What others are saying

"Many aquarium books are almost all fluff and no substance. *Aquatic Systems Engineering* is heavy on the substance and very light on the fluff. Anyone interested in building or maintaining a small or large aquarium installation will find a gold mine of essential information within these pages."

—*Martin A. Moe, Jr., Author of:* The Marine Aquarium
Handbook
and The Marine Aquarium Reference

"So many times we see aquatic systems fail to flourish despite being equipped with all the requisite accessories—not properly utilized. With the publication of *Aquatic Systems Engineering* by Pete Escobal, we finally have a graphic, as well as a verbal guide to maximizing the benefits of aquarium equipment. A must-read for hobbyists and professionals alike; required reading for my staff."

—*Marc Weiss: World Wide Fish Farm USA*

"A truly outstanding book! *Aquatic Systems Engineering: Devices And How They Function* by Pete Escobal is an absolute "must have" reference and textbook for any serious hobbyist, professional aquarist, retail store owner, or student of the aquatic sciences. In the pages of this definitive text, the author explains virtually everything you need to know about filters, sterilizers, reactors, venturis, skimmers, pumps, heat, and ozone, along with installation and turnover times.

"Using a graphical presentation, P.R. Escobal introduces new subject matter fundamental to the proper operation of aquatic life support systems. Equally as important, the author establishes a new approach with which they can be analyzed, understood, and properly installed by the serious hobbyist and retailer alike.

"I highly recommend this book for your consideration."

—*Don Dewey, Publisher: Freshwater And Marine Aquarium
Magazine*

More Comments on Next Page

"Good job! A great text to help advance aquaculture. Our tropical aquaculture needs to take giant steps to reach needed production goals. This book will serve an important purpose in helping to make our industry more professional."
—*Warren R. Savidge: Florida Tropical Fish Farmers Association*

"I think the structure of your book to give first the results and then the analytic proofs is very convenient. Very useful are the problems and examples with the answers at the end of each chapter. So, I think your book will be very interesting for the experienced hobbyist and for retailers."
—*Hubert Kleijkers: Teacher and Translator (Europe)*

"Finally! A book that every marine hobbyist who cares about their system should read. A must for people who have heard an opinion from everyone. Nothing can reach the marine aquarist like *Aquatic Systems Engineering*."
—*Richard Freed, Owner: Aquascape Aquarium*

"As always, a complete and thorough job, with more detail than one could have imagined possible. Despite the appearance of equations, tables and graphs, the text is quite readable and there are numerous interesting tidbits of information waiting to be discovered. For advanced aquarists waiting to be challenged—the wait is over."
—*Ed Bauman, Editor: Aquarium Fish Magazine*

"Theory becomes reality with this informative practical guide to successful aquarium management."
—*Jeff Grieco: Pet Warehouse*

"Full of hard to find needed technical data."
—*Alan Sperling, Publisher: Pondscapes Magazine*

More Comments on Next Page

"The valuable information contained will save a great deal of time and money to anyone setting up a tank system. It's a must to read and understand for every serious aquarium shop owner."

—*Michael Wimbert, Owner: Mr. Fish*

"When it comes to all the implements that can be used on aquariums, hobbyists often have a difficult time understanding their purpose and grasping how to exactly install the various pieces of equipment that are used today in modern aquariums. The author went way beyond what you would expect to find. This book is not only detailed and easy to understand, but covers just about any device you may consider using on your aquarium. I really strongly recommend it and am going to use it as a reference myself. Pete Escobal has done the hobby a great service by compiling all this information and making it available. This book was dearly needed."

—*Albert J. Thiel: Theil Aqua Tech*

"Great book every marine hobbyist should own."

—*Boyce E. Phipps, Publisher: Marine Fish Monthly*

AQUATIC SYSTEMS ENGINEERING

AQUATIC SYSTEMS ENGINEERING:
Devices and How They Function

P.R. ESCOBAL
President, Aquatronics
President, Filtronics

Expanded
Second Edition

Dimension Engineering Press • Oxnard, California

AQUATIC SYSTEMS ENGINEERING:
Devices And How They Function
by
P.R. Escobal

Published by:

DIMENSION ENGINEERING PRESS
Post Office Box 2457
Oxnard, California 93033 U.S.A.

Copyright ©1996 by P.R. Escobal

First Printing 1996, Second Printing 2000

Printed in the United States of America

Escobal, Pedro Ramon.
    Aquatic systems engineering: devices and how they function /P.R. Escobal. — 2nd ed.
    p. cm.
    Includes bibliographical references and index.
    LCCN: 99-96286
    ISBN: 1-888381-10-8

    1. Aquariums. 2. Pumping machinery. 3. Water --Aeration. 4. Water--Purification—Foam fractionation. 5. Water--Purification--Filtration. 6. Water--Purification--Disinfection. I. Title

SF457.E73 2000   639.34'028
                    QBI99-1673

DEDICATION

From dawn's first arising
to twilight's last gleaming,
I offer you thanking
and love without yielding.

Your Husband

For my wife Gayle, who during the generation of this book, helped me in this project with much patience. Her support, comments, and assistance has no equal measure that I can ever repay.

ABOUT THE AUTHOR

P.R.Escobal received his Bachelor of Arts, B.A., and Bachelor of Aeronautical Engineering, B.A.E., from New York University. Prior to graduation he was awarded the Chance Vought Memorial Prize for jet airplane design. His fascination with rockets and the space age led him to seek employment at Rocketdyne, where he worked on the F-1 motors which subsequently were used in the Apollo project to propel man to the moon. At the same time, he earned his Master of Science, M.S.,from U.C.L.A. To follow the Apollo program, the author moved to the Aerospace Corporation and subsequently to TRW Systems Group. At this time, he wrote the graduate texts *Methods of Orbit Determination,* followed by *Methods of Astrodynamics.* Both his texts, without the author's knowledge, were translated into Russian. He is the author of over 200 articles and reports in the aerospace industry. While at TRW, he was appointed Assistant Department Manager and his group continued to work on the Apollo project. The end of the Apollo project was a great disappointment and lead him to seek employment elsewhere. The ten years spent at Jet Propulsion Laboratories found him involved in numerous projects, including the direction of a project which he named Multilateration, which through software simulation, showed excellent potential for earthquake prediction. Unfortunately, for political reasons, the project and its detailed engineering report was shelved.

From the very early days of his life, the author was fascinated with tropical and marine fish, as much as with aerospace engineering. He and his wife founded Aquatronics in 1969. Amazingly enough, this was the very year man landed on the moon. P.R. Escobal became its president and, except for some consulting, separated himself from the aerospace industry. His efforts were now directed to the aquatic industry. He founded Filtronics in 1971.

Countless new medical treatments were developed. He molded Aquatronics into the producer of the world's most complete line of aquatic medications and pioneered the concept of *a specific medication for a specific cure.* His insistence on safety required placement of the correct labeling and the listing of all ingredients on all products. The author's engineering was applied to the development of magnetic drive pumps, ultraviolet sterilizers and air-producing devices. He holds two patents on the Hydroram™ and Hydroair™ aeration equipment. Lately, he has written a number of scientific articles for the aquatic industry. His belief that the scientific method should be applied to aquatic systems gave birth to this book. The author is listed in *International Who's Who of Professionals.*

ACKNOWLEDGMENTS

A hundred times everyday, I remind myself
that my inner and outer life are based on the
labors of other men, living and dead, and that
I must exert myself in order to give in the same
measure as I have received.

Albert Einstein

This book took years to evolve, and over those years many people contributed to the final work you hold in your hands. To name everyone involved in this production would be impossible. It goes without saying that this book would not have been possible except for the many brilliant scientists whose names are forged indelibly into the history of mankind. These scientists will be formally acknowledged in the text upon use of the principles they have so firmly established.

Many times the foundation necessary for solution to an existing problem by an investigator is established by a single spoken word or sentence provided by another person. This spark, which engenders the subsequent path toward the solution is usually unintentionally forgotten. Of course, the extraction of the solution from conception to completion is far removed from being a trivial operation. Nevertheless, should I have omitted a reference or direct acknowledgment on a fundamental issue, apologies are tendered.

To those unrelated discoveries encountered by chance when in quest to solutions to specific problems, serendipity, I wish to thank the Power from above.

For the first indenture typing of the manuscript, I wish to thank Julie Grant, Ruby Gonzales, my wife Gayle, and others who have contributed over the duration required to generate this work. The painful job of reproducing the manuscript many times was performed by Lucy Huezo. Final typesetting and editing thanks are extended to Kim Scaramastro. Construction of some of the unique devices peculiar to this book is due to the efforts of Ed Moure. To Alan Colvin belongs the distinction of turning my line drawings and cover into works of art. Some ideas, comments and inclusion of material were due to the suggestions of Tom Aurand. Corrections to the first edition and typesetting plus illustration enhancement of the added chapters and appendix are to be noted and thanks are extended to Pat Wiese. The insight provided to me by Robert Chase on ozone reactions must be noted. I am also grateful to Lionel Ramirez for a careful proofreading effort. Comments and additional suggestions by my wife also need to be noted.

Finally, to the reviewers who provided much needed comments, I shall always remain indebted.

P.R. Escobal

AQUATRONICS/FILTRONICS
MARCH 1996, JANUARY 2000

AQUATIC SYSTEMS ENGINEERING

FOREWORD

Many aquarists, especially us hobbyists, usually "fly by the seat of our pants." This phrase, now a part of the American lexicon, was coined to describe a pilot flying without benefit of instruments or ground control instructions, using only experience, intelligence, and the "feel" of the airplane around him to guide the plane safely home. The critical engineering an aquarist "flying by the seat of the pants" puts into the construction of an aquarium project is often summed up in the phrase, "Yeah, that looks about right." If the aquarist is well seasoned, this approach may be successful, but it often leads to the frustrations and failures that stem from an inadequately engineered aquarium system. In most instances, it is a lack of essential information that induces this casual approach to design and construction of aquarium systems. The critical information on water movement through the pipes, filters, and pumps of modern aquarium systems, what happens to it within these filters and other devices, and exactly how to do the calculations that identify the precise requirements of particular aquatic systems were not easily understood or available to serious aquarists.

Who better than an aeronautical engineer with almost 30 years of aquatic engineering experience to decipher for us the science and mathematics of engineering aquarium systems. In this book, *Aquatic Systems Engineering*, Pete Escobal has given us "seat of the pants" aquatic flyers the tools and instruments we need to understand the science behind the operation of aquarium devices, and the formulary to be precise about aquarium system design. Any confusion an aquarist might have between water turnover rate, filtration, and water circulation is thoroughly dispelled. The operation and flowrate through sterilizers and skimmers is carefully analyzed, and the complex relationships between these devices, pump capacity, and head loss from friction and filters, is mathematically defined and described. A graphical approach, however, is stressed wherever possible, and along with many specific examples, makes it very easy for non-technical readers to determine most system and sub-system requirements. Heater selection, ozone use, installation hydraulics, pumping air by both conventional and new methods, and many other basic topics make this a most useful book for serious hobbyists and professional aquarists. In fact, anyone who pumps or pushes water through pipes will find something of value within these pages.

Martin A. Moe, Jr.

AQUATIC SYSTEMS ENGINEERING

PREFACE

Star Trek, the television series about the continuing voyages of a spaceship named U.S.S. Enterprise, made its entry into history in 1966. This series was responsible for the later birth of a second series Star Trek: The Next Generation. Subsequently appeared a third and a fourth series. All these series continue to air as of 1996. Quite a phenomenon. The second series, with Captain Jean-Luc Picard at the helm dealt with the science which investigates the facts and principles of reality and of human nature and conduct. The first series was not as philosophical, but it certainly did have moments which caused one to reflect on the subject matter. In one episode of Star Trek, Captain James T. Kirk asks Chief Engineer Montgomery Scott, appropriately named Scotty, to perform a feat tantamount to making the sand in an hourglass pass through the neck of the glass at a higher speed than that provided by gravity. The reply given by Scotty, in a stressed Scottish brogue, is a classic statement of the truth. Since his reply comes from my memory, the use of quotation marks would be inappropriate, but within *acceptable parameters* it was: Ay capt'in, but ah can-na change dah laws of physics. Indeed, the laws of physics are inflexible and cannot be changed. The laws, when applied to a problem under investigation, can be violated quite easily, but the penalty incurred would be the attainment of a false or spurious solution. Violation of these laws usually comes about due to a lack of knowledge of their very existence. This is what this book is all about—providence of the laws which rule the correct use of aquarium devices. Remember, that a lack of knowledge of these laws is equivalent to changing the laws of physics because false principles are being substituted for true ones, even though the false principles may not be intentionally known to the user or manufacturer.

Aquatic Systems Engineering: Devices and How They Function, was written for serious hobbyists and, of course, the owners of retail outlets dealing in the aquatic trade. It was also written as a text book with the hope that the science peculiar to the aquatic systems might be taught formally at the undergraduate level. Nevertheless, the problems at the end of each chapter, along with the answers, provide a test as to the understanding of the subject matter for all concerned with the proper operation of aquatic devices used to maintain a closed ecological system. Many worked examples are interjected into the text in order to clarify how the material presented therein should be applied.

At first sight it might appear that the book is equation dependent. Unfortunately, there is no way to prove the assertions made in the text without them, but the good news is that the reader need not delve into the equations at all. How is this possible? It is possible because of the format of the book. The hobbyist or retailer can read the introduction and first few sections of each chapter until the graphical data peculiar to the subject matter at hand is encountered. Armed with the graphical data, the end user should have sufficient ammunition to permit the question of interest to be answered. In some cases, a division or multiplication is unavoidable. To reiterate, the results, whether graphic or analytic, are given first and the analysis follows. Actually, this format is carried to extremes with ultraviolet sterilizers and skimmers. Chapter 4 presents sterilizers from a graphical point of view: Chapter 5 amplifies Chapter 4 and has the back-up analysis. Skimmers are analyzed graphically in Chapter 8, followed by the theory in Chapter 9. It would benefit the reader to proceed as far as possible into the back-up chapters of these two subjects. To assist the reader not versed in elementary algebra, appeal can be made to the Appendix. Examination of this Appendix will show that only the simplest of mathematical operations need to be understood, and this is only necessary if the reader does indeed wish to understand the theory in further depth. The only exception to the previous discussion is Chapter 11, which deals with hydraulics, fluid flow, and pump sizing for a given installation. In this case, only the analytic approach is possible. However, the Appendix has all the necessary information to deal with Chapter 11. Given the complexity of the subject matter, the reader may be amazed at the simple manner with which the entire systems analysis of a given installation falls into place. To this end, the list of tables and graphs following the table of contents will be of assistance. An advanced look at Chapter 14, which deals with the individual component selection for a given installation may be in order. Should this be done, the reader will finally encounter the section which deals with pump selection. At this point, just skip over this section. Unless Chapter 11 has been read, the material will not make sense.

Chapter 1 attempts to collect, in brief summary, the devices to be discussed and their subcomponents. A brief description of the nitrogen cycle was included because it is fundamental to any installation. For further understanding and more detail, the reader should consult the references therein. Some important foundational points are also stressed in this chapter. Even though it might seem fruitless to a knowledgable reader, I think it should be read by all.

Wherever possible in this book, different ways of obtaining established results are presented and new concepts are introduced. This is especially true in Chapters 2 and 3, which discuss the duration required to have all the water in an aquatic system pass through a given device. Chapter 5 demonstrates that ultraviolet sterilizers have an optimal diameter, while Chapter 7 brings into focus unique new techniques for pumping air. In Chapter 9 will be found the analysis that shows the importance of skimmer diameters. Installation hydraulics, as discussed in Chapter 11 is specially simplified for aquatic applications. Chapter 12 and 13 provide additional new methods of looking at old problems.

Each chapter of Aquatic Systems Engineering, with the exception of Chapter 14, is self contained. In other words, the user interested in a specific discipline can proceed to extract information on the subject matter without having to refer to other chapters for symbol definitions, mathematical constants, graphs, tables, etc. In a few cases, repetition is unavoidable. However, the practical use of the book is greatly enhanced by this format. Symbol definitions are a slight problem. Due to the broad range of the distinct branches of science discussed in this book, no attempt has been made to have every parameter have a distinct symbol. However, as mentioned, each chapter is self-contained and the symbols peculiar to the subject matter are unique within the chapter which is being read. It is hoped that this book will find acceptance as a guide to the proper use of aquatic life support devices. Since new ground is under exploration in this book, the possibility of error on my part exists. However, I disavow the application of the material in this book. I welcome criticism of a concrete nature fortified by analytic proofs, but welcome not unsubstantiated singular opinions.

As parting words, I would like to say that this book is not anywhere as formidable as it might seem upon flipping through the pages. The subject matter can be applied quite easily without the math, but the math can be interesting, and if mastered, it can also provide much satisfaction, and as Scotty might say, in a pleasant Scottish brogue, "Ay capt'in, amm glad ya see that ya can-na change dah laws of physics."

P.R. Escobal

Malibu, California, 1996

PREFACE TO THE SECOND EDITION

It is a wonderful reward to know that so many copies of this book are now in the hands of hobbyists, professionals, retailers, and fish farmers. To be candid, it was a surprize that the book actually did fly—not like Mr. Hughes' Spruce Goose, but actually much, much higher. Had this not been the case it goes without saying that this second and enlarged edition would not be forthcoming. It also would not be in existence had it not been for the wonderful first edition reviews and comments of thanks from readers that were thirsty for the information provided therin. As a one-to-one gesture of appreciation this second edition can be obtained directly from the publisher for one half the cover price upon return of the used first edition. Please see the last page of this book for the exchange form.

But there is a second fundamental reason why I have chosen to be executor for this work: I want Scotty's words, "Ay Capt'n, amm glad ya see that ya can-na change dah laws of physics," to be heard with great resonance. It is an unfortunate circumstance that there are still manufacturers and retailers that due to lack of knowledge are still perpetuating their own unproven laws of physics. It is hoped that a second injection of knowledge will provide some protection against this rather shaky brick wall of misinformation and existing flim flam.

For the sake of thousands of users that have utilized the first edition of this book as a reference, I decided not to change the organization of the existing chapters except for updates, removal of unfortunate typographic errors, and necessary corrections. The two new chapters were just appended to the tail end of this work. Since these are specialty chapters, added at the request of readers, I see no harm or disruption forthcoming to users that are now accustomed to the format.

Chapter 15 details the manner in which it is possible to predict the number of fish a given tank can safely hold in an ecologically balanced aquarium, and how this number can be increased by use of auxiliary devices such as fluidized beds. Finally, Chapter 16 returns to the material presented in Chapter 6 and details the operation of reactors. It is one thing is to install a reactor but it is quite a different matter to correctly determine the water and gas flowrate plus additives that need be supplied so as to achieve the water quality desired by the user. Two new appendices have been included. Appendix 1 provides a brief introduction to aquarium light requirements and Appendix 3 collects handy conversion factors.

As well you know, at this juncture in our history the computer reigns supreme. Whether this reign is for the good is moot, but with a priori apology for a pedantic utterance: the computer is here to stay. In the two years between the first and second editions I undertook the project of writing a computer disk, i.e., CD that obtains all the parameters peculiar to this book in a yes/no format. This CD, by the name of ACE which in short stands for Aquatic Computer Engineering was by no means designed to replace the book. Fundamental knowledge can never be replaced by a non-thinking device. Perhaps in the future microchips will think or at least mimic thought. I am very glad I will be on the other side when this comes about. The computer CD is a fantastic aid to avoid the drugery of computational arithmetic and algebra and it is lightning fast. The CD defines the devices and contains many opticals. Both the book and the CD go hand in hand and should be used simultaneously. If you are interested in the CD ask your retailer or use the form on the last page of this book.

As the second millinnium begins I wish you the best of health, happiness, and extended knowledge in your fishkeeping endeavors to reach the lofty but easily attainable goal: achievement of a correctly managed tank.

P.R. Escobal

Malibu, California, 2000

CONTENTS

LIST AND LOCATION OF TABLES:

LIST AND LOCATION OF GRAPHS

1 Devices and Definitions: Aquarium Hardware and Terms in Common Use

I am an idealist. I don't know where I'm going,
but I'm on my way.

Carl Sanburg

1.1 SUMMARY OF AQUARIUM DEVICES

Throughout this book reference will be made to different mechanical devices. Even though the device may be explained at the point of referral, it will be beneficial to review the function of each different device from a general point of view.

1.1.1 AIR PUMP

A device that takes in atmospheric air, compresses the air and delivers the air to a secondary device such as an air stone. Some air pumps are of variable output design. Their design usually employ rubber diaphragms, but others use no diaphragms, bellows or pistons to produce the needed air. See Hydroram™ (1.1.16), Hydroair™ (1.1.15).

1.1.2 ALGAE-SCRUBBER

Algae-Scrubbers are denitrifying systems that rely on Heterothropic bacteria to metabolize and break down dissolved organics in the aquarium. Algae then utilize the organic and inorganic nutrients obtained from the bacterial activity. These units produce dramatic reduction in unwanted nitrate levels, as well as supplying much needed dissolved oxygen. They consist of elongated waterproof boxes which have a full spectrum light overhead. Water is pumped into one end and extracted from the other side. Media which permits the algae to grow is placed inside the unit.

1

1.1.3 BIO-MASS

An expression, in suitable units, which denotes the amount of living matter in the tank. Sometimes referred to as "pounds or inches of fish per gallon" even though pounds is not a unit of mass. Pounds divided by the acceleration of gravity (g=32.174 ft/sec^2) is a mass unit.

1.1.4 BIO-MEDIA

Any suitable material on which bacteria can grow. There are many such materials such as small plastic balls of irregular surface, including cylinders, and chips. In large systems even ping-pong balls are used.

1.1.5 BIO-TOWER

This is a watertight large diameter tube with a bottom drain. Water is injected at the top of the tower and is diffused by an appropriate device. The water droplets, which have been oxygenated by the diffusion process, then run over suitable media and chemicals to further treat the water. These units are also called ammonia towers because of their ability to strip water clean of ammonia.

1.1.6 CARBON DIOXIDE REACTOR

This reactor consists of a watertight cylinder through which water flows in and out along the bottom. A bleed valve on top extracts all the trapped air and causes the water to rise to the top of the tube. The bleed valve is then shut down and pure carbon dioxide is injected through a secondary valve. The carbon dioxide forces the water down to some fixed level. As time goes by the water flowing through the reactor absorbs the carbon dioxide and thus raises the value of the dissolved carbon dioxide level in the aquarium water. Carbon dioxide is very beneficial to plants, and is commonly used to reduce the pH in many reef aquariums.

1.1.7 CARTRIDGE

These are hollow cylinders made of some appropriate material which have a fine porous surface. They are placed in watertight housings through which water is pumped so that it travels through the cartridge from the outside to the hollow internal core. The water exists the housing from the inner core and is thus filtered to the rated value of the cartridge.

1.1.8 CHILLER

This is a device used to drop the water temperature. The desired water temperature can be dialed and maintained at the set level required by a given species. Advanced models also heat the water so as to permit total climate control.

1.1.9   CIRCULATION PUMP

Usually, these devices are referred to as powerheads. They can have a large output of water but have a low pressure rating. They are used to enhance water movement in tanks and have some applications to run low pressure devices.

1.1.10   FILTER

A device which removes particulate matter from an aquarium or pond. It is a housing which holds media or cartridges (See 1.1.7) that can trap particles. The media becomes clogged as time goes by and must be replaced so as to restore the original water flow in and out of the filter.

1.1.11   FLOWMETER

These are instruments used to measure the flow in a given line. The Sphere™ Flowrater™ is an inexpensive version of this device. Flowrate determination is of great importance for proper use of many devices because contact time depends on the flowrate value.

1.1.12   FLUIDIZED BED

A device consisting of a sealed tube through which water, and air are injected through the bottom into a suitable media such as fine quartz silica sand. The water and air cause the silica sand to remain in constant swirling motion. The media is lifted about three quarters of the way up the tube leaving a clear amount of water at the top. This water is then returned to the aquarium. The large surface area of the moving internal media promotes excellent biological activity.

1.1.13   FOAM FRACTIONATOR
See **PROTEIN SKIMMER** (1.1.27)

1.1.14   HEATER

This is an electrical device which raises the water temperature to some desired value. Advanced models have a separate temperature sensing probe and external controller on which the temperature that is desired can be dialed.

1.1.15 HYDROAIR™

This device is inserted into a pipe through which water is flowing, and the unique internal construction (venturi) suctions air into it. Air and water then leave the Hydroair™. The patented model is adjustable so that it can vary air output.

1.1.16 HYDRORAM™

By using a Hydroair™ device as a subsystem, the Hydroram™ can produce pure air just like an air pump (1.1.1). It is capable of producing high pressures (up to 6-7 psi) as opposed to most vibrator type airpumps (3-4 psi). Furthermore, air is stripped clean of airborne pollutants.

1.1.17 HYPERBARIC REACTOR
See OXYGEN REACTOR (1.1.24)

1.1.18 INCUBATOR

A small plastic enclosure that hangs on the inside of the breeding tank that is full of water nearly to the tank water level. Fish ready to give birth are placed in this trap so that the young fry can escape through small holes on the side of the trap.

1.1.19 "JAY" TUBE

This is a curved siphon tube used to extract or introduce water into a tank and is usually positioned on one of the tank walls. Second generation "J" tubes have a check valve on the top curved section that permits easy priming of the tube so as to evacuate the air and leave it full of water. One side of the "J" tube is below the water level and the other side is connected via a flexline to another device so as to complete a closed loop of water.

1.1.20 LIGHTS

Usually these are long fluorescent bulbs that provide the plants with actinic radiation and the fish with color rendering radiation. Lights usually are positioned in tank covers or hoods with the actinic and color rendering lights connected to different timer circuits. Actinic bulbs are run only four to five hours per day. To stimulate the growth of symbiotic algae found in many corals and bi-valves, the actinic bulbs can be run eight to ten hours per day.

1.1.21 LOOP (SPLIT)

This is a plumbing connection that ensures that the water level in a given device stays at a constant level. The effect of the valves and tubing makes sure that whatever water the pumping device introduces into unit, it also removes the same amount. In this type of connection line voltage fluctuations from the utility company will not upset the fine balance of an operating system. In case of a power outage correct operating conditions are resumed when power is restored.

1.1.22 MAGNETIC WATER SOFTENER

A device that passes water through two powerful magnetic fields. For water scale to buildup, the water needs centers (points) for initial crystallization to occur. The magnetic flux prevents this from occurring, and scale build on tank walls, etc. is greatly reduced. The devices last indefinitely.

1.1.23 NITROGEN REACTOR (DENITRIFIER)

This is a hollow cylinder which contains a long length of opaque tube curled inside. Water enters the reactor via a feeder line operating under gravity or suction and runs down the winding coil. It is discharged at the bottom of the sealed external hollow cylinder, fills the cylinder and escapes at the top. Water flow through the winding inner coil is very slow. The units work because Chemoautotrophic bacteria thrive in a near zero oxygen environment but need nitrates as a food source, hence they eliminate them.

1.1.24 OXYGEN REACTOR

A closed hollow cylindrical tube filled with small plastic balls or cylinders with large surface area through which water is pumped, along with air at higher pressure than that of the water. The air pressurizes internally and forces the water down to a small degassing vent. Once the degassing has occurred, the water rises until it is again pushed down by the air to the degassing vent. This cycle continues as long as the reactor operates. The air which is introduced into the reactor and cascades over the large surface area plastic balls will thus force oxygen into the water.

1.1.25 OZONE REACTOR

This device is the same as an oxygen reactor except ozone gas is used instead of air. It is a device used primarily for water disinfection. The ozone gas is produced in an ozone generator which must be fed dry air in order to operate correctly. The excess ozone must also be passed through a cartridge containing carbon in order to remove it from venting into the atmosphere. Algae build-up is greatly reduced by the use of these reactors. Burns off protein waste.

1.1.26   PRE-FILTER

Good practice dictates the placement of a sealed tube or open box filled with low resistance filter media prior to letting the water enter expensive equipment. The pre-filter will thus trap large particulate matter such as gravel, leaves, etc. from entering the equipment, especially pumps, and wet dry systems (1.1.39).

1.1.27   PROTEIN SKIMMER

This is a hollow tube through which water is introduced while air is pumped into the bottom of the tube. The bubbles collide with the water and bombard the water droplets with mechanical and chemical action. This action generates foam which is collected at the top of the skimmer and discarded. The foam carries out dissolved organics and pollutants. There are various designs. If ozone is used, a carbon cap on top of the skimmer should be used to absorb excess ozone before it goes into the atmosphere.

1.1.28   PUMP (MAGNETIC)
move water through exbit exhibit.

A device that removes water from a tank at low pressure, imparts energy to the water and expels it at high pressure. A magnetic drive pump has a hollow magnet attached to the axis of a motor into which a smaller magnet attached to an impeller (fan) is inserted. The smaller magnet is separated from the large magnet by a small cup which forms part of the entire front end of the pump. Hence, water in the front end never comes in contact with the larger magnet, i.e., the lines of magnetic flux travel through the small cup to the inner concentric magnet and cause it to spin. The spinning action causes the pressure increase in the water.

1.1.29   REACTOR (CELL)

A general term used to denote a device that holds some media with some specific objective in mind. These include oxygen, carbon dioxide reactors, etc. There are also devices that hold media that absorb unwanted pollutants. These are denoted as negative reactors because the media they hold subtract substances which are not desired to be constituants of aquarium water, e.g., extraction reactors which hold carbon, ion exchange resins, etc.

1.1.30 REVERSE OSMOSIS SYSTEMS

Reverse osmosis devices usually consist of a carbon pre-filter and a second chamber that contains a very fine membrane through which water is forced through under pressure. They are used to create "ultra pure" water and usually remove 99.8% of all dissolved minerals, etc. The water is so pure that required chemicals (trace elements) must later be added to the tank. However, one can be certain that all offensive chemicals have been removed.

1.1.31 SELF-LEVELING DEVICE
See **LOOP SPLIT** (1.1.21)

Sand Filter—
removes particulates
and growing bacteria

1.1.32 SKIMMER
See **PROTEIN SKIMMER** (1.1.27)

mechanical

1.1.33 STERILIZER (U.V.)

This device is a long ultraviolet bulb placed axially in a closed tube with a water entrance and exit port. When water is introduced into the sterilizer at the proper flowrate, and the construction of the outer closed tube is of the proper diameter so as to have the required contact time, the ultraviolet bulb will deliver what is called the proper "Zap" dosage to kill the target organism which has been selected. Perhaps, this is the second most important device that can be used after having a proper mechanical filter.

1.1.34 SUB-SAND FILTER (BIOLOGICAL)

These are flat plates which are perforated with holes or slits placed at the bottom of tanks . They are lifted from the bottom of the tank by a small space. Hollow tubes are placed on the ends of the plates which go through the flat plates, reach up to the water surface but permit the water to enter at the bottom. An air stone is dropped down each hollow tube and air is pumped in so as to create a current that lifts the water to the tank surface. This action causes water to go through the aquarium gravel, bottom plate and thus creates circulation through the gravel.

1.1.35 SUMP

An auxiliary tank connected to and placed under another tank for purposes of water filtration, heating, etc., and in some cases to control water overflow should a power outage occur.

1.1.36 THERMOMETER

A device to measure the water temperature. Advanced models are placed externally on the tank wall and a probe placed into the tank measures the temperature.

1.1.37 ULTRAVIOLET STERILIZER
See **STERILIZER** (1.1.33)

1.1.38 VENTURI *Mazzi injectors*

This is a tube which slowly contracts to a minimum diameter and then expands again to its original diameter. The device has the effect of increasing the water velocity at the minimum diameter, called the "throat" and decreasing the water pressure at the same point. Hence, air will be suctioned into the flowing water. *or ozone.*

1.1.39 WAVE GENERATOR

A wave generator is a timing relay that can be adjusted so as to turn on one or more pumps or powerheads at different times. It provides a left and right electric pulse duration which can be adjusted as desired. Advanced models use solid state electronics that do not spark or create electrical interference. It can turn on a pump or powerhead (circulation pump) placed on opposite ends of an aquarium so that water jets placed near the water surface create waves. These waves help to create needed circulation within the tank.

1.1.40 WET-DRY SYSTEM *Bio and Mechanical*

This device is a large box placed below the tank through which water from the aquarium enters at the top of the box and travels through a plate perforated with holes or, even better through what is called a rotating spray bar (inverted lawn sprinkler). This action oxygenates the water which then flows down through appropriate media wherein beneficial bacteria are cultivated. The bacteria condition the water. Then the water travels through a series of traps that contain some filtration and chemical conditioning elements. Finally, the water is returned to the tank. Sometimes an additional prefilter hangs on the side of the tank. Advanced models are protected so that the wet-dry system and the tank can never overflow.

1.2   BIOLOGICAL CYCLE

Some of the devices described in Section 1.1 are important in maintaining the critical balance of biological activity within a closed ecological system in check. This cycle of biological activity involves the process of nitrification. In short, this cycle is called the nitrogen cycle. Maintenance of a properly balanced nitrogen cycle is of paramount importance in aquariums and ponds.

To understand this cycle, consider that fish introduced into an aquarium immediately start to excrete waste products in the form of respiration and digested food products. These waste products produce ammonia (NH_3). As the ammonia accumulates to toxic levels, usually measured in parts per million (PPM=0.7 to 0.8) the fish will die. Fortunately, before the toxic levels are reached, the ammonia promotes the growth of Nitrosomonas species of bacteria. These bacteria use the ammonia as their food source and in turn produce nitrite (NO_2). In about 10 to 14 days a safe concentration of ammonia is attained but only at the expense of producing an increased level of nitrite. Unfortunately, nitrite is also toxic to fish around concentrations of 15 to 20 PPM. Reduction of the excess nitrite is now the job of a new group of bacteria known as Nitrobacter whom have become active due to the excess nitrite. The Nitrobacter break down the nitrite into nitrate (NO_3). Nitrate levels less than 35 PPM are relatively non-toxic to fish. However, some corals and invertebrates are attacked if the nitrate level reaches even 20 PPM. The removal of excess nitrate is called denitrification.

Denitrification can be accomplished by regular water changes or by the use of devices such as a nitrogen reactor (1.1.23) or algae scrubber (1.1.2). These devices remove the nitrates naturally by the grace of a new bacteria of the Chemoautotrophic species. These bacteria thrive in an oxygen deficient environment and use nitrates as their food source. They transform the nitrates into nitrogen gas which dissipates through normal water circulation and gas exchange within the aquarium.

Hence, what is required for a total balanced aquarium are devices that aid the nitrification cycle, e.g., sub-sand filters (1.1.34), biotowers (1.1.5), wet-dry systems (1.1.40), fluidized beds (1.1.12), and those that promote denitrification or nitrate removal such as mentioned before. Correct use of these devices, not necessarily all of them, will permit a natural balance to be achieved in a closed ecological system.

1.3 MECHANICAL FILTRATION

Apart from obtaining a natural aquatic balance by the devices mentioned in Section 1.1, good mechanical filters (1.1.10) are necessary to remove excess free floating particulate matter. These devices also aid in promoting circulation, but as will be seen in Chapter 3 they should not be taxed into providing total circulation requirements. Filters can be loaded with all sorts of media which also helps to remove unwanted chemicals and gas which are either introduced into the aquarium for medicinal reasons or are due to the normal biological activity of the living organisms. For example carbon or ProOre™ can remove (adsorb) unwanted waste organics and greatly sweeten the water. Mechanical filtration to some degree also aids the natural biological process peculiar to all aquariums and ponds. Protein skimmers (1.1.27) also do an exceptional job at removing dissolved (particulate) organic debris.

1.4 CIRCULATION

The healthy state of an aquarium is directly linked to the circulation present within its confining retention panels. Air pumps (1.1.1). Hydrorams™ (1.1.16) and Hydroairs™ (1.1.15) can all be used to pump oxygen into an aquarium. The stream of air bubbles rising from the bottom of the tank set up water currents that provide circulation. For some people the rising air curtains are visually attractive, others care not for these air displays. Circulation requirements can be achieved without air pumps by means of circulation pumps (1.1.9) or regular pumps (1.1.28) which just keep the water in motion. Wave generators (1.1.39) also aid in setting up a rhythmic pattern of circulation. Proper circulation aids the mechanical filter to function with greater efficiency.

1.5 OXYGENATION

The air devices discussed in Section 1.4 provide a means of increasing the dissolved oxygen levels in an aquarium. The dissolved oxygen level should never fall below five PPM. Should bubbling air not be introduced into an aquarium other devices such as algae-scrubbers (1.1.2) or Oxygen (Hyperbaric) reactors (1.1.24) can be employed. Wet-dry systems (1.1.40) especially those with rotating spinner bars also provide oxygen to the tank. Actually, the last two devices are much more efficient at providing dissolved oxygen. Proper or elevated oxygen levels are most important especially if medications are to be used. Most medications will destroy some of the free floating bacteria and this is in turn will drop the oxygen level below acceptable limits.

1.6   STERILIZATION

The greatest plague the aquarium hobbyist or professional must fight is disease generating bacteria. Chemical treatments are available and at times there is no recourse but to employ medications so as to target and destroy the bacteria. Specifically, if the bacteria or parasites are on the fish, medications must be used. However, the use of ultraviolet sterilizers (1.1.33) is highly recommended as a method of making the water bacteria free. Sterilizers only affect the water flowing through them, so they do not destroy any beneficial bacteria present in the filter bed. Only free floating bacteria, protozoans and algae are affected. The importance of this device is so great that two full chapters are devoted to its proper usage (Chapters 4 and 5).

Another option is to use ozone for sterilization. This accomplished by the use of an ozone generator (see Chapters 13 and 16) which provides the gas to an ozone reactor (1.1.25) or to a protein skimmer (1.1.27). There are many benefits to ozone sterilization if the gas is properly handled.

1.7   SUMMARY

There are many aquarium devices. They were briefly outlined in this chapter. Not all of them need to be used but at least a subset of them is needed to have a functional nitrification/denitrification cycle, i.e., to have a correctly operating biological cycle. A brief overview of how the devices listed interact was given with respect to biological activity, mechanical filtration, circulation, oxygenation and sterilization.

1.8   PROBLEMS

1.8.1 Draw a diagram of what happens in a complete biological cycle so that aquatic life can exist.

1.8.2 List the hazardous levels of ammonia, nitrate, nitrate and oxygen that must be avoided in a closed system.

1.8.3 What are the three types of bacteria which dominate the biological cycle?

1.8.4 What is the difference between an airpump, Hydroram™ and Hydroair™?

1.8.5 Name the aquarium devices you consider to be of the greatest importance to maintain a well balanced aquarium.

1.9 REFERENCES

1.9.1 M.A. Moe, Jr., *The Marine Aquarium Handbook*,
Green Turtle Publications, Plantation, Florida, 1995.

1.9.2 M.A. Moe, Jr., *The Marine Aquarium Reference*,
Green Turtle Publications, Plantation, Florida, 1992.

2 The Duration Required to Pass All the Water in a Body of Water through a Specified Device.

Trust yourself. You know more than you think.

Benjamin Spock

2.1 GENERAL DISCUSSION

In order to have a concrete basis for the development of the turnover formula an ultraviolet sterilizer will be used as an example. As will be seen, the analysis developed herein applies to any device that does not offer *a time varying resistance to the flow of water.* Obviously, a filter offers more and more resistance to the water flow as it slowly becomes clogged. This case will be discussed in Chapter 3. Note that, there are many devices that do not offer increasing resistance as a function of elapsed time, e.g., an ultraviolet sterilizer, an oxygen reactor, an algae-scrubber, etc. Hence, the formula developed in this chapter is perfectly general and has many applications. However, a greater focus on the process of water turnover will be achieved by selecting one device, such as a U.V. sterilizer and discussing the results in relation to this specific device. The use of the basic turnover formula for other devices is demonstrated by various problems in Section 2.5.

The frequently asked question which relates to the length of time that an ultraviolet sterilizer must be run to completely strip clean a quantity of water is answered in this chapter. It is demonstrated that the total duration to have all the water in a tank or pond pass through a sterilizer with a fixed gallon per hour rating is directly proportional to the total gallons to be sterilized, and inversely proportional to the sterilizer flowrate in gallons per hour. Specific formulas are derived and tables for the required calculations are given. The results obtained

13

in this chapter are important because they will ensure proper sterilization and greatly extend the lifetime of ultraviolet bulbs. Chapters 4 and 5 delve much deeper into the use of ultraviolet sterilizers. But these chapters will be completely dependant on the results introduced herein.

Sterilizers used in aquariums and aquaculture have fixed rates. These ratings denoted in this chapter by the symbol $\dot{F}_o$ which signifies the number of gallons per hour (GPH) that are permitted to be passed through the sterilizer for correct operation, depend on three factors: 1) the amount of water contained in the sterilizer; 2) the intensity or power rating of the ultraviolet bulb; 3) the contact time of water flowing in the direction of the axis of the bulb. All manufacturers of sterilizers should supply this rating and have the backup calculations to substantiate the stated rating.

Connection of the sterilizer so as not to exceed the rated value, will involve a by-pass line so that only the rated gallons pass through the sterilizer while the excess gallons provided by the pump are returned to the tank, either by a second line or by a line containing a check valve which joins back to the by-pass line. Apart from the sterilizer rating, $\dot{F}_o$, one also has to keep in mind the pump rating, i.e., the number of gallons the pump delivers per hour. This is denoted by the symbol $\dot{G}$. A typical installation is illustrated in Figure 2.1.

2.2   THE TURNOVER FORMULA

Knowledge of differential and integral calculus is necessary to understand how the results developed herein are obtained; however use of the results stated in this section have no such requirement. The interested reader may wish to follow the analytic development to see how the results were obtained.

One must remember that this is a difficult problem because the sterilizer is stripping out bacteria at a slow rate and returning the bacteria free water to the main tank or pond. The sterilized water now mixes with the unsterilized water which is yet to be sterilized and this mixture is then passed through the sterilizer. So the question is: How many hours should the sterilizer be run so that the water is sterilized? The answer is:

$$T = a\,(G/\dot{F}_o)\,, \tag{2.1}$$

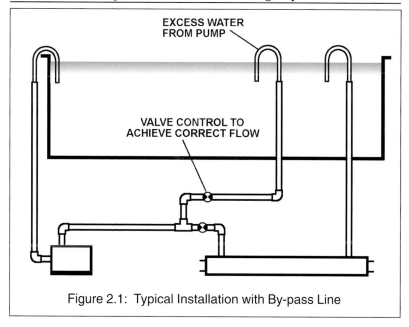

EXCESS WATER
FROM PUMP

VALVE CONTROL TO
ACHIEVE CORRECT FLOW

Figure 2.1: Typical Installation with By-pass Line

where:

T = Hours of sterilization required,
G = Gallons in tank,
$\dot{F}_o$ = Sterilizer flow rating (GPH),
a = Purity coefficient.

The purity coefficient is displayed in Table 2.1. It is arbitrarily selected as being equal to 9.2 which implies that 99.99% of the water in the tank will be sterilized within time T. The analytic development which follows shows how this coefficient is obtained and why the value is taken to be 9.2. Table 2.1 provides other choices.

2.3 ANALYTIC DEVELOPMENT

The sterilizer installation depicted in Figure 2.1 can be illustrated equivalently as shown in Figure 2.2.

Instead of having a tee connection and control valves as shown in Figure 2.1 it has been elected to place a small pump (pump 1) that supplies the sterilizer with the proper flow, for example, (50 GPH) for a sterilizer which has a rating of 50 GPH. The second pump (pump 2) now acts as the by-pass. As is obvious, the by-pass line extracts water from the tank and returns the water without any sterilization action of any sort. On the other hand pump 1 supplies the sterilizer with a mixture of sterilized and unsterilized water and returns totally sterilized water to the tank or pond. Figure 2.2 is now combined back to the installation depicted in Figure 2.1.

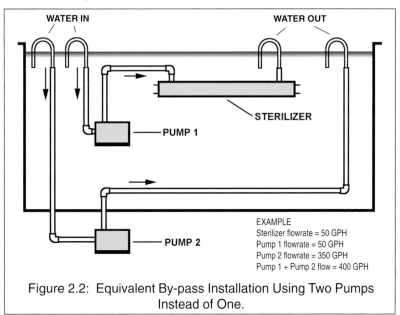

EXAMPLE
Sterilizer flowrate = 50 GPH
Pump 1 flowrate = 50 GPH
Pump 2 flowrate = 350 GPH
Pump 1 + Pump 2 flow = 400 GPH

Figure 2.2: Equivalent By-pass Installation Using Two Pumps Instead of One.

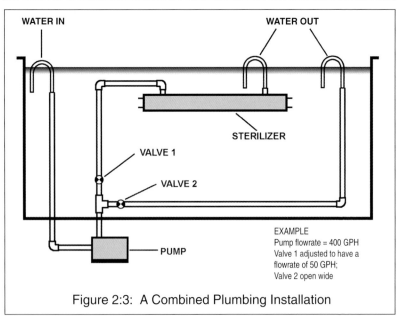

EXAMPLE
Pump flowrate = 400 GPH
Valve 1 adjusted to have a
flowrate of 50 GPH;
Valve 2 open wide

Figure 2:3: A Combined Plumbing Installation

A little thought reveals that the systems illustrated in Figure 2.2 and Figure 2.3 are equivalent but clearly shows that the return by-pass line only recirculates the water.

The analysis proceeds as follows. Figure 2.4 illustrates a tank or pond containing G gallons of water:

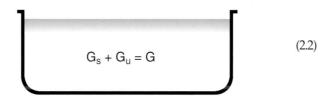

$$G_s + G_u = G \tag{2.2}$$

Figure 2.4: Tank full of water

By defining a coefficient b as:

$$b = (G_s/G) = \frac{\text{Total Gallons of Sterilized Tank Water}}{\text{Total Gallons in Tank}}, \tag{2.3}$$

it is easy to see that at the time sterilization is started $b = 0$, i.e., no water has been sterilized and the total gallons in the tank, G, are equal to G_u, the number of gallons of unsterilized water. However, at any given time, the water flowing into the sterilizer is a mixture of sterilized and unsterilized water. In actuality the sterilized water reaching the entry port just flows through the sterilizer and is re-sterilized but has no effect on the rate of change of the total sterilized gallons, $\dot{G} = dG_s/dt$, in the tank, where t is time.* More specifically, the rate of change in the tank of sterilized water depends on the actual percent of sterilized water in the tank or pond. This can be stated as:

$$\dot{G} = (1 - b)\,\dot{F}_o = (1 - G_s/G)\,\dot{F}_o, \tag{2.4}$$

which says that when there is no sterilized water in the tank, $G_s = 0$, and the rate of change of sterilized water is equal to $\dot{F}_o$, i.e., in the first second or so of operation only unsterilized water enters the sterilizer and totally sterilized water exists the sterilizer. But as the ratio (percent) of sterilized water rises, less and less unsterilized water enters the

---

*The overhead dot placed over any symbol indicates the time rate of change of the symbol or variable: therefore $\dot{x} = dx/dt$ where dx and dt are differential quantities. For example, velocity, $\dot{p}$, is the time rate of change on position, p, or $\dot{p} = dp/dt$, (See Appendix 2.).

sterilizer. When b or G_s/G reaches one, only sterilized water enters the sterilizer and is just re-sterilized so that the rate of change of sterilized water is equal to zero. It is assumed herein that the sterilized and unsterilized water in the tank mix very quickly. Over a sterilizing cycle this assumption is true from an average point of view. Rearranging Eq. (2.4) yields:

$$\dot{G}_s + (\dot{F}_o/G)\,G_s = \dot{F}_o \tag{2.5}$$

or,

$$dG_s/dt + (\dot{F}_o/G)\,G_s = \dot{F}_o. \tag{2.6}$$

Hence, the controlling equation of the sterilization process is a differential equation of the first order. Obtaining the solution of Eq. (2.6) is outside the scope of this work. The interested reader is directed to Refs. (2.5.1, 2.5.2) for methods of solving these types of equations. The solution, as time starts at $t = 0$ and ends at $t = T$ (where T is the total hours required for sterilization) is:

$$T = (G/\dot{F}_o)\,\log_e\,(G/[G - G_s]), \tag{2.7}$$

where the logarithm is taken to the base e. Most calculators display natural logarithms to the base e, sometimes denoted by $\ln = \log_e$. Please see the Appendix for the laws of logarithms.

An interesting result obtained from Eq. (2.7) is that as G_s gets closer and closer to G, the total gallons in the tank, $(G - G_s) \rightarrow 0$ which makes the logarithm become infinite. This implies that T is infinite. Therefore, it will take an infinite amount of time to totally sterilize the tank. A little thought will reveal that since sterilized water is always being mixed with unsterilized water, it is possible to reduce the unsterilized water to any desired percent — *but it is not possible to get rid of it completely.* To this end, let:

w = PERCENT OF STERILIZATION DESIRED,

namely 99%, 99.9%, 99.99%, etc. Equation (2.7) can now be written as:

$$T = (G/\dot{F}_o)\,\log\,(1/[1 - w/100]), \tag{2.8}$$

since $G_s = wG/100$, where w is stated in percent. However, since $\log(x/y) = \log(x) - \log(y)$ and $\log(1) = 0$:

$$T = -\,(G/\dot{F}_o)\,\log\,(1 - w/100). \tag{2.9}$$

Table 2.1 is a display of the value of the factor $a = \log(1 - w/100)$, which is negative and thus cancels the minus sign in Eq. (2.9).

TABLE 2.1

Percent Sterilization vs. Purity Coefficient

w (Percent)	Purity Coefficient (a)
99.0	-4.6
99.9	-6.9
99.99	-9.2
99.999	-11.5
99.9999	-13.8
99.99999	-16.1

As can be seen in Table 2.1 the greater the purity of the water desired, the longer it takes to sterilize the water (since a increases). However, when one considers that, e.g., in a 100 gallon tank 99.0% sterilization means that only 1 gallon remains unsterilized; 99.9% means that only 12.8 ounces remain unsterilized, and 99.99% means that only 1.28 ounces remain unsterilized, it becomes obvious that a trade-off decision must be made. This is especially true because the second time water goes through the sterilizer ($t > T$), the residual unsterilized water will all but vanish. A conservative but realistic choice for w for all cases would be w = 99.99%. This permits Eq. (2.9) to be written as:

$$T = 9.2 \ (G/\dot{F}_o). \tag{2.10}$$

The previous discussion points out the importance of understanding the physics of sterilization so that the correct size sterilizer is purchased for the volume of water in the tank or pond.

EXAMPLE: Turnover Duration

How long will it take for all the water in a 50 gallon tank to pass through a sterilizer or other aquarium device (skimmer) if the water flow through the device is 60 gallons per hour? Assume the purity coefficient is taken to be 9.2.

Just use Eq. (2.10) with $G = 50$ and $\dot{F}_o = 60$, i.e.,

$$T = 9.2 \ (G/\dot{F}_o) = 9.2 \times 50/60 = 7.66 \ \text{HRS}.$$

As can be seen, around three turns per day will be realized. Pretty simple?

2.4 SUMMARY

A formula has been developed that correctly predicts the duration for 99.99% of the water in a tank or pond to pass through a given device. The formula applies to devices that do not offer increasing resistance to the water flow as a function of time. The case of increasing resistance is handled in the next chapter. It was noted that the purity coefficient can be adjusted to increase the percentage of processed water but that all the water in the tank can never be filtered totally. Figure (4.3) depicts relationship (2.10) graphically.

2.5 PROBLEMS

2.5.1 A sterilizer can deliver the proper dose if water is pumped through it at 50 gallons per hour (GPH). The net gallons in the tank are 100 gallons. What is the duration so that 99.99% of the water in the tank has gone through the sterilizer?

Ans: 18.4 HRS

2.5.2 An oxygen reactor is adjusted so that the flowrate through it is just 60 GPH. The rest of the water just flows around the reactor via a by-pass line. How long will it take for all the water in a 70 gallon tank to be oxygenated?

Ans: 10.73 HRS

2.5.3 It is desired to have 4 complete water exchanges per day in a 100 gallon tank through a clean bio-tower. What is the required flowrate? Assume the bio-tower contains 15 gallons.

Ans: 176.3 GPH

2.5.4 It is desired to pass 99.999% of the water in a tank through a chemical tower which offers little or no resistance. The entire system is comprised of 400 gallons. For the chemicals to enter into solution a flowrate of 100 GPH has been determined so as to dissolve the chemicals in 24 hours. It is wished to treat the tank twice daily. What is the flowrate through the tower?

Ans: 383.3 GPH

2.5 REFERENCES

2.5.1 Coddington, E.A., *An Introduction to Ordinary Differential Equations*, Prentice Hall, Englewood Cliffs, N.J., 1961

2.5.2 Hartman, P., *Ordinary Differential Equations*, John Wiley, New York, 1964

3 Theory of Filtration: Turnover and Circulation

See Mystery to Mathematics Fly.

Alexander Pope

3.1 GENERAL DISCUSSION

Proper filtration systems can only be installed when the foundations for a theory that establish proper water management are understood. For a given size tank, the questions of interest are: What duration is required for all the water in the tank to pass through the filter system when filtered water is being mixed with unfiltered water? How many hours per day should the filter be run? What is the difference between the filtration and circulation of water in a closed aquatic system? These are the questions addressed in this chapter.

In order to be effective, quality filtration systems require an analytic theory based on scientific principles so that equipment is used correctly and economically. To meet these objectives, the critical parameters required as inputs need to be identified. These parameters will be identified and utilized to answer the listed questions. As will be seen it is much more effective to run the filter with a predetermined on-off cycle (or number of short cycles) wherein each cycle is defined as the duration that all the water in the tank is filtered to a specified percent in purity. This duration is referred to as one *turn* of the tank water. Unfortunately, the correct definition of one turn has not truly been defined in a rigorous manner until it was introduced in Ref. (3.10.1) and Chapter 2. In fact, the common usage is usually in error because there is a tendency just to divide the number of gallons in the tank by the pump flowrate and adopt the resulting time as one turn. This is wrong for two reasons. First, the value of the flowrate leaving the filter, not the rated pump flowrate, must be used in the calculations. Second, the process wherein filtered and unfiltered water is being mixed together has been ignored. The error occasioned due to the incorrect flowrate assumption easily is fixed by insertion of a flowmeter or inexpensive Flowrater™ aft or in front of the filter. Unfortunately, the formula obtained in Chapter 2 can only be used when the flow through a given tank accessory, such as an ultraviolet sterilizer does not vary with time. But in a filter the flowrate does vary with time due to debris build-up, and thus a more general formula for the filtration related definition of one turn needs to be sought. This formula will be obtained in the sections to follow. However, to make the simple turn formula of use to those who care not as to how it is obtained, it will be stated first along with an example in order to clarify how the formula is used.

The analytic theory of filtration makes an important distinction between the process of water filtration and that of water circulation. To attempt to satisfy circulation requirements in a closed ecological system at the expense of the filtration equipment is neither optimal or desired. Filtration is the slow deliberate stripping of water to remove particulate matter and pollutants. Circulation encompasses the objective of water movement to create currents so as to cause surface agitation and help the water become oxygenated. Circulation loops in aquariums and ponds can also be used to condition water by passing it through devices that have one function or another but whose mechanical filtration capability is limited or nonexistent, e.g., chemical towers, sterilizers, protein skimmers, reactors, etc. Circulation loops should be operational at all times. Some devices can be on timers, e.g., U.V. sterilizers, but the water should still continue its journey to and from the aquarium via bi-pass lines. Usually, circulation loops can be powered by pumps or powerheads which draw small amounts of current and are thus economical to operate. The heavy duty work that will satisfy filtration requirements need not be continuous.

3.2   FILTRATION ELEMENT LIFETIME

Removal of debris from water is accomplished by the placement of screens in specially built containers. These screens have holes in them that prevent the undesired particulate matter from passing through. A screen need not be a membrane but can be a plug of loose gravel, charcoal, zeolite, ProOre™, etc. In these cases the miniature tunnels in the loose media of choice act as traps wherein undesirable particulate matter of large size is held back. In professional filtration systems such as the Torpedo Tower™ or N-Stage™ (See Chapter 11) filters, specially manufactured cartridges are used whose screen size is usually referred to in micron units (1 micron = 0.000038 inches). In theory a one micron cartridge will remove particulate matter that has a mean diameter of one micron. These cartridges, due to manufacturing limitations, have holes larger and smaller than the standard rating. Water, seeking the path of least resistance will go through the large holes and clog them first. Thus as time goes by the water will pass through smaller and smaller holes till obstruction of flow is complete. What is the lifetime of these cartridges? Very rough estimates are displayed in Table 3.1.

TABLE 3.1

Approximate Lifetime of Filter Cartridges
(length = 9-3/4" • diameter = 3")

Microns	Lifetime (weeks)*
1	0.5
5	1.0
10	2.0
20	3.0
50	4.0

*FOR ESTABLISHED TANKS:
NOT FOR NEW INSTALLATIONS

A little thought will reveal that the lifetime of the cartridge D, i.e., the duration before the filter elements need to be replaced is an important factor in the theory of filtration. The trouble with an exact determination of D is that: 1) This parameter can be made as large as one wishes by just increasing the quantity of cartridges used; specifically D is related to filter size; 2) This parameter depends on the local bio-mass pollution production rate; and 3) It also depends on whether or not the tank or pond is in a steady state of operation or some disturbance has created a spike in the amount of free floating pollutants. These factors all add up to saying that the rough lifetime expressed in Table 3.1 can only be used for an estimate of what D might be. To obtain D for a given system, it must be measured empirically—but this is easy to do. Actually, the analysis developed herein does not require an explicit determination of D for determination of the turnover duration. However, a reasonable value of D will be required in order to determine the filter service interval.

It is almost obvious that a filter with as large a filtration area as possible should be selected so as to minimize the period between element cleaning or cartridge replacement. Specifically, one would expect that a filter which holds two cartridges of the same micron rating as those displayed in Table 3.1 would last twice as long. Hence, once the filter size (area) is selected, the filter (pump) can be turned on and the flowrate measured over the next few weeks. If the initial flowrate (GPH) is denoted by the symbol $\dot{F}_o$, and the present flowrate is defined by the symbol $\dot{F}$, the coefficient of exhaustion, e, can be defined as:

$$e = \dot{F}/\dot{F}_o. \tag{3.1}$$

A good rule to follow is take e = 1/2, i.e., to assume that when the flowrate leaving the filter is reduced by 50%, the filter needs to be serviced. The value of e can be taken as desired should the 50% rule not be acceptable. However, whatever value is chosen, when the ratio for the flowrates is equal to the adopted value, e.g., e = 1/2, the time that was required to reach this value will be known. This time is the true empirically determined value of D. This value of D should be determined with the tank in a steady state operation as opposed to a tank which has just been installed. In summary, choose e and observe the system until this value is attained. The continuous running duration from filtration initiation with clean elements until e is reached is taken as the value of D. This value of D need only be determined once unless the user changes the micron rating of the cartridges. It specifically tells the user when the filter is to be cleaned. Lastly, the value of D needs to be reduced by the amount of time the filter is off (if it is).

3.3   RATE OF EXHAUSTION

In order to use the theory developed herein the rate of change at which the filter elements, e.g., cartridges, reach exhaustion at the adopted value of e needs to be expressed mathematically. Since the filter experiences what is referred to as "filter damping." The method used herein is to assume linear damping, namely, that the cartridges/media reach exhaustion or need to be replaced on a time scale which is proportional to time. Since the initial flowrate with clean elements, $\dot{F}_o$, is easily measured, the instantaneous flowrate, $\dot{F}$, can be mathematically modeled by the linear equation:

$$\dot{F} = \dot{F}_o + Rt, \tag{3.2}$$

where $\dot{F}_o$ and R are constants and t is the elapsed time since filter start-up. This equation can be solved for R, which is the rate of exhaustion, i.e.:

$$R = (\dot{F} - \dot{F}_o)/t. \tag{3.3}$$

However, since at exhaustion $t = D$ then by Eq. (3.1), $\dot{F} = e\dot{F}_o$ and R can be expressed as:

$$R = (e - 1) \dot{F}_o/D. \tag{3.4}$$

Obviously, by adopting $e = 1/2$, and since $\dot{F}_o$ along with D previously have been measured empirically, the value of R becomes known.

EXAMPLE: Average Filtration Flowrate Determination

A Flowrater™ device measured the flowrate of a clean filter as 300 GPH. It is observed that this flowrate is reduced to half of the original value three weeks later. What is the flowrate one week after start-up? What is the average flowrate in the first week of operation?

Let $e = 1/2$, $\dot{F}_o = 300$ GPH, $D = 3$ weeks $= 504$ HRS. and use Eq. (3.4) to determine R:

$$R = (e - 1) \dot{F}_o/D = (1/2 - 1) \times 300/504 = -0.298 \ G/H^2.$$

Next use Eq. (3.2) with $t = 1$ week $= 168$ hours:

$$\dot{F} = \dot{F}_o + Rt = 300 - 0.298 \times 168 = 249.9 \ GPH.$$

Therefore the average flowrate (See the Appendix) in the first week is $(300 + 249.9)/2 = 274.9$ GPH.

3.4   TOTAL NET GALLONS OF WATER IN TANK

The true amount of water in a tank can be determined by the displacement principle due to Archimedes. By placing all the gravel (in bags), subplates, decorations, etc. into the tank and then filling the tank, it follows that upon removal of these items the water level will drop. Everything in the tank need not be arranged in the ultimate final beauty, it just needs to be put in the tank any which way. The drop in water height when everything is removed, ΔH, (measured in inches) is related to gallons as displayed in Table 3.2.

Table 3.2

SHAPE	GALLONS
Rectangular	$0.004329 \times \Delta H \times L \times W$
Circular	$0.002299 \times \Delta H \times D^2$
Hexagonal	$0.002812 \times \Delta H \times W_m^2$

All dimension in inches; Drop in height = ΔH, Length = L, Width = W; Maximum Width = W_m.

The gallons so determined are subtracted from the total gallons which the tank will hold. Hopefully, the manufacturer provides this for you. If not just set $\Delta H = H$, where H is the water level height and calculate the true gallon rating of the empty tank.

3.5   DETERMINATION OF TURNOVER DURATION

The previous sections have identified the necessary input parameters, namely, the initial flowrate, $\dot{F}_o$; the adopted value of e; the flowrate exhaustion rate, R; and the total net gallons in the tank G.

Since knowledge of the methods of solution of differential equations is central to obtaining an analytic expression of the turnover duration only the results of the analysis will be presented in the next section.

The theory of filtration is complicated by the fact that the water entering the filter is returned to the tank in a filtered state where it is then mixed with unfiltered water. It is this time changing mixture that the filter senses on subsequent passes of the water through the filtration elements. Chapter 2 derives a rigorous derivation for the turnover formula, namely:

$$T = a \, (G/\dot{F}), \qquad (3.5)$$

where:

T = Number of hours for all the water in the tank to pass through a given device (HRS),

$\dot{F}$ = Water flowrate through the device (GPH),

a = Purity coefficient = 9.2 (Dimensionless),

G = Total net gallons in the tank (GAL).

A purity coefficient of 9.2 implies that 99.99% of the water has passed through the device. As discussed in Chapter 2, 100% of the water will never pass through the device because of mixing. Formula (3.5) assumes that the device through which the water flows does not offer increasing flow resistance as a function of time, e.g., an ultraviolet sterilizer. However, in a filter the flow decreases as indicated by Eq. (3.2). Therefore:

$$T = aG/(\dot{F}_o + Rt). \tag{3.6}$$

This equation indicates that the turnover time, T, is constantly changing. The simplest approach is to determine an average turnover time within which the filter will operate until exhaustion. The result of performing the time averaging procedure is:

$$T_{ave} = 12.75 \, G/\dot{F}_o, \tag{3.7}$$

where G is in gallons, $\dot{F}_o$ in gallons per hour, and where the purity coefficient is taken as 9.2 and e is adopted as 1/2. Note the differences between Eq. (3.5) which applies with little or no water resistance and Eq. (3.7) which assumes linear damping of the water. The next section derives this equation. If Eq. (3.7) is accepted, the next section may be skipped.

EXAMPLE: Average Turnover Time

A 200 gallon tank is observed and it is noted that the initial flowrate of 600 GPH through the filter decreases to 1/2 the original value in 400 hours. What are the start, final and average turnover durations?

Select Eq. (3.6) with $t = 0$ to obtain the start duration:

$$T_s = aG/(\dot{F}_o + Rt) = 9.2 \times 200/(600 + 0) = 3.07 \, HRS.$$

Note that $a = -9.2$ so that a negative sign should be placed in front of the equation. This sign is usually omitted. Equation (3.7) yields the average as:

$$T_{ave} = 12.75 \, G/\dot{F}_o = 12.75 \times 200/600 = 4.25 \, HRS.$$

The final turnover duration $(t = D)$ just prior to cleaning is:

$$T_f = 2 \, aG/\dot{F}_o = 2 \times 9.2 \times 200/600 = 6.13 \, HRS.$$

The importance of the average turnover equation is that the parameter D is not present and need not be determined. Figure 3.1 displays the average turnover time as a function of the total net gallons in the tank and the initial flowrate.

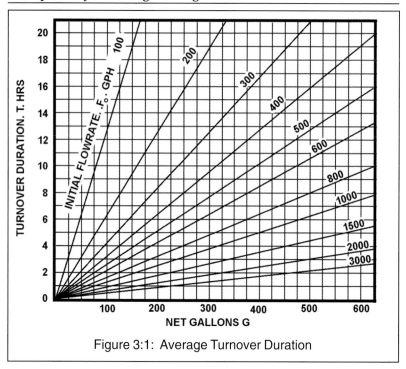

Figure 3:1: Average Turnover Duration

3.6 TIME AVERAGING

Since the turnover duration is constantly changing as a function of time (Eq. 3.6), it is best to use an average value of this parameter during the time span of operation, D, i.e., from t = 0 to t = D. This averaging procedure can be expressed via Eq. (3.6) as:

$$T_{ave} = (1/D) \int_0^D aG/(\dot{F}_o + Rt)\, dt.$$

Performing the integration (See the Appendix) yields:

$$T_{ave} = (aG/RD)[\log \dot{F}_o - \log (\dot{F}_o + RD)],$$

which by the laws of logarithms can be written as:

$$T_{ave} = (aG/RD) \log [\dot{F}_o/(\dot{F}_o + RD)].$$

However, for linear damping Eq. (3.4) states that $R = (e - 1)\dot{F}_o/D$. Performing the indicated substitution yields:

$$T_{ave} = aG \log (1/e)/([e - 1]\dot{F}_o). \tag{3.8}$$

As discussed previously, if the exhaustion parameter, e, is adopted at e = 1/2 and a is taken as -9.2, then:

$$T_{ave} = 12.75\ G/\dot{F}_o.$$

3.7 FILTER ON-OFF TIMES

In order to save electric power and pump wear the filter can be put on a timer and started for a discrete number of turns each day. Obviously as discussed earlier, circulation loops using, e.g., powerheads, should be run continuously. Each turn of average duration T_{ave} will filter out all tank pollutants (particulate matter). However, during the T_{ave} cycle additional particulate matter will be generated. Hence, it would be wise to spread the on-off cycles evenly throughout the day. Three to four complete T_{ave} cycles a day should be sufficient. Spreading the cycles evenly will also prevent build-up of anaerobic bacteria.

3.8 SUMMARY

The parameters peculiar to establish the foundations of a rigorous formula when filters are to be used are identified. Flowrate is then modeled as a linear function. This permits the standard turnover formula for devices that offer no resistance to be adjusted for devices that offer resistance, e.g., filters. The new formula is then averaged over time to obtain a simple relation that can be used for determination of the on-off times of filtration loops. It is emphasized that circulation of tank water should not be confused with the process of water filtration.

3.9 PROBLEMS

3.9.1 What is the average turnover rate for a 100 gallon tank when a flowrate of 50 gallons per hour is flowing through the filter?

Ans: 25.5 HRS

3.9.2 It is desired to filter water in a 500 gallon tank to 99.9999% purity. What purity coefficient should be used? Assume $e = 1/2$ and 400 GPH flowrate is going through the filter. What is the turnover duration?

Ans: 23.9 HRS

3.9.3 Two turns of water are desired each day in a 500 gallon pond. What flowrate should the pump provide?

Ans: 531 GPH

3.9.4 Three 30 gallon tanks plus a sump of 20 gallons are used in a breeder installation. What filter flowrate should be used till the flowrate falls to 1/3 the original valve? Assume 4 turns per day.

Ans: 556 GPH

3.10   REFERENCES

3.10.1   Escobal, P.R., "The Time Required to Sterilize a Body of
Water with an Ultraviolet Sterilizer."
Fresh Water and Marine Aquarium Magazine,
January 1991

3.10.2   Coddington, E.A., *An Introduction to Ordinary Differential
Equations,* Prentice-Hall, Englewood Cliffs, N.J., 1961

4 Sterilizer Selection:
Practical Solution Via Graphics

It is truth very certain that, when it is not in our power to determine what is true, we ought to follow what is most probable.

Rene Descartes

4.1 OVERVIEW

Fishwise, the single most important device available today, ranking second only to a well designed mechanical filtration system is the ultraviolet sterilizer. It is an unfortunate circumstance that use of these devices for eradication of unwanted organisms in aquariums and ponds produced only marginal beneficial results for many end users. The fault in attainment of end results of a striking beneficial nature is not due to the sterilizers; it is directly traceable to the use of the sterilizer.

For a sterilizer to function correctly it must deliver the proper dose to kill the unwanted target organisms, i.e., it must emit the proper *zap* dosage. The concept of zap dose, namely, the energy required for 100% kill of a specified target organism was first introduced in Ref. (4.10.1). But how is the proper dosage to be attained by a given sterilizer? The answer is: *by selection of the proper flowrate that must pass through the sterilizer.* As simplistic as this statement is, the importance of selection of the proper flowrate can not be understated.

This chapter incorporates the results of two previous articles, Refs. (4.10.1), (4.10.2), into a single theory which will give birth to a unified sizing chart that permits the end user to correctly use ultraviolet sterilization technology correctly and successfully. Absolutely no attempt is made herein to prove the results. The analytic proofs from which the results presented in this chapter are derived from can be found in the stated references and in Chapter 5. Furthermore, a graphical approach is adopted in this chapter which permits the user to determine the proper parameters with a minimum of computation. Prior to presentation of the prerequisite graphical results and associated examples, a quick review of some necessary fundamentals and definitions will be undertaken in a question and answer format.

4.2 PRELIMINARIES

It will be beneficial to restate certain facts about U.V. sterilization. First, a question which is asked repeatedly is: "Will U.V. sterilization present a hazard to fish?" The answer is no, because only the water passing through the sterilizers is treated. The beneficial bacteria are safe in the filter bed, rocks and on the tank panels. Certainly, both good and bad bacteria are destroyed in the free floating form as they travel through the U.V., but there are products that can replenish the good bacteria if one insists on having beneficial bacteria floating around the tank. But remember, once established the good bacteria are perfectly safe in their aquatic home. Obviously, the fish are not irradiated and they are perfectly safe. However, when seeding a tank with beneficial bacterial cultures, turn the U.V. sterilizer off for 24 hours.

Second, "Are quartz sleeves necessary?" The answer is *no* unless the temperature is below 55°F. Quartz sleeves are secondary glass tubes which encase the actual bulb. General Electric has demonstrated that radiation is decreased by 26 percent when it passes through the sleeve; see (4.10.3). Furthermore, the bulb operates at hotter temperatures and this may shorten its lifetime. The slight increase in efficiency due to the encased bulb is nowhere offset by the 26 percent loss caused by the radiation traveling through a second glass enclosure. Some manufacturers advocate that the sleeve will make it easier to change the bulb. This is true, but what they have forgotten to tell you is that if the sterilizer is sized correctly for a given tank, and it is run the required number of hours, *it will be necessary to clean the quartz sleeve before the bulb is replaced.* The quartz sleeve just raises the cost of the sterilizer, is subject to breakage and reduces sterilizer efficiency for all tanks while the operating temperature is in the 65° to 85°F range.

Third, "Why is the diameter of the sterilizer important?" The reason for the sterilizer to have a specific diameter involves the systems analysis of *three separate actions.* Action *one* is characterized by the decrease of radiation as the distance perpendicular to the bulb is increased. The radiation falls off as the inverse square of the distance.

Action *two* is associated with the fact that the radiation is degraded the longer the distance it must travel through water of varying turbidity. Actions one and two demand that the diameter be as small as possible. In opposition, as the diameter is made smaller, so is the volume internal to the sterilizer. Since what is sought is for the sterilizer to deliver a maximum dose (which is the product of bulb intensity and time) the diameter should be increased so as to lengthen the contact time. Thus, action *three* says to make the diameter as large as possible. Reference (4.10.1) and Chapter 5 shows that these three actions lead to an algebraic equation of degree four (See the Appendix) that has only one unique solution for the diameter (See the Appendix). This diameter turns out to be *three and only three inches*. If the diameter is smaller, less dose is supplied, and if the diameter is larger, the dose also decreases.

Fourth, "What dose should be delivered?" There is no one answer to this question. However, as presented in Ref. (5.12.2) it is possible to tabulate the zap dosage for numerous target organisms. The table is repeated here (Table 4.1).

TABLE 4.1

Zap Dosage in Microwatt - Sec/cm^2

ORGANISM	ZAP DOSE	ORGANISM	ZAP DOSE
BACTERIA		**BACTERIA**	
Bacillus Anthracis	8,700	Streptococcus Lactis	8,800
Bacillus Megatherium sp (veg)	2,500	Streptococcus Viridans	3,800
Bacillus Megatherium (spores)	5,200	**YEAST**	
Bacillus Paratyphosus	6,100	Saccharomyces Ellipsoideus	13,200
Bacillus Subtilis (mixed)	11,000	Saccharomyces Sp.	17,600
Bacillus Subtilis (spores)	22,000	Saccharomyces Cerevisiae	13,200
Clostridium Tetami	22,000	Brewer's Yeast	6,600
Corynebacterium, Dephtheriae	6,500	Baker's Yeast	8,800
Dysentery Bacilli	4,200	Common Yeast Cake	13,200
Eberthella Typhosa	4,100	**MOLD SPORES**	
Escherichia Coli	6,600	Penicillium Roqueforti	26,400
Micrococcus Candidus	12,300	Penicillium Expansum	22,000
Micrococcus Piltonensis	15,000	Penicillium Digitatum	88,000
Micrococcus Sphaeroides	15,400	Aspergillus Glaucus	88,000
Mycobacterium Tuberculosis	10,000	Aspergillus Flavus	99,000
Neisseria Catarrhalis	8,500	Aspergillus Niger	330,000
Phytomonas Tumefaciens	8,500	Rhisopus Nigricans	220,000
Proteus Vulgaris	6,600	Mucor Racemosus A	35,200
Pseudomonas Aerugenosa	10,500	Mucor Racemosus B	35,200
Pseudomonas Flourescens	6,600	Oospora Lactis	11,000
Salmonella	10,000	**VIRUS**	
Salmonella Enteritidis	7,600	Bacteriophage (E. Coli)	6,600
Salmonella Typhimurium (ave)	15,200	Tobacco Mosaic	440,000
Sarcina Lutea	26,400	Influenza	6,800
Serratia Marcescens	6,160	**PROTOZOA**	
Shigilla Paradysenterlae	3,400	Paramieum	200,000
Spirillum Rubsum	6,160	Nematode Eggs	92,000
Staphylococcus Albus	5,700	Chlorella Vugaris (algae)	22,000
Staphylococcus Aureus	6,600	**FUNGI**	45,000
Streptococcus Hemolyticus	5,500		

A compromise value of 50,000 microwatt-second/cm^2 can be adopted. This will incinerate all organisms up to and including free floating fungi. If protozoa are the target organism then dosage levels up to 100,000 are indicated. On the other hand control of algae in ponds requires a dose of only 22,000.

Fifth, "What watt sterilizer should be used in a given size tank?" This is the question that presently will be addressed with easy to use graphical aids. To reach the indicated dosage levels presented in Table 4.1, it will be evident that even for small tanks (above 20 gallons) selection of a sterilizer rated at less than 25 watts is a very poor choice. Furthermore, the price difference between an eight or 15 watt sterilizer and that of a 25 watt unit is minimal, and even this price difference is quickly offset by the duration the unit need be run. The shorter the run duration, the longer the bulb will last and less electrical energy will be consumed. For these reasons sterilizers of less than 25 watts are not even discussed in this chapter. The reader might extrapolate the curves presented here and see why this system decision was adopted.

4.3   DELIVERY DOSAGE

Chapter 5 presents explicit equations for the calculation of the dose delivered by ultraviolet sterilizers of increasing wattage. The formulas depend directly on the flowrate going through the sterilizer. The interaction between flowrate and dosage is now presented graphically in Figure 4.1.

The curves in Figure 4.1 are for the optimal three inch diameter models. For a two inch diameter sterilizer decrease the dosage by about 33 percent. If the diameter is greater than three inches, also correct appropriately, i.e., a four inch diameter sterilizer, if it exists, would yield also about 33 percent less dosage. This percent decrease when calculated backwards, says that a three inch diameter sterilizer yields 50 percent more output than a two inch or four inch diameter U.V.

Since the delivered dosage is flowrate dependent it is also obvious that the ultraviolet sterilizer *must* be connected in-line with an additional by-pass line as illustrated in Figure 4.2. This is the only way a sterilizer can be connected. Combined filtration and U.V. systems with no flow control regulation into the sterilizer are totally and completely incompetently installed.

Hence, as illustrated, by adjustment of the control valves, the proper flowrate through the sterilizer can be attained. The flowrate can be

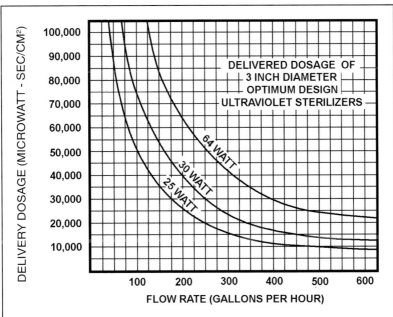

Figure 4.1: Delivery Dose as a Function of Flowrate for Optimal Diameter Sterilizers

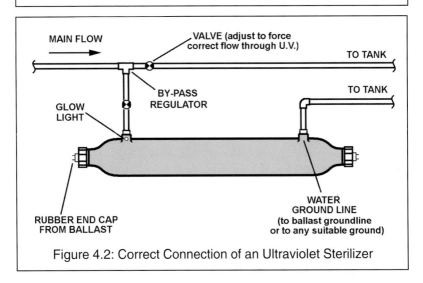

Figure 4.2: Correct Connection of an Ultraviolet Sterilizer

measured by timing the *flow into a bucket*, the use of a flow meter, or by the use of an inexpensive Flowrater™ such as are currently available. Correctly designed sterilizers have a ground wire which should be used to prevent static shock.

From Table 4.1 the target organism zap dose can be selected, and Figure 4.1 now determines the flowrate that must pass through the sterilizer to deliver the required dosage. So far so good, but it is unwise to forget that it takes a certain amount of time for all the water in the tank to travel through the U.V. sterilizer loop.

4.4 WATER EXCHANGES PER DAY

As water is passed through a sterilizer, if the flowrate is correct, it will be completely sterilized with respect to the target organism. However, the water is then returned to the tank or pond and mixed with unsterilized water. In effect, the target organism is thinned out in relation to its original concentration. The question now is: "How long will it be before all the water is sterilized?" The answer to this question can be obtained by the use of calculus as was presented in Chapter 2. It turns out that it would take an infinite amount of time for all the water in the tank to pass through the sterilizer. This is due to the mixing process just discussed. Chapter 2 shows that by adopting a purity coefficient equal to 9.2 that 99.99 percent of the water will have gone through the sterilizer, e.g., in a 100 gallon tank all except 1.28 ounces would have been irradiated. The duration required for this occurrence is the correct definition of *one turn* or *one water exchange*. The analytic formula defining the duration of this process is a function of the purity coefficient, the net gallons in the tank and the flowrate through the sterilizer. References (4.10.1), (4.10.2) and Chapter 2 prove the previous statement. Figure 4.3 displays the results graphically. The straight line nature of the graph permits easy extrapolation to volumes of water greater than 500 gallons.

EXAMPLE

What is the duration of one turn for a 50 gallon tank if a zap dose of 50,000 mw-sec/cm^2 is to be delivered with a three inch diameter 25 watt sterilizer?

Enter the ordinate axis of Figure 4.1 at 50,000, intersect the 25 watt curve and read the abscissa axis which defines the flowrate as 100 gallons per hour.

Enter the abscissa axis of Figure 4.3 at 50 gallons, intersect with the 100 GPH flowrate line and read the turn or exchange time as 4.5 hours from the ordinate axis.

In theory then, a 25 watt sterilizer could be installed with a timer

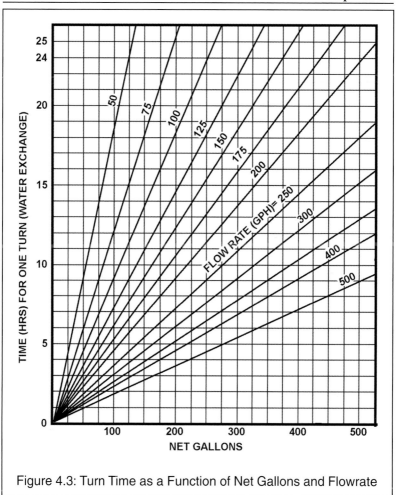

Figure 4.3: Turn Time as a Function of Net Gallons and Flowrate

and run only 4.5 hours per day such as to kill every target organism whose zap dose is below 50,000 (as listed in Table 4.1). Unfortunately, the correct use of a sterilizer is not that simple. The next section explains why.

4.5 REQUIRED WATER EXCHANGES

Bacteria and other organisms require time to multiply. Antibiogram kits currently available on the market instruct the user to take a swab, touch it to the infected fish and then smear the swab onto a small petri dish. Small diskettes impregnated with assorted antibiotics are then placed on the petri dish. Within 36 hours the bacteria has grown everywhere except in those areas surrounding the unique antibiotic diskettes which inhibit the bacteria. Obviously the fish would be treated with those unique antibiotics. Repeated use of these kits has demonstrated that 24 hours is a reasonable expected time of arrival for the first observable traces of bacteria to appear. But some bacteria, no doubt, breed prior to 24 hours. Furthermore, fish are fed at least twice daily and bacteria are introduced at these times. So, in compromise, let 12 hours be adopted as the bacteria cycle.

One exchange or turn of water per day corresponds to the theoretical minimum sterilization requirement. Two exchanges per day are accepted as optimal. The exchanges would be performed so as to divide the 24 hour period equally.

More than two exchanges per day are not required and to do so just would shorten bulb lifetime (estimated by General Electric as 10-11 months of continuous operation.)

By letting the duration be 12 or 24 hours a graph can be generated that fixes the total required flowrate as a function of the size of the tank or pond. The linear nature of Figure 4.4 permits easy extrapolation if the number of gallons is greater than 600.

The acceptable operating range for selection of the system flowrate is bounded by the two straight lines. Operation exactly on the two exchange line defines the optimal system flowrate selection criterion.

EXAMPLE

What size sterilizer should be selected for a 150 gallon? The user is interested in total eradication of all target organisms, including protozoans.

From Table 4.1 select a dosage level of 100,000 mw-sec/cm^2 (Nematodes).

Enter Figure 4.4 on the abscissa axis at 150 gallons and intersect the *two total water exchanges per day* line. Read the ordinate as 115 gallons per hour (approximately). This is the required system flowrate.

Enter Figure 4.1 on the ordinate axis at 100,000 and intersect the 25 watt curve. Read the abscissa and note that the flowrate is less than 115 gallons per hour. The 25 watt U.V. is not strong enough. The abscissa reading on the 30 watt U.V. also falls short of the required flowrate. The 64 watt line provides a reading of 125 gallons per hour; this is close enough. A 64 watt U.V. is required.

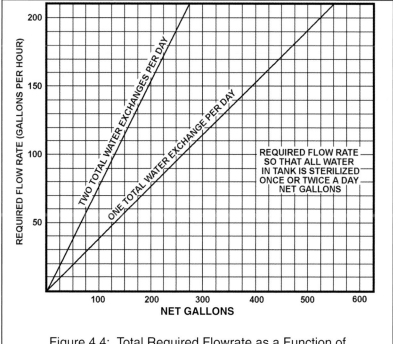

Figure 4.4: Total Required Flowrate as a Function of System Volume in Gallons (Sterilizers)

Enter Figure 4.3 at an abscissa reading of 150 gallons (tank size) and intersect with the flowrate obtained from Figure 4.1, i.e., 125 gallons per hour. Read 11 hours from the ordinate axis. Note that the flowrate through the sterilizer is adjusted to a 125 gallons per hour—not 115.

Set the timers so as to turn on the 64 watt U.V. every 11 hours with a one hour off time between burns. Two turns of water per day are thus realized. In this case about a 10 percent bulb lifetime extension will be realized if timers are used. Obviously, adding another 25, 30 or 64 watt sterilizer will further shorten the total burn time.

EXAMPLE

What size 3″ diameter sterilizer is required to control algae in a 300 gallon pond? Read Table 4.1 and obtain a zap dosage of 22,000.

Enter Figure 4.4 on the abscissa axis at 300 gallons and intersect with the *two total water exchanges per day* line. Extrapolate the line and read 230 gallons per hour on the ordinate axis.

Enter Figure 4.1 on the ordinate axis at 22,000 and intersect the 25 watt line. Read the abscissa as 225 gallons per hour. The 25 watt U.V. (3 inch diameter) just about makes it, as can be seen from Figure 4.3, which yields a turn time of 12 hours. The U.V. would have to burn 24 hours a day. Selection of a 30 watt sterilizer would be a wiser choice because the duration would be decreased and, in the long run, less bulbs would be used because lifetime of the bulbs would be increased. The reader may wish to verify that to deliver the required dose, the 30 watt model needs to run only 8.5 hours, with a flowrate of 312 gallons per hour.

4.6 GRAPHICAL ANALYSIS

The examples presented previously have demonstrated the manner in which the graphics are used. A review now follows.

Step 1: Use Table 4.1 to select the proper zap dose which will destroy the target organism of choice. For general water management, a dose of 50,000 mw-sec/cm^2 is indicated.

Step 2: For the size tank or pond, use Figure 4.4 by entering along the abscissa (in gallons) and intersect the *two total water exchanges per day* line. Read the required system flowrate from the ordinate axis. Should the curve need to be extrapolated, the required flowrate can be found from:

$$\text{FLOWRATE} = 0.766G,$$

where G is the net gallons in the tank or pond.

Step 3: Enter Figure 4.1 along the ordinate axis for the zap dose level selected in Step 1, and then intersect with the watt line whose corresponding value of the flowrate on the abscissa is equal to or greater than the total system flowrate obtained in Step 2, if the value of the flowrate from Figure 4.1 is too small for the required zap dose, then more than one ultraviolet sterilizer will be required. If the U.V. is two inch instead of three inch in diameter, remember to decrease the dose by 33 percent.

Step 4: Enter Figure 4.3 on the abscissa axis for the size tank or pond in gallons and intersect with the flowrate line determined in Step 2. Read the turn or water exchange time in hours from the ordinate. Obviously, if the flowrate is taken exactly as discussed in Step 2, this time will be 12 hours. Choosing a larger sterilizer, or more than one sterilizer, will reduce the turn time and lengthen bulb lifetime.

EXAMPLE

A 600 gallon pond is to be sterilized at the nominal 50,000 mw-sec/cm^2 dose. What sterilizer should be used? Assume the optimum 3 inch diameter model will be used.

Step 1: The dose is 50,000 mw-sec/cm^2.

Step 2: The value of the required flowrate for 600 gallons falls off Figure 4.4. Calculate it as:

FLOWRATE = 0.766G = 0.766 x 600 = 460 GPH.

Step 3: From Figure 4.1, enter the ordinate at 50,000 and intersect the 25, 30 and 64 watt lines. The flowrates are too low. For example, the 25 watt line yields a value of 100 GPH on the abscissa axis. So a solution would be to choose five 25 watt sterilizers. A better choice is to use the 64 watt curve line which gives an abscissa reading of 250 GPH. Thus two 64 watt sterilizers will also solve the problem: etc.

Step 4: A small extrapolation of the 460 GPH flowrate line and the abscissa line verifies that the turn line is exactly 12 hours, as it should because of the choice in Step 2. But if two 64 watt sterilizers were used, the turn time for a combined flowrate of 500 GPH would be about 10 hours.

4.7 UNIVERSAL (UNIFIED) SIZING CHART

This final section integrates all the previous sections into a single graphical display that can be used directly to select the proper size sterilizer for a tank or pond containing a known number of gallons. This display assumes that two turns or water exchanges per day will be the adopted standard. It is obtained by cross plotting or performing a linear transformation on the flowrate axis of Figure 4.1 as dictated by Figure 4.4. In order to make the scales of the transformation compatible and easily used a convenient truncation of the gallon scale is performed which causes a very slight error in the tank size, e.g., for a 250 gallon pond, a three gallon error is generated. Given the physics of the U.V. sterilization, this error is negligible.

Figure 4.5 displays the universal sizing chart. It is a repeat of Figure 4.1, with a second scale that represents the total net gallons in the tank or pond that is the candidate for a U.V. sterilizer.

The unified sizing chart is easy to use. Basically, one enters the chart on the abscissa axis (the net gallon scale) and moves vertically to

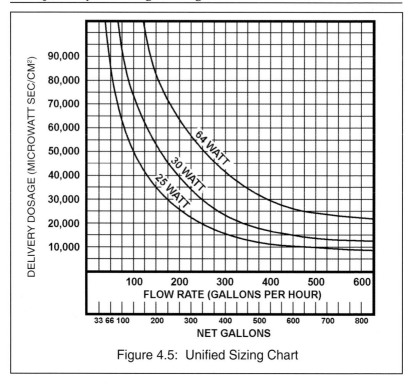

Figure 4.5: Unified Sizing Chart

intersect with each watt curve so that the dosage can be read off the ordinate axis. Selection of the sterilizer wattage can thus be made so as to handle the target organism. However, note that if a larger size sterilizer is selected, which will shorten the turn time, a new flowrate will be found by dropping vertically from the selected curve. The observation that the net gallon scale now indicates a larger tank size than the existing tank can be ignored, and the flowrate noted. With the noted flowrate, just use Figure 4.3 with the actual tank size to determine the turn time. For each on/off cycle of the sterilizer, i.e., set the timer so as to have two equally spaced cycles of the determined duration throughout a 24 hour period.

EXAMPLE

What size three inch diameter sterilizer should be selected for a 150 gallon tank so that protozoans (nematodes) are destroyed?

Enter the unified sizing chart at 150 gallons. Note each square is 33 gallons; half a square is about 16 gallons, etc. Note that only the 64 watt U.V. will deliver the desired dose, and from the complementary abscissa axis, it must be run with a flowrate of 125 gallons per hour to deliver a 100,000 mw-sec/cm^2 dose.

EXAMPLE

What size three inch diameter sterilizer should be selected for a 50 gallon tank?

Enter the unified sizing chart at 50 gallons. Halfway between 33 and 66 is close enough and note that a 25 watt sterilizer will be able to handle even protozoan problems if run at a flowrate of about 47 gallons per hour.

Note that a better choice might be a 30 watt sterilizer because it would do the same job with a flowrate of about 70 gallons per hour. Enter the vertical scale at 100,000, intersect the 30 watt curve and drop vertically to obtain 70 GPH. Forget the net gallon scale.

The 25 watt sterilizer, as dictated by Figure 4.3 would need to be run almost 20 hours a day. In contrast, the 30 watt U.V. needs to be run only 12 hours (Figure 4.3 gives six hours for one turn, but two are needed.). In the first case the bulb would be replaced in about 10 months, but the 30 watt U.V. bulb would burn for almost 20 months before a replacement is necessary.

4.8 SUMMARY

It is necessary to purchase the sterilizer of a wattage so that at least two water exchanges per day can be performed. The sterilizer must be correct in relation to the selected target organism zap dose. Increasing the wattage shortens the turn time and lengthens the bulb lifetime. Install the U.V. correctly with the proper by-pass line.

4.9 PROBLEMS (Can all be solved graphically)

4.9.1 Discuss in length why a by-pass line is required when a sterilizer is to be installed. See Figure 4.2. Would the by-pass line be used on other mechanical devices?

4.9.2 A sterilizer is to service a 200 gallon tank and make sure that all the net water in the tank passes through the sterilizer three times per day. What is the flowrate through the by-pass line?

Ans: 250 GPH

4.9.3 Protozoa (Nematodes) are to be controlled in a 100 gallon tank. What zap dosage is required? What about algae control?

Ans: Protozoa: 92,000 mw-sec/cm^2
Ans: Algae: 22,000 mw-sec/cm^2

4.9.4 What wattage sterilizer will eradicate the protozoans in Example 4.9.3? Control the algae?

> Ans: Protozoa: 25 watt with 50 GPH
> 30 watt with 75 GPH
> 64 watt with 133 GPH
>
> Ans: Algae: 25 watt with 240 GPH
> 30 watt with 325 GPH
> 64 watt with 625 GPH

4.9.5 Assuming that three turns of water will be required on a daily basis for the sterilizers discussed in Problem 4.9.4—what size sterilizer needs to be selected for a 75 gallon tank for protozoan elimination? For algae elimination?

> Ans: Protozoa: 64 watt with 88 GPH
> Ans: Algae: 25 watt with 88 GPH

4.9.6 Use the Universal Sizing Chart (Figure 4.5) to determine the flowrate through a 30 watt sterilizer so that two turns a day are performed in a 230 gallon tank if the target organism is of a fungal nature.

> Ans: 175 GPH

4.9.7 For a large pond installation containing 1600 gallons, a general zap dose of 22,000 mw-cm/sec^2 is desired for full fledged algae-control. What is the number of sterilizers (and size) required?

> Ans: Two 64 watt units hooked in
> parallel, each having a flowrate
> of 625 GPH

4.10 REFERENCES

4.10.1 P.R. Escobal, "Inside Ultra Violet Sterilizers," *Aquarium Fish Magazine,* January 1993

4.10.2 P.R. Escobal, "The Time Required to Sterilize a Body of Water with a U.V. Sterilizer," *Freshwater and Marine Aquarium Magazine,* February 1991

5 Analytic Theory of Ultraviolet Sterilizers: Flowrate, Power and Diameter

Seek Simplicity and Distrust It.

Alfred North Whitehead

5.1 ULTRAVIOLET STERILIZATION

The stars, of which our sun is one of countless millions, emit ultraviolet (U.V.) energy. This energy reaches the Earth and encounters the protective atmosphere which shrouds our planet. The atmosphere acts as a filter and renders harmless the most effective wavelength of ultraviolet light at which germicidal action is most pronounced. Actually, the atmosphere is such a fine filter that only about 10 percent effectiveness of the irradiation will be realized for sterilization.

Today, as in the past, the effectiveness of sunlight, even at ultraviolet levels below ten percent, is well established, and there are few doubts as to the ability of this part of the sun's spectrum to kill micro-organisms. Everyone is familiar with the beneficial effects of fresh air. In applications related to the aquarium the benefits of fresh water are sought. To be able to derive such benefits, a source of irradiation is desired which has a wavelength at which the relative germicidal effectiveness is maximized.

With the advent of fluorescent lamps and the discovery of the unique wavelength at which germicidal effects are maximized (2537 angstroms), an atomic element that would emit such a wavelength upon vaporization was sought. This element was mercury and when placed on a fine wire, it gave birth to today's low pressure germicidal or mercury lamps. These short wave ultraviolet energy sources deactivate

45

micro-organisms which are not protected by an absorbing medium such as our deep atmosphere. The deactivation of harmful micro-organisms in an effective manner will therefore be dependent upon the proper exposure to such lamps, where exposure or dose is the product of intensity and time.

In aquariums experiments have demonstrated that ultraviolet irradiation when properly used decreases the number of free-floating bacteria, yeast, mold spores, viruses, protozoa (algae) and fungi.

This chapter attempts to lay a firm foundation based on scientific analysis for selection of operating variables whose proper values will ensure that U.V. irradiation does indeed satisfy the objective goal for which it was intended. Unfortunately, the knowledge of operating details on ultraviolet sterilization in the aquarium industry is deficient, and in fact, some claims made by reputable manufacturers are not only confusing, but are in substantial error. It is for this reason that end users run, for example, eight watt sterilizers at flowrates of 300 gallons per hour, and then come to the conclusion that ultraviolet sterilization does not seem to control disease. The recommendations presented in this chapter will ensure that ultraviolet sterilization will not only do the proper job, but will even exceed the end users' expectations as to what irradiation can accomplish.

To orient the reader, this chapter is outlined as follows: First, the *zap* dosage is defined and values of the zap dosage for a wide variety of organisms is listed. Next germicidal lamps are discussed and explicit formulas for intensity output as a function of the distance from the bulb are presented based on the data from General Electric. In the next Section, a formula which corrects the intensity as it penetrates into water is developed. This is followed by a simple formula for the number of gallons contained in the sterilizer as a function of the radius and length of the sterilizer. This will permit the contact or, dwell time, of the water within the radiation chamber to be determined. *At this point a single expression for the dosage delivered by the sterilizer can be obtained by multiplying together the intensity, the intensity correction factor and the dwell time.*

An important refinement is discussed subsequent to obtaining this formula, by letting the radius of the sterilizer be an unknown and solving for the value of the radius which causes the dosage to be maximized. The reader should bare in mind that the larger the diameter of the sterilizer, the greater the dwell time of the water, and this will yield an increase in the dosage. However, as the radius of the sterilizer increases the farther the radiation must travel. This causes a decrease in the generated dosage. The questions now are: What is the value of the radius of the sterilizer which will maximize dosage output? Is the diameter of the sterilizer you intend to purchase correct? These questions will be answered in this chapter. As will be seen, performance of the optimal sterilizers are up to 50 percent higher than sterilizers of an equal wattage which have smaller diameters.

Lastly, the result of the analysis developed in Chapter 2, is restated. These results give a formula which correctly defines how long the sterilizer must be run so that all the water in the tank is sterilized, i.e., it correctly defines what "one turn" of water means, especially when sterilized and unsterilized water is being mixed as it goes through the U.V. on subsequent cycles. This formula can also be used to correctly determine the wattage required for a given tank size.

5.2   THE ZAP DOSAGE

Since intensity, I, has the units of microwatts per square centimeter, and time, t, can be measured in seconds, the dose, D, is given by:

$$D = I \times t \ [\text{microwatt-sec/cm}^2]. \qquad (5.1)$$

The question now is: What is the dosage which will inhibit population growth by 100 percent? Experiments have demonstrated that this dosage which is called herein the *Zap Dosage*, can be determined quite well, see Ref. (5.12.2). The results are collected in Table 5.1.

A well designed sterilizer that can deliver such zap dosages will therefore be of great benefit to successful aquarium management.

Those readers that just wish to use the results need read no further. Just use Table 5.1 to obtain the zap dosage required for the selected target organism. Next use Table 5.3 or 5.5, with the scale formula listed in each table to see what flowrate is required to do the proper job. The examples will also clarify the correct method of application.

5.3   GERMICIDAL LAMPS

A low-pressure germicidal mercury lamp is designed so that as much energy as possible can be generated at a wavelength of 2537 angstroms. To accomplish this, 60 percent of the input energy (watts) is required. A loss occurs in passing through the special glass because it only permits 74 percent of the 60 percent of the input to be realized, i.e., a little less

TABLE 5.1

Zap Dosage in Microwatt - Sec/cm^2

ORGANISM	ZAP DOSE	ORGANISM	ZAP DOSE
BACTERIA		**BACTERIA**	
Bacillus Anthracis	8,700	Streptococcus Lactis	8,800
Bacillus Megatherium sp (veg)	2,500	Streptococcus Viridans	3,800
Bacillus Megatherium (spores)	5,200	**YEAST**	
Bacillus Paratyphosus	6,100	Saccharomyces Ellipsoideus	13,200
Bacillus Subtilis (mixed)	11,000	Saccharomyces Sp.	17,600
Bacillus Subtilis (spores)	22,000	Saccharomyces Cerevisiae	13,200
Clostridium Tetami	22,000	Brewer's Yeast	6,600
Corynebacterium, Dephtheriae	6,500	Baker's Yeast	8,800
Dysentery Bacilli	4,200	Common Yeast Cake	13,200
Eberthella Typhosa	4,100	**MOLD SPORES**	
Escherichia Coli	6,600	Penicillium Roqueforti	26,400
Micrococcus Candidus	12,300	Penicillium Expansum	22,000
Micrococcus Piltonensis	15,000	Penicillium Digitatum	88,000
Micrococcus Sphaeroides	15,400	Aspergillus Glaucus	88,000
Mycobacterium Tuberculosis	10,000	Aspergillus Flavus	99,000
Neisseria Catarrhalis	8,500	Aspergillus Niger	330,000
Phytomonas Tumefaciens	8,500	Rhisopus Nigricans	220,000
Proteus Vulgaris	6,600	Mucor Racemosus A	35,200
Pseudomonas Aerugenosa	10,500	Mucor Racemosus B	35,200
Pseudomonas Flourescens	6,600	Oospora Lactis	11,000
Salmonella	10,000	**VIRUS**	
Salmonella Enteritidis	7,600	Bacteriophage (E. Coli)	6,600
Salmonella Typhimurium (ave)	15,200	Tobacco Mosaic	440,000
Sarcina Lutea	26,400	Influenza	6,800
Serratia Marcescens	6,160	**PROTOZOA**	
Shigilla Paradysenterlae	3,400	Parameium	200,000
Spirillum Rubsum	6,160	Nematode Eggs	92,000
Staphylococcus Albus	5,700	Chlorella Vugaris (algae)	22,000
Staphylococcus Aureus	6,600	**FUNGI**	45,000
Streptococcus Hemolyticus	5,500		

than half the input energy is used. About two percent goes into visible light and 48 percent into heat (Ref. [5.12.3]). It is interesting to note that if a sleeve of this special quartz material is placed around the bulb, as some manufacturers advocate, the sleeve will cause a loss of another 26 percent. For very low temperature systems (T = 50°F or less) the sleeve will help, otherwise it is not of much use. This statement is made in light of the fact that: if the sterilizer is run the correct number of hours (as will be discussed), the sleeve would need to be removed for cleaning before the bulb requires replacement. Furthermore, these sleeves cost the user added expense and are subject to breakage. To make matters even worse, the addition of a sleeve causes an additional displacement of water inside the U.V. chamber which reduces contact time, unless the diameter of the chamber is increased.

General Electric provides intensity data on 25, 30, and 64 watt germicidal lamps as listed in Table 5.2

The value I_0, i.e., the intensity at the glass surface is not provided by General Electric. This value was obtained by using a smooth second degree Lagrange interpolating polynomial and represents the theoretical maximum output.

TABLE 5.2

Bulb Intensity in Clean Air Perpendicular to Bare Tube

INTENSITY (watts/ft^2)	DISTANCE (inches)	25 WATT	30 WATT	64 WATT
I_8	8	1.00	0.77	0.88
I_4	4	2.07	1.50	1.72
I_2	2	4.20	3.00	3.40
I_0	0	7.39	5.26	5.91
DIAMETER		1"	1"	3/4"
LENGTH		17"	35"	59"

To use the data for computation of the intensity at any distance, p, perpendicular to the bulb, an analytic function, needs to be found that can represent the intensity output. Examination of Figure 5.1 shows that the analytic form required should be a function equal to I_0 when $p=0$ and then smoothly decrease to zero as p becomes infinite.

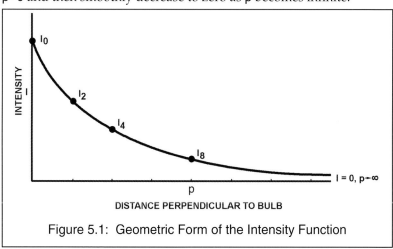

Figure 5.1: Geometric Form of the Intensity Function

An analytic form which satisfies the end boundary conditions and passes through the intermediate first three data points is:

$$I = A/[p-C]^2 + B/[p-C]),$$ (5.2)

where A, B, and C are constants. Using the data in Table 5.2, these constants can be obtained. The resulting analytic functions for p less than 5″ are:

$$I_{25} = \frac{6263.629}{(p+16.104)^2} - \frac{269.953}{p+16.104}$$ (5.3)

$$I_{30} = \frac{4174.384}{(p+15.796)^2} - \frac{181.178}{p+15.796} \tag{5.4}$$

$$I_{64} = \frac{4962.392}{(p+16.169)^2} - \frac{211.351}{p+16.169}, \tag{5.5}$$

where I is determined in watts/ft^2 when p is input in inches. These formulas represent the data in a convenient form which will enable further analysis to be performed. Note that I_{25} for a G25T8 bulb (or other sizes) manufactured by General Electric, will be very close to a G25T8 bulb made by an alternate manufacturer since the bulb outputs are standardized.

EXAMPLE

What is the intensity in watts/ft^2 in clean air at one inch from the surface of a G30T8 (30 watt bulb).

From Eq. (5.4) letting p = 1, it follows that:

$$I_{30}(1") = \frac{4174.384}{(1+15.796)^2} - \frac{181.178}{1+15.796}$$

$$= 14.797 - 10.786 = 4.01 \text{ (watts/ft}^2\text{)}.$$

5.4 DEPTH DISSIPATION

When 90 percent of the energy is absorbed by a liquid the effective or maximum depth for sterilization is reached. General Electric data shows that this distance, call it p^*, can vary widely from 0.1 inch in wines and syrups to five inches in drinkable water of low transmission. In aquariums the only recourse is to adopt a safe limit, especially if dye medications or cloudy water with bacterial blooms are present. The best estimate that can be provided here is to pick $p^* = 2$ inches. By defining a coefficient of dissipation, c, where:

$$c = (1 - p/p^*), \tag{5.6}$$

with p and p^* both measured in inches. A corrected value of the intensity in water, call it I^*, can now be written:

$$I^* = cI = (1-p/p^*)(A/[p-C]^2 + B/[p-C]). \tag{5.7}$$

This is an expression to correct for the energy dissipation which occurs through water or any other liquid. As mentioned $p^*=2$ inches is a safe value. Obviously when $p=p^*$ it follows that $l^* = 0$.

5.5 DWELL OR CONTACT TIME

To develop an expression for the time that water stays in the body of the sterilizer requires a knowledge of the volume of water within the unit. Therefore, since the volume of any cylinder is:

$$V = \pi r^2 L,$$

where r is the radius and L is the length, one can write:

$$V = (\pi[p+r_b]^2 - \pi r_b^2)L, \qquad (5.8)$$

which is the volume of the annular ring of water once the volume of the bulb is subtracted, and where r_b is the radius of the bulb, L is the length of the bulb, and as before p is the distance perpendicular to the bulb to the inside wall of the sterilizer. The previous expression can be simplified to read:

$$V = \pi L(p^2+2r_b p)/231, \qquad (5.9)$$

where if the lengths are in inches, the conversion factor, 231, gives V in gallons.

To find the dwell time T_D one has only to divide V by the flowrate $\dot{F}_o$, i.e., the gallons per hour going through the sterilizer. Specifically:

$$T_D(HRS) = V(GAL)/\dot{F}_o(GAL/HR). \qquad (5.10)$$

5.6 THE DOSAGE EQUATION

At this point the expressions to obtain the dose delivered by the sterilizer are available. Since the definition is given by Eq. (5.1), it follows that by multiplying Eq. (5.7) and (5.10) with the appropriate conversion factors, one has:

$$D = 52700(L/\dot{F}_o)(1-p/p^*)(p^2+2r_b p)(A/[p-C]^2 + B/[p-C]), \qquad (5.11)$$

where

D	= Dose (microwatt-sec/cm^2),
L	= Sterilizer Length (inches),
$\dot{F}_o$	= Sterilizer Flowrate (GPH),
p*	= Dissipation Distance (inches=2 in),
r_b	= Radius of Bulb (inches),
A,B,C	= Intensity Constants (Eqs. 5.3,5.4,5.5),
p	= Distance Perpendicular to Bulb from Surface (inches).

EXAMPLE

What dosage is delivered with a 25 watt sterilizer at the inner wall of the sterilizer housing? The G25T8 bulb diameter is one inch; the length is 17 inches. Assume that water is flowing at 500 GPH and that a two inch diameter STARTRONICS unit, (Ref. 5.12.5), is used.

In this example p = (1"-1/2"), $\dot{F}_o$ = 500 GPH, L = 17", p* = 2" (adopted), A = 6263.629, B = -269.953, C = 16.104.

Substitution of these values into Eq. (5.11) yields:

$$D=52700[17/500][1-0.5/2][0.5^2+2 \times 0.5 \times 0.5][6263.629/(0.5+16.104)^2$$

$$-269.953/(0.5+16.104)]$$

$$=6512 \text{ microwatt-sec/cm}^2.$$

EXAMPLE

What would be the dosage delivered in the above example if the flowrate is cut to 70 GPH? Against what organisms would this dosage be effective?

Since the flowrate is just a scale factor in the D equation, the new dose for an $\dot{F}_o$ = 70 GPH would be:

$$D = 6512 \times 500 \text{ GPH}/70 \text{ GPH}$$

$$= 46514 \text{ mw-sec/cm}^2.$$

Examination of Table 5.1 shows that fungi, algae and most organisms would be killed.

For purposes of reference, the values of the dosage function are collected in Table 5.3.

TABLE 5.3

Dosage Delivered by Various Wattage Sterilizers

Flowrate = 500 GPH, Diameter = 2", p* = 2"

Size	Dosage (mw-sec/cm$^{2)}$
25 Watt	6512
30 Watt	9548
64 Watt	18406

Note that to obtain the dosage at different flowrates,
Dosage (at new flowrate) = Dosage (at 500 GPH) x 500/New Flowrate

5.7 OPTIMUM STERILIZER DESIGN

The equation which defines the dosage, uses the distance p as a variable. A little thought will reveal that as the diameter of the sterilizer is increased, the dose also increases, but as p increases, the depth which the U.V. radiation can penetrate falls off and the dose decreases. The intensity also decreases. So at what value of p is the dose a maximum? The theory of maxima and minima from differential calculus states that either a maximum or minimum of an analytic function is attained when the derivative of the function is equal to zero. Without belaboring the point, the end product of performing this analytic operation results in an algebraic equation of the fourth degree, namely:

$$a_0 p^4 + a_1 p^3 + a_2 p^2 + a_3 p + a_4 = 0, \tag{5.12}$$

where in terms of the constants peculiar to Eq. (5.12),

$a_0 = +2B/p^*$
$a_1 = +A/p^* - B - 5BC/p^* + 2r_b B/p^*$
$a_2 = +3BC - 6r_b BC/p^* - 3AC/p^* + 3BC^2/p^*$
$a_3 = +2A[r_b + C] - 2BC[C - r_b] - 4r_b AC/p^* + 4r_b BC^2/p^*$
$a_4 = -2r_b C[BC - A]$.

Note that since Eq. (5.12) has been equated to zero, the multiplicative factor 52700 (L/$\dot{F}_o$) does not enter into the problem, i.e., the optimization does not depend on the U.V. sterilizer length or the flowrate through the unit. Equation (5.12) can be solved for p in closed form using the methods developed in the theory of equations of algebraic structure, Ref. (5.12.4). The results are collected in Table 5.4.

TABLE 5.4

Sterilizer Diameter for Maximum Output (p*=2)

Bulb	Diameter (Inches)
G25T8 (25W)	3.19"
G30T8 (30W)	3.17"
G64T6 (64W)	3.0"

Examination of Table 5.4, i.e., the results obtained by solving Eq. (5.12), shows that the optimum solutions cluster around a value for the diameter of three inches. Since it would be impractical to manufacture sterilizers with precisely the values tabulated in Table 5.4, it follows that a very close compromise is to adopt a value for the diameter equal to three inches. The corresponding dosage which is delivered by the optimal design sterilizers is shown in Table 5.5, along with the percent increase in delivered dosage from the slimmer two inch diameter sterilizers (see Table 5.3).

TABLE 5.5

Optimum Diameter Sterilizer Output
Flowrate = 500 GPH, Diameter = 3", p* = 2

Size	Dosage (mw.-sec/cm^2)	Percent Gain
25 Watt	10,083	55%
30 Watt	14,793	54%
64 Watt	25,084	34%

Note that to obtain the dosage at different flowrates
Dosage (at new flowrate) = Dosage (at 500 GPH) x 500/New flowrate

The increase in performance is striking. It is obvious that the advantages are that faster flowrates can be utilized to treat a body of water, and fewer sterilizers are required for larger tanks. Keep in mind that making the diameter greater than three inches lessens the dose output. Smaller values of the dissipation parameter, p*, would reduce these values, but the increased performance would still be realized. These wide bodied sterilizers are currently available for sale. The modest increase in purchase price is far outweighed by their outstanding performance.

5.8 THE LENGTH OF TIME REQUIRED TO RUN AN ULTRAVIOLET STERILIZER

How long should a sterilizer be run to sterilize all the water in a body of water? The analytic proof of the results repeated herein was presented in Ref. (5.12.1) and Chapter 2. Only the final formula is stated here in order to complete the last link required for successful use of the ultraviolet sterilization process. The formula is not only useful because it correctly defines what one "turn" of water actually means, but because it also answers the question: What size sterilizer is required for an aquarium or body of water containing a given number of gallons?

One must remember that the problem related to the determination of the turn or cycle time is difficult because the sterilizer is stripping out organisms at a slow rate and returning the organism free water to the main body of water where it is mixed with unsterilized water. Hence the ratio of sterilized to unsterilized water is constantly changing as it goes through the sterilizer chamber. As explained in the reference, the sterilizer must be connected with a by-pass line should the flowrate in the main line exceed the maximum rating of the sterilizer, i.e., a tee must be installed in the main line with valves which divide the flow so that only the correct water flow goes through the sterilizer. Two independent lines can then be returned to the tank. With this understanding the question now is: How many hours should the sterilizer be run so that all the water in the tank is sterilized?

The answer is:

$$T = a(G/\dot{F}_o),\tag{5.13}$$

where

$$\begin{aligned}
T &= \text{hours of sterilization required (HRS)} \\
G &= \text{gallons in tank (net gallons)} \\
\dot{F}_o &= \text{sterilization flowrate (GAL/HR)} \\
a &= \text{purity coefficient (dimensionless).}
\end{aligned}$$

The purity coefficient is displayed in Table 5.6.

Since 100 percent of the water can never be sterilized (see Chapter 2), a good compromise is to select $a = 9.2$. This selection implies that, for example, in a 100 gallon tank only 1.28 ounces of water would elude sterilization. A hefty penalty is payed in extended duration if higher and higher values of a are adopted. At any rate, once a is adopted at, say, 9.2, then Eq. (5.13) can be used to determine the time required to

TABLE 5.6

Percent Sterilization and Required Purity Coefficient

Percent Sterilization	Purity Coefficient
99.00000	-4.6
99.90000	-6.9
99.99000	-9.2 (adopted)
99.99900	-11.5
99.99990	-13.8
99.99999	-16.1
100.00000	Infinite

make one sterilization pass, i.e., one "turn". *This equation defines what one turn really means.* As explained in Chapter 2 the negative in front of a is omitted.

EXAMPLE

What is the time required to sterilize a 100 gallon tank with a 30 watt slim line sterilizer with a two inch diameter if the user is satisfied with delivering a dose equal to 50,000 mw-sec/cm^2 (sufficient to kill free floating fungi)?

Since the base value for a 30 watt sterilizer is given by Table 5.3 as 9548 mw-sec/cm^2 for a flowrate of 500 GPH, the flowrate required is (see the flowrate formula also listed in Table 5.3):

$$D(new) = D(at\ 500\ GPH) \times 500/New\ flowrate$$
$$50,000 = 9548 \times 500/\dot{F}_o,$$

or the new flowrate would be:

$$\dot{F}_o = (9548/50,000) \times 500 = 95\ GPH.$$

Equation (5.13) now yields:

$$T = a(G/\dot{F}_o)$$
$$= 9.2 \times 100/95 = 9.68\ hours.$$

Hence, in 10 hours 99.99% of the water will have been stripped clean of every organism listed in Table 5.2 (whose zap dosage is below 50,000 mw-sec/cm^2).

EXAMPLE

What on/off duration should be set on a timer in a 75 gallon tank with a 30 watt slim line sterilizer with a two inch diameter if the user wishes to zap everything save the Tobacco Mosaic Virus and a few mold spores which are usually not found in a tank?

From Table 5.3 the base value for D is 9548, so that from Table 5.1 using D(new) = 100,000

$$\dot{F}_o = 9548 \times 500/100,000 = 48 \text{ GPH}.$$

The duration required for all the water to pass through the sterilizer is:

$$T = 9.2 \times 75/48 = 14.39 \text{ hours}.$$

Hence, setting a timer with an on/off cycle of 15 hours will accomplish the job.

5.9 PROPER WATTAGE LEVEL OF A STERILIZER

The number of on/off cycle (turns) required per day is certainly not more than three, especially if one is armed with the knowledge that each cycle is indeed zapping everything that presents a danger in the tank. Furthermore, by limiting the number of turns to only those required to do the correct job, one can economize on bulb replacement (lifetime in continuous operation of germicidal lamps is only about 10 months), power consumption, and added heat transference. To this end, Eq. (5.13) can be used backwards to answer the question: What size sterilizer should be purchased for a given tank size? Let $T = 24/N$ where N is the number of on/off cycles per day (24 hours). A realistic value for N is at most three. Solving for the flowrate $\dot{F}_o$ in Eq. (5.13) one has:

$$\dot{F}_o = aGN/24. \tag{5.14}$$

This equation determines the total flowrate which must pass through the sterilizers (one or more) to accomplish the sterilization.

EXAMPLE

A store owner has a 1000 gallon central system. What size sterilizer(s) should be purchased? From Eq. (5.14), letting N = 3,

$$\dot{F}_o = aGN/24 = 9.2 \times 1000 \times 3/24 = 1150 \text{ GPH}.$$

Obviously, for a large system this number implies more than one sterilizer. Since the owner wishes to zap nearly everything that swims up and including fungi, it would be wise to select the zap dosage from Table 5.1 as 50,000 mw-sec/cm^2. From Table 5.3 selecting a 64 watt sterilizer:

New flowrate = 18406 x 500/50,000 = 184 GPH,

since the dosage at 1150 GPH is supposed to be 50,000 mw-sec/cm^2. The number of 64 watt slim line sterilizers required would therefore be given as:

$$Number = 1150/184 = 6.25,$$

or six 64 watt two inch diameter sterilizers plumbed in parallel should be used. If the optimum three inch diameter sterilizers are purchased, since they are 36 percent more efficient, only four of these models would be required.

EXAMPLE

What size sterilizer should a user purchase for a 60 gallon tank?

When this question is asked, the user usually means: What wattage is required to disinfect the water? Obviously, a three inch diameter sterilizer would be better than a two inch model (if that is the question).

The two options available are a 25 watt model and a 30 watt model. Assuming a reasonable dose of 50,000 mw-sec/cm^2 is used, the flowrates can be determined for each size from Table 5.3 (for a two inch diameter sterilizer) as:

$$\dot{F}_o = \text{new flowrate} = D(\text{at 500 GPH}) \times 500/D(\text{desired}),$$

so that;

$$\dot{F}_o \text{ (25 Watt)} = 6512 \times 500/50,000 = 66 \text{ GPH},$$
$$\dot{F}_o \text{ (30 Watt)} = 9548 \times 500/50,000 = 96 \text{ GPH}.$$

The turnover time for each size is now given by:

$$T = aG/\dot{F}_o$$

or

$$T \text{ (25 Watt)} = 9.2 \times 60/66 = 8.3 \text{ hours}$$
$$T \text{ (30 Watt)} = 9.2 \times 60/96 = 5.75 \text{ hours.}$$

Assuming that three turns a day are desired, the total time for each sterilizer would be:

$$3T \text{ (25 Watt)} = 3 \times 8.3 = 24.90 \text{ hours}$$
$$3T \text{ (30 Watt)} = 3 \times 5.75 = 17.25 \text{ hours.}$$

As can be seen, both sizes will do the job, but since the lifetime of the bulbs is about 312 days (7500 hours), the 25 watt U.V. bulb would need to be replaced in 312 days, while the 30 watt U.V. bulb would last 434 days. Therefore, the 30 watt sterilizer is more cost effective over a long period of time. The differences become more pronounced as the number of gallons in the tank increases. Use of a three inch diameter sterilizer would increase bulb lifetime up to 50 percent.

5.10 SUMMARY

Once the proper zap dosage is selected, the determination of the proper flowrate through a sterilizer can be determined. The flowrate through the sterilizer is the single most important factor in achieving proper U.V. sterilization. A three inch diameter sterilizer can increase performance by up to 50 percent, as opposed to standard two inch models. The turnover rate can be computed by means of the special formula presented in this chapter. The same formula can be used to determine the correct amount of wattage that is required from a knowledge of the proper flowrate.

5.11 PROBLEMS

5.11.1 A three inch diameter 60 watt sterilizer is under consideration to control algae in a 500 gallon pond. What is the zap dosage? Three turns a day are desired. What is the flowrate through the sterilizer?

Ans: 22,000 mw-sec/cm^2
Ans: 575 GPH

5.11.2 Explain in detail how and why a by-pass line should be used to connect an ultraviolet sterilizer of any size.

5.11.3 Two 25 watt two inch diameter sterilizers are connected in series, i.e., the output of one sterilizer is fed directly into the input of the next sterilizer. If the flowrate through the sterilizers is 600 GPH, what is combined zap dosage?

Ans: 10853 mw-sec/cm^2

5.11.4 Three three inch diameter 30 watt sterilizers are connected in parallel, i.e., the flow through each sterilizer is one third the total flowrate. If the total flowrate is 1500 GPH, what is the combined zap dosage of the sterilizers?

Ans: 44379 mw-sec/cm^2

5.11.5 Explain in detail what happens when the diameter of a sterilizer is increased. What are the three trade-off factors of consideration?

5.12   REFERENCES

5.12.1 P.R. Escobal, "The Time Required to Sterilize a Body of Water with an Ultraviolet Sterilizer," *Freshwater and Marine Aquarium Magazine,* Vol. 14, No. 2, February 1991

5.12.2 R.W. Legan, "U.V. Disinfection Chambers Require Custom Designing," Water and Sewage Works, Reference Edition, June 30, 1980

5.12.3 General Electric, "Germicidal Lamps and Application," Technical Document LS-179

5.12.4 J.V. Uspensky, *Theory of Equations,* McGraw-Hill Book Company, New York 1948

5.12.5 Filtronics, P.O.Box 2457, Oxnard, California 93033

6 Reactors:
Water Conditioning Devices

Civilization advances by extending the number of important operations which we can perform without thinking about them.

Alfred North Whitehead

6.1 FUNCTION OF REACTORS

Reactors are sealed cylindrical tubes through which water flows. Each of these devices is designed to operate on the water and either add or subtract some wanted or unwanted constituent. Some reactors handle more than one function. They are usually positioned externally in relation to the aquarium. Depending on their function, the flow rate of the water within the reactor can be a very important parameter. This is so because the volume of the reactor and the flow rate determine what is called the "dwell time," i.e., the duration that the water spends in the reactor. Many chemical reactions and processes require unique contact times in order to function optimally and correctly. The ultraviolet sterilizer (Chapters 4 and 5) is not classified as a reactor, but the dwell time parameter was shown to be of paramount importance. So shall it be with all reactors.

6.2 DETERMINATION OF DWELL TIME

Since reactors are usually cylindrical, the volume, V, is given as the product of the cross-sectional area and the length (height) of the reactor, namely:

$$V = \pi D^2 L/4, \qquad (6.1)$$

where $\pi = 3.1415$, D is the diameter and L is the length, all measured in inches. Actually, if the reactor is partially filled with water, L should be

61

adjusted so that only the volume of the water is determined. Since reactors are usually filled with bio-media (1.1.4), the determination of V is best accomplished empirically by filling the loaded reactor with water and then extracting the water into gallon bottles. This operation yields V directly in gallons. Obviously, the same ploy can be used in a reactor of any shape. The dwell time, T, is now given directly by:

$$T = V/\dot{F}_o, \qquad (6.2)$$

where $\dot{F}_o$ is the flow rate passing through the reactor (GAL/SEC), V is the water volume (GAL) and T is in seconds.

6.3   THE BY-PASS CONNECTION

Chapter 4 introduced the concept of the by-pass connection. Installation of reactors with this type of connection is almost mandatory. Figure 6.1 illustrates the plumbing peculiar to the by-pass connection.

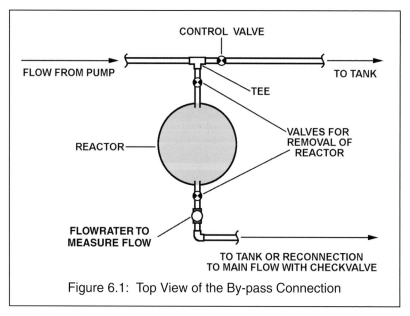

Figure 6.1: Top View of the By-pass Connection

    As can be seen, by closing the control valve, more and more water is forced through the reactor. By closing the removal valves and opening the control valve, all the water is diverted around the reactor. Installation of a flowmeter or an inexpensive Sphere™ Flowrater™ (1.1.11) is a wise decision so as to be able to monitor the flow through the reactor and thus by Eq. (6.2) determine the dwell time.

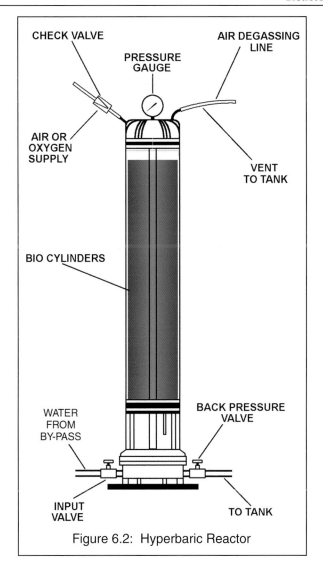

Figure 6.2: Hyperbaric Reactor

6.4 OPERATION OF REACTORS

6.4.1 The Oxygen Reactor (Hyperbaric Reactor)

A typical oxygen or ozone reactor is illustrated in Figure 6.2. This type of reactor is a long cylinder usually filled with bio-media in the form of small bio-cylinders or bio-balls (small plastic balls with many perforations or projecting spikes). The removal valves are open and the reactor is filled with water via a central tube which ejects the water at the top of the reactor. A plate with perforated holes which permits water to pass but retains the biocylinders is placed at the bottom of the reactor. This leaves a portion of the reactor not filled with the bio-media. Air or ozone is injected at the top under pressure. The gas forces the water level to drop below the bottom plate and below a small orifice (thin pipe on right below plate) called the degas-vent. When the gas reaches the vent, it escapes in a puff via the small diameter degassing airline which returns to the tank. The degassing line always spits out gas and a small quantity of water. This is why the line must be hung over the top edge of the tank via a small "jay" tube (1.1.19). Since gas has escaped, the water level rises above the degas-vent until the entering gas starts to push the water down the reactor. It again drops to a level below the degas-vent. This perpetual dance continues with the water in the reactor oscillating a few inches up and down near the bottom bio-media retaining plate.

This entering gas thus envelops the upper column of bio-media. The fractionation of the water over the large surface area inherent to the bio-media causes the pressurized gas to dissolve into the water and thus raises the dissolved oxygen or ozone level of the water leaving the reactor.

When a reactor is installed and no gas is pumped in, the water pressure gauge will read a certain value. This value can be adjusted by use of the water removal valve exiting the reactor. Use the valve to raise the pressure two to three psi above normal flow. Higher pressures than those indicated present a hazard because nitrogen might be forced into the water. When air, etc., is pumped in, the air pressure from the airpump or Hydroram™ (1.1.16) should be adjusted so that the reactor oscillates in a predetermined number of seconds (see Chapter 16). Specific input flowrates are required. An airpump or Hydroram™ capable of six psi pressure is mandatory.

6.4.2 The Carbon Dioxide Reactor (CO_2)

Living plants are very fond of carbon dioxide. Lush foliage will be attained by the proper control of this gas. Optimal values as indicated by a CO_2 test kit should be 8-10 PPM. Figure 6.3 illustrates an inexpensive CO_2 reactor.

In a CO_2 reactor, water enters the bottom through the front removal valve (nearest to the control valve illustrated in Figure 6.1) and fills the entire reactor with water as soon as the top air bleed valve is open.

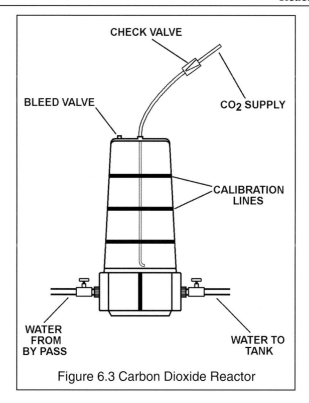

CHECK VALVE

BLEED VALVE

CO_2 SUPPLY

CALIBRATION LINES

WATER FROM BY PASS

WATER TO TANK

Figure 6.3 Carbon Dioxide Reactor

When the water reaches the top of the reactor, the bleed valve is closed. Carbon dioxide is now pumped into the reactor via a second port containing a check valve. An injector which uses disposable CO_2 cartridges is a most convenient method of delivering the gas to the reactor. The small disposable cartridges hold a surprising amount of CO_2. In the FILTRONICS™ Diffusin™ system, one cartridge will fill the reactor about 38 times. By use of the gas injector, the reactor is filled to one of the calibration lines placed on the reactor to aid the user to relate to tank size. Carbon dioxide is soluble in water. By adjustment of the left removal valve, the amount of water that enters the reactor can be easily adjusted for a given tank. The CO_2 in the reactor should slowly deplete itself over a long duration. The gas should be added continuously during the day (with light). For an exact analysis see Chapter 16.

6.4.3 Bio-Tower Reactors

Bio-towers are very useful reactors. They can be used as true reactors and as hybrid wet/dry systems (1.1.40). Many of the functions performed in the square type wet/dry system can also be satisfied by a bio-tower. A bio-tower is just a large diameter tube of varying length which is sealed at the bottom and has a top cover that can be removed. A top water entry port and lower drain are provided. It can be filled with just about any type of media. Figure 6.4 illustrates a typical bio-tower. Water is introduced through the top entry port and is caused to flow through the media which acts on the water. The water exits through the bottom port. Bio-towers filled with zeolite or ProOre™ (substances that absorb ammonia are called ammonia towers). Those filled with ion exchange resins go by the name ion exchange reactors. Ion exchange resins transform nitrite, nitrate, ammonia, copper, etc. into harmless by-products. Carbon reactors are bio-towers filled with activated charcoal.

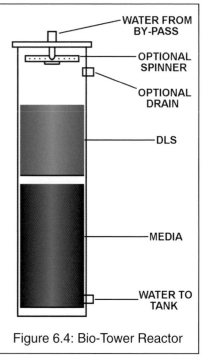

Figure 6.4: Bio-Tower Reactor

If a rotating spinner bar (sort of an inverted lawn sprinkler) is placed underneath the top cover and the unit is filled with bio-cylinders or balls on the bottom, topped off with a roll of DLS (reinforced polyester matting), the unit functions as a wet/dry system. The spinner bar helps to oxygenate the water, the DLS filters and helps the beneficial bacteria colonize, etc.

The bio-tower can be used as a fluidized bed (1.1.2) by pumping water in through the bottom drain into a unit partially filled with fine silica. The enormous surface area of the swirling sand has great benefit to the achievement of a correct biological cycle. The treated water is extracted from a side port near the top (See Chapter 15.).

As can be seen, bio-towers have many applications. As usual, correct contact times are of prime importance.

6.4.4 Nitrogen Reactors

As mentioned in Section (1.2), the control of elevated nitrate levels is

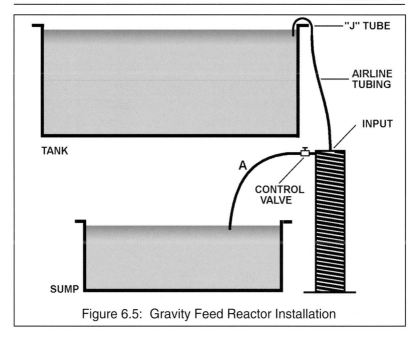

Figure 6.5: Gravity Feed Reactor Installation

very important. To this end, the nitrogen reactor (1.1.23) is an important asset. Figure 6.5 displays the method of installing the reactor.

To operate, apply suction at (A) with the control valve fully open. Water will fill the reactor and start flowing into the sump. Close down the control valve until 40 to 50 drops per minute exit at (A) into the sump.

A nitrogen reactor is a hollow cylinder with a long opaque coiling flexible inner hose of small diameter. Water enters the top of the reactor via a feeder line which operates under gravity or suction and runs down the winding coil. It is discharged at the bottom of the sealed external hollow cylinder, fills the cylindrical tube and escapes from the reactor at the top. The water flow through the internal coil is exceedingly slow. Because of the slow rate, it will take up to three or four weeks to obtain a reduction in nitrate levels.

It has been demonstrated that once nitrate levels drop to 5 PPM, the regulator valve must be completely open to feed the bacteria on water turnovers, otherwise, there is a risk of bacterial die-off which can result in the production of hydrogen sulfide gas.

A second method of installation is displayed in Figure 6.6. For this type of installation, no sump needs to be employed.

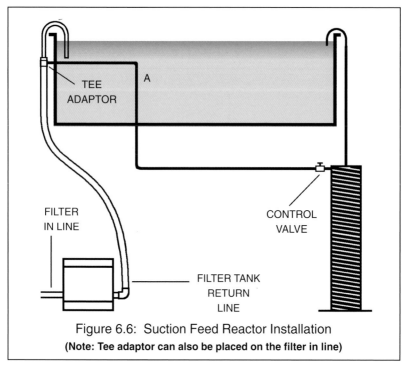

Figure 6.6: Suction Feed Reactor Installation
(Note: Tee adaptor can also be placed on the filter in line)

This method of operation requires the use of a tee with a spout to where the tubing can be attached. To operate, open the control valve and apply suction a (A). Water will fill the reactor. Reconnect airline tube to adaptor. Turn on the filter (pump). Water will siphon into the main line. When water flow in airline tube is steady, close the control valve. Remove reactor "jay" tube from tank and place in a one ounce bottle full of tank water. Open the control valve, and determine the flow (equivalent to about 40 to 50 drops per minute). Just time how long it takes for the water in the one ounce bottle to drop half way down the bottle. Since a one ounce bottle contains about 600 drops, it follows that the half way mark should be reached in six to seven minutes (when the valve is correctly set).

6.5   SUMMARY

Reactors are very useful devices capable of performing a wide variety of functions. However, they need to be installed correctly by use of a by-pass connection. The by-pass connection permits control of the flow rate into the reactor. This in turn, based on the volume of water contained in the unit permits the dwell or contact time to be determined. Many chemical reactions require time to attain completion. Some dwell times can be obtained theoretically, but in reactors the empirical approach is simpler. The use of reliable test kits that measure dissolved oxygen, ammonia, nitrite, copper (such as the Aquatronics Accutron™ test kits), etc., permit proper flow rates to be introduced into the reactor via the by-pass connection.

6.6 PROBLEMS

6.6.1 In the by-pass connection why is the control valve placed after the "tee" fitting shown in Figure 6.1?

6.6.2 What is the proper flow rate into a reactor which holds 15 gallons of water if the ion exchange resins require 45 seconds of contact time to perform their objective?

Ans: 1200 GPH

6.6.3 Why is a check valve necessary in the by-pass connection if water leaving the reactor is to be combined back into the main flowline? Can you think of a good reason the flow exiting the reactor should not be recombined into the main flowline?

6.6.4 Why should the pressure in an oxygen reactor not be in excess of 2-3 psi over nominal operating conditions?

6.6.5 Describe a plan for determination of the flow rate that should be supplied to a carbon dioxide reactor.

6.6.6 How do nitrogen reactors reduce nitrate levels? Discuss generally.

6.7 REFERENCES

6.7.1 M.A. Moe, Jr., *The Marine Aquarium Handbook,* Green Turtle Publications, Plantation, Florida 1995

6.7.2 M.A. Moe, Jr., *The Marine Aquarium Reference,* Green Turtle Publications, Plantation, Florida 1992

7
Venturi:
A Velocity Pressure Transformation

Daniel Bernoulli has been called the father of mathematical physics.

Eric Temple Bell

7.1 DEFINITION OF THE DEVICE

A venturi, what is it? It is a cylindrical hollow tube with a unique shape through which fluid flows. The unique shape takes the form of an hourglass, i.e., the tube has a given entrance diameter which tapers down to a smaller diameter, and finally returns to its original diameter. This device was invented by Clemens Hershel (7.10.1). What does it do? The fluid flow enters the venturi with a given pressure and velocity. As the tube tapers down to a minimum constricting diameter the velocity of the fluid increases. This increase in velocity, to satisfy the law of conservation of energy, causes the pressure to decrease to a minimum at what is called the throat of the venturi. From the minimum diameter or throat, the venturi now expands so that, in the absence of frictional loss, the original entrance velocity and pressure is recovered. If the venturi is well designed the overall pressure loss is about 15 percent of the pressure differential that exists between the inlet and the throat.

What applications does a venturi have? Apart as its use as a fluid flow measurement device, it can be used to inject air into the fluid (water) by opening a small hole at the outside perimeter of the throat. As long as the pressure at the throat is less than atmospheric pressure (14.7 pounds per square inch at sea level) air will be suctioned into the venturi. As will be discussed, these devices have three main applications in aquatic systems.

The first application consists of using the air injection capability to mix air and water. The air/water mixture is returned to the aquarium or pond and let to impinge against a flat vertical rock or slab. The upward cascade of bubbles will dramatically increase aeration and circulation. To make a concrete identification, the device performing this task is referred to as an *injector*. A second application would be to use the venturi to produce only air by separating the air from the water. This device is referred to as a Hydroram™. The Hydroram™ can be used to power up conventional air stones, etc. The very important third applications consists of using either an injector or Hydroram™ to operate a protein skimmer. Actually the injector will be abandoned for a much more powerful device.

7.2 BERNOULLI'S EQUATION

Any text on fluid mechanics can be consulted to find the derivation of this famous equation due to Daniel Bernoulli. It can be obtained by using the basic principle of physics which states that the work (product of force times distance) performed on a given mass is equal to the change in kinetic and potential energies of the mass. For the venturi depicted in Figure 7.1, Bernoulli's equation can be stated as follows:

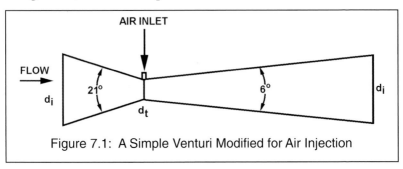

Figure 7.1: A Simple Venturi Modified for Air Injection

$$(p_i/w) - (p_t/w) = (V_t^2/2g) - (V_i^2/2g) + Z_t - Z_i, \qquad (7.1)$$

where,

p_i = inlet pressure (lbs/ft^2),
p_t = throat pressure (lbs/ft$^{2)}$,
w = water density (62.4 lbs/ft^2),
V_t = water velocity at throat (ft/sec),
V_i = water velocity at inlet (ft/sec),
g = acceration of gravity (32.174 ft/sec^2),
Z_i, Z_t = elevation of inlet and throat above some reference (ft).

Since the flowrate of water, $\dot{G}$, measured in gallons per hour, or cubic feet per second must be the same at the inlet and throat, the velocity terms are not independent, because $\dot{G} = AV$, where A is the cross sectional area of the venturi. Furthermore, since the area is equal to $\pi d^2/4$ it follows that:

$$d_i{}^2 V_i = d_t{}^2 V_t. \qquad (7.2)$$

Substitution of Eq. (7.2) into Eq. (7.1) with the appropriate conversion factors yields:

$$p_t - p_i = 3.1125 \times 10^{-7} \, [(1/d_i{}^4)-(1/d_t{}^4)]\dot{G}^2, \qquad (7.3)$$

where p is measured in pounds per square inch, d is measured in inches and $\dot{G}$ is measured in gallons per hour. Note that it has been assumed that the venturi is horizontal so that $Z_t - Z_i = 0$, or $Z_t - Z_i$ is negligible and that $3.1125 \times 10^{-7} = 3.1125/10000000$.

Equation (7.3) is fundamental in the design of venturi devices because for a given inlet diameter and desired flowrate, one can compute the required throat diameter. A return visit to Eq. (7.3) will be forthcoming.

7.3 THE VARIABLE THROAT VENTURI

The trouble with a simple venturi is that the throat is fixed. This is a limitation because atmospheric pressure is different throughout the country, e.g., consider mile high low pressure, Denver, Colorado, U.S.A., and that different applications require different back pressures. The patented variable throat Hydroair™ (7.10.2) has the advantage of being able to select a unique throat diameter for each situation that might be encountered. This device is illustrated in Figure 7.2

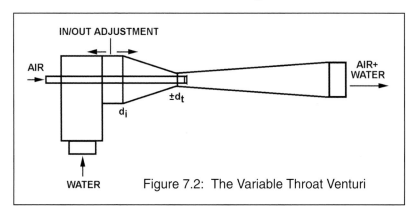

Figure 7.2: The Variable Throat Venturi

As can be seen, air is not injected perpendicular to the throat (as in Figure 7.1) but is injected axially. Furthermore, the air delivery tube can slide in or out and thus create a throat of any size. This patented device is called a Hydroair™.

7.4 APPLICATION: HYDROAIR (VENTURI)

Figure 7.3 illustrates skematically how a Hydroair™ device can be used in "piggy back" fashion to provide a tank or pond with aeration and circulation.

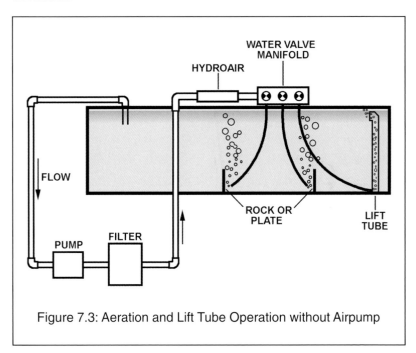

Figure 7.3: Aeration and Lift Tube Operation without Airpump

For proper operation, the Hydroair™ should be positioned near the water level in order to avoid overhead water pressure. Note that as long as the pump is on, free air delivery is obtained by just placing the device on the return line from the filter. The maximum flow is achieved by throttling the Hydroair™ to obtain the proper throat area. The water and air exiting the venturi can then be returned to the tank via a single line or fed to a manifold consisting of valves so as to split the air/water mixture for aeration or lift tube operation. As the amount of bubbles decrease, one also can clearly see when the filter needs cleaning.

7.5 APPLICATION: HYDRORAM™

Suppose only air is desired, e.g., to run a pressurized trickle filter or a protein skimmer, etc. How can the water and air be separated? The schematic of such a device is shown in Figure 7.4.

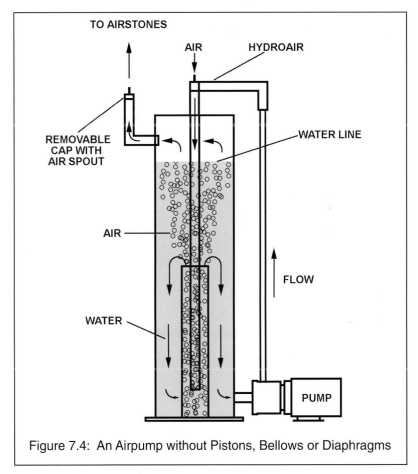

Figure 7.4: An Airpump without Pistons, Bellows or Diaphragms

By insertion of a Hydroair™ device into a closed cyclindrical tube partially filled with water and the connection of a pump to form a closed water loop, the air can be separated from the water. In the Hydroram, Ref. (7.10.3), the pump suctions water out of the bottom of the unit and returns it to the adjustable Hydroair on top. The air and water travel down a thin central pipe into an inner tube which is sealed at the bottom. Water and air impinge at the bottom and the flow direction is reversed. The bubbles rise to the top where they separate from the water. This device is to air what a protein skimmer is to water, i.e., the air which is produced is scrubbed clean of dirt, pollutants, etc. After a given duration the water in the device needs to be replaced; it becomes quite dirty.

Hence, if one wanted to deliver super clean air to a protein skimmer, a Hydroram™ device would be indicated. This device also finds use in deep tanks because it does not care about back pressure. There is nothing that can be damaged such as a diaphragm. It also finds application in pressure reactors. But how much pressure can such a device produce? To answer this question one must go back to Eq. (7.3).

EXAMPLE

By measurement of the flow and pressure into a Hydroram™ constructed with a half inch return line from a magnetic drive pump capable of delivering up to 500 gallons of water per hour (under a one foot head), it was observed that:

$$G = 48 \text{ GPH}; \; p_i = 10 \text{psi}.$$

The venturi inlet and throat diameters were 0.480 inches and 0.335 respectively. The air injection tube diameter (which runs axially down the Hydroram™) was 0.190 inches. This diameter must be subtracted from the inlet and throat diameters because water does not occupy this cross-sectional space. Hence, by Eq. (7.3):

$$p_t - 10 = 3.1125 \times 10^{-7} \, [(1/0.290^4) - (1/0.145^4)] \times 48^2,$$

so that $p_t = 8.47$ psi. Assuming that sea level conditions apply, i.e., atmospheric pressure = $p_a = 14.7$ psi, it follows that the difference $p_a - p_t = 6.22$ psi. This is a remarkable pressure value. Note that for water, each 2.308 feet of depth equals one psi. This implies that this device can pump air down to more than 14 feet. Most air pumps only achieve two to three psi. A few vibrator type air pumps will also achieve six psi, but it is not known how long the diaphragm will last. Also, the air is not purified.

Lastly, it should be pointed out that the throat diameter was obtained by throttling the venturi until the minimum throat pressure was obtained. Obviously different size venturis will produce more air, etc.

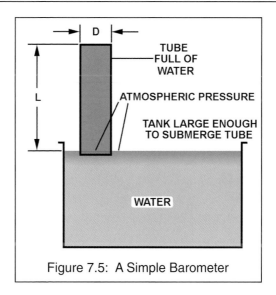

Figure 7.5: A Simple Barometer

7.6 VOLUME OF AIR

Let's look at a simple barometer as illustrated in Figure 7.5:

If a tube of any diameter is submerged in water and the air is evacuated, the tube can be extracted vertically and it will retain the water as long as it is not totally pulled out of the water. If the length L is measured (see Fig. 7.5), and the inside tube diameter is known, then the volume of water in the tube is $\pi D^2 L/4$, in say, cubic inches. To obtain the volume of air pumped per minute, one need only insert the airline from the pumping device into the tube and time how long it takes for the water to be displaced. Therefore, one can obtain the cubic inches per minute rating of any air pump. It is a puzzlement why most manufacturers do not give you this number, so that you know what you are purchasing. The small venturi peculiar to the Hydroram™ application previously described can produce in excess of 600 in³/min. Note that if you desire to build an atmospheric barometer, then some air needs to be left in the riser tube. This type of barometer can then be calibrated from radio reports which broadcast barometric pressure.

7.7 APPLICATION: PROTEIN SKIMMER

Protein skimmers are popular devices that remove dissolved organics from aquariums. There are three types: counter-current, co-current, and venturi-current. In counter-current skimmers, the flow of bubbles rise to oppose the flow of water within the device. The theory of counter-current skimmers is presented in detail in Chapter 9. Co-current skimmers, i.e., where the air bubbles and water flow in the same direction, are not as efficient as counter-current designs because of contact time considerations. Both of these designs require the use of an air pump or a Hydroram™. As mentioned earlier, should a Hydroram™ be used as the air source, then highly purified air will be fed to the skimmer. Venturi-current skimmers need to use a Hydroair™ to inject the air into the skimmer. These types of skimmers perform as if they were a combination of counter and co-current skimmers. The air and water mixture can be injected axially straight up from the bottom to cause a swirling action (co-current and counter-current design). Another design, called the bounce design, injects air and water from the top of the skimmer and lets the mixture impinge on the bottom of the skimmer so that the flow of the mixture is reversed (co-current and counter-current). Some sophisticated venturi skimmers recycle the water a number of times so as to achieve the proper contact time. Counter-current skimmer designs are the most efficient, but selection of the design depends on installation contraints.

7.8   SUMMARY

Clemens Herschel's venturi device can be modified so as to have an adjustable throat diameter. Adjustability of this device permits the user to select the throat diameter so as to achieve optimal performance. Devices that deliver both air and water or just air are available. The theory for the proper design of venturis depends on Bernoulli's equation.

7.9   PROBLEMS

7.9.1   Explain clearly how fixed throat venturis differ from those that possess a variable throat. What are the advantages of the variable model?

7.9.2   What is a Hydroair™? A Hydroram™?

7.9.3   What is the throat pressure in a simple venturi? The inlet pressure is 16 psi. Inlet and throat diameters are 3/4″ and 1/4″ respectively. The flowrate is 650 GPH.

Ans: -17.25 psi

7.9.4   A three inch diameter tube of 20″ length which is closed at the top is submerged in water and is lifted upwards as illustrated in Figure 7.5. An airline is used to introduce air into the open bottom of the tube. It takes 27 seconds for the water to be pushed out of the vertical tube. How much air is the airpump attached to the airline producing?

Ans: 314.2 in^3/min.

7.9.5 A Hydroram™ developes a pressure of seven psi. How deep will the device pump air?

Ans: 16.2 ft.

7.10   REFERENCES

7.10.1 C. Herschel, "The Venturi Meter", paper presented before the American Society of Civil Engineering, Dec. 1887

7.10.2 P.R. Escobal, "Apparatus for Air Delivery System," U.S. Patent 5,054,423, Oct. 1991

7.10.3 P.R. Escobal, "Apparatus and Method for Pumping Air," U.S. Patent 4,687,494, Oct. 1983

7.10.4 P.R. Escobal, "Inside Protein Skimmers," *Aquarium Fish Magazine,* Feb. 1995

8 Introduction To Protein Skimmers: A Graphical Approach

Thought is only a flash between two long nights,
but this flash is everything.

Henri Poincaré

8.1   THE PROTEIN SKIMMER

A protein skimmer is a device that strips out or removes dissolved organics and debris from an aquarium or pond. Basically, it is a cylindrical hollow column of plastic material containing water through which air or ozone is flowing from the bottom with or against the current of water passing through the same column. When the air and water move in opposite directions, the skimmer is called one of counter-current design. A skimmer which uses a venturi (Chapter 7) to inject the air is appropriately called a venturi skimmer. When air and water ascend in the same direction, the skimmer is called one of co-current design. As will become evident in Chapter 9, the counter-current design is more efficient than the co-current or venturi design. Apart from many other factors, two points must be clarified from the start. First, as will be demonstrated in Chapter 9, the diameter of the skimmer is as equally important as the length (height) of the skimmer. However, when the diameter of the skimmer is discussed it is implied herein that this is the diameter of the column containing the rising air bubbles. Some skimmers are designed with an inner co-axial tube through which the bubbles rise, so it is the inner tube diameter which must be used in the analysis to follow. Actually, inner co-axial tube skimmers are quite less efficient because of the loss of cross-sectional area inherent in their designs. Secondly, the skimmer length, L, means the height of the water column within the skimmer. The skimmers are illustrated in Figure 8.1.

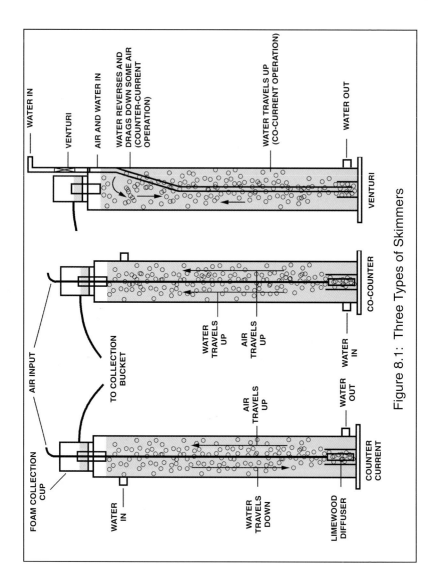

Figure 8.1: Three Types of Skimmers

8.2 THE LAWS OF SKIMMER OPERATION

An in-depth discussion and proof of the laws which govern skimmer operation is presented in Chapter 9. At this point only a statement of these fundamental laws will be made. Subsequent to this, charts which permit the correct diameter of skimmers required for a given installation will be graphically displayed.

The concept of the bombardment rate, i.e., the number of times an ascending clean air bubble hits or rubs against a descending or ascending drop of water, similarly, is presented without the benefit of the discussion given in Chapter 9. The bombardment rate, R_B, is a critical parameter in skimmer selection. It will be discussed in more detail shortly. However, the intent of this chapter is to present a graphical approach to skimmer selection free of but the most fundamental analytic formulas. To this end the laws are:

FIRST LAW: Flowrate through a given skimmer is fixed from the start by the gallons in the tank and the number of complete water exchanges required each day.

SECOND LAW: The bombardment rate, depends only on the duration of the tank water exchange and the diameter of the skimmer.

THIRD LAW: Increased skimmer length or height only raises the value of the absolute contact time but does not affect the bombardment rate.

FOURTH LAW: The maximum volume of air in a skimmer can only be about 16 percent the volume of the skimmer.

FIFTH LAW: The air flowrate entering a skimmer should produce a full upward blossom of bubbles without excessive turbulence and is theoretically determined as a function of skimmer diameter, length, bombardment rate and absolute contact time.

SIXTH LAW: The value of the bombardment rate within the skimmer, its length, diameter and airflow must all be properly chosen for optimum operation.

SEVENTH LAW: If the skimmer diameter required is greater than the skimmer diameter which is available, then selection of a fixed number of skimmers of cross sectional area less than the required cross-sectional area, but whose total individual cross-sectional areas sum to the required cross sectional area, is equivalent from a performance point of view.

These skimmer laws, as presented herein for the first time, may sound formidable from the point of view of implementation, but as will be seen, the basic requirements can be displayed on a unified sizing chart (see Chapter 9). However, to correctly use the Filtronics™ graph presented herein, a number of points must first be clarified. The next section addresses the facts that should be understood prior to use of the graphical data.

8.3   THE THEORY OF SKIMMER SELECTION

The question most frequently asked is: "How tall a skimmer should be purchased for a given tank?" It will be proven in the next chapter that this is only one half of the correct question. The correct question is: "What diameter and height skimmer should be purchased for my tank?" This question will be answered presently. However, before this question is addressed, some trade-off factors need to be considered.

First, for a tank of given size, all the water in the tank should pass through the skimmer a certain number of times each day. But how long a duration is required to have all the water in the tank pass through the skimmer? Reference (8.9.1), and Chapters 2, 4 and 5 address this question in relation to ultraviolet sterilization. However, the analysis presented in Chapter 2 also applies to protein skimmer operation. The analysis performed therein shows that it takes a given duration in hours for all the water in the tank to pass through an external device such as a sterilizer or protein skimmer. One must consider that water is going through the external device and is being delivered back to the tank where it is mixed with water that has not gone through the device. So what duration is required for all the water in the tank to go through the device? The answer is:

$$T = 9.2 \, (G/\dot{F}_o), \tag{8.1}$$

where the factor is 9.2 is the purity coefficient (Table 2.1, Chapter 2). This number implies that 99.99 percent of the water in the tank will have gone through the device (skimmer) in, T hours, for a tank containing, G gallons, with an attached skimmer that has a flowrate $\dot{F}_o$ in gallons per hour. Hence, T defines one complete "turn" of water correctly.

If a skimmer is designed and operated at the correct design parameters, then experimental observation indicates that two turns a day will suffice to process the water. By setting $T = 12$ hours in Eq. (8.1); the ratio G to $\dot{F}_o$ becomes a fixed number or better said: For a tank of, G gallons, the flowrate through the skimmer is fixed. Not only is the flowrate fixed, but as will be seen, the flowrate value is low, which is what is desired.

As will be demonstrated in Chapter 9, the value of the bombardment rate is given for marine systems as:

$$R_B = 4.53d_s^2 \, (T/G) \pm 2.19. \tag{8.2}$$

In contrast for freshwater systems:

$$R_B = 11.61d_s^2 \, (T/G) \pm 2.19, \tag{8.3}$$

where in the two previous equations, T is measured in hours, G is in gallons and the skimmer diameter, d_s is input in inches; the lower sign is for counter-current designs, while the upper sign controls co-current designs.

If, as discussed in the next chapter R_B is taken equal to 10 and two complete water exchanges through the skimmer will suffice, then generation of the next graph is possible.

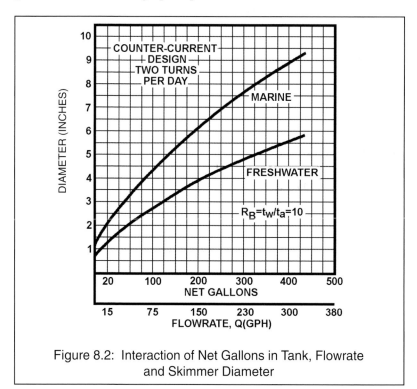

Figure 8.2: Interaction of Net Gallons in Tank, Flowrate and Skimmer Diameter

As is evident from the graphical data peculiar to counter-current skimmers, the selection of the skimmer diameter is obtained by entering the horizontal axis (abscissa axis) at the value of the net gallons contained in the tank and reading off the diameter of the skimmer on the vertical axis (ordinate axis).

EXAMPLE

What skimmer diameter should be selected for a 100 gallon marine tank so that two water exchanges a day will occur? What is the correct skimmer flowrate?

Enter the horizontal scale of Figure 8.2 at 100 gallons (net) and read 4.4 inches off the vertical scale. Obviously, a skimmer of this diameter is not likely to be found. The seventh law can be employed to select the skimmer. A 4.4 inch diameter skimmer has a cross-sectional area equal to $\pi D^2/4 = 3.1415 \times 4.4^2/4 = 15.2$ in^2. A three inch skimmer has the area $3.1415 \times 3^2/4 = 7.1$ in^2. So two three-inch diameter skimmers placed on each side of the tank have a combined area of 14.2 in^2. The one square inch error is negligible. To determine the flowrate through the three inch skimmer, enter Figure 8.2 at three (3) on the vertical scale and select 35 GPH from the horizontal flowrate scale. This is the flowrate in each of the skimmers.

8.3.1 CO-CURRENT SKIMMERS

If installation requires the use of a co-current skimmer, then several points should be made clear. First, a co-current skimmer provides bombardment of the water with only rear hits. This is less efficient. Furthermore, if the water and air travel in the same direction, the contact time of the air and water is reduced. This second point should be well noted (see Chapter 9). Since turnover is faster with a co-current design, it is easy to show that the diameter of the co-current skimmer is less than the corresponding counter-current skimmer. The turnover times (Eq. 8.2) for a marine counter-current and co-current skimmer are:

$$T = 2.336 \ G/d_s^2 \ \text{(counter-current)}; \quad T = 1.787 \ G/d_s^2 \ \text{(co-current)}. \tag{8.4}$$

Hence, by equating the turnover times for the same size tank, it follows that:

$$d_{co} = 0.8747 \ d_{cc}, \tag{8.5}$$

i.e., the diameter (in inches) of the co-current skimmer can be smaller, but this is not of fundamental importance. The advantage in performance clearly falls over to the counter-current skimmer.

8.3.2 VENTURI SKIMMERS

Venturi skimmers utilize a venturi (Chapter 7) to simultaneously inject both air and water into the skimmer. If injected with the air/water mixture at the bottom of the skimmer, the mixture travels toward the top of the skimmer in a co-current mode. Some swirling motion of the mixture may be of advantage, but this is yet to be proven. When the air and water reach the top collection tube, the direction of the water slowly becomes reversed since it is to be extracted at the bottom of the skimmer. This reversal of the water carries some of the air bubbles downward. The bubbles will then tend to rise upward in a counter-current mode. If air and water is introduced at the top of the skimmer and is moved through a pipe to the bottom of the skimmer (see Figure 8.1) where the flow is bounced upwards in a co-axial inner tube, the flow upwards is still of a co-current nature. The water trying to escape at the bottom of the skimmer drags some of the air with it to the point where the upward bubbles must start to rise. Usually about two-thirds of the skimmer is filled with air and water, but the bottom one third is just pure water. A correctly adjusted venturi skimmer is not supposed to eject both air and water. Only bubble free water should exit the skimmer.

The previous discussion seems to place the venturi skimmer in the classification of being a *hybrid skimmer* with both co-and-counter-current operational features. A reasonable compromise is that it is an operational device that is about one third less efficient than a counter-current skimmer. However, both of the co-and-counter-current activities are being handled simultaneously. This seems to imply that venturi skimmers (given the proper airflow) are close in their performance rating when compared to counter-current designs. The graphical data for counter-current designs is closely applicable. The venturi protein skimmer will be examined in more detail in Chapter 11.

8.4 SUMMARY

Three types of skimmers were introduced, namely: The counter-current, co-current and venturi. Each have application depending on installation requirements. The concept of the bombardment rate was introduced. Then, the laws of skimmer operation were stated but not proved. These laws are examined in detail in Chapter 9. A discussion of skimmer selection was presented, with an emphasis on the proper flowrate that should be input into the skimmer. A graph was presented to aid in the selection of the proper diameter of a skimmer for a given size tank. The conclusion seems to be that a counter-current skimmer is a reasonable choice, both from a performance and cost point of view. Venturi skimmers have appeal in some installations and closely follow the performance rating of counter-current skimmers.

8.5 PROBLEMS

8.5.1 Select the proper counter-current skimmer for a 180 gallon marine aquarium. What is the required flowrate? Assume two turns per day and a bombardment rate of 10.

> Ans: 6″
> Ans: 135 GPH

8.5.2 Why is the turnover formula (Eq. 8.1) applicable to skimmers as well as an ultraviolet sterilizer?

8.5.3 The flowrate through a nine inch counter-current skimmer is 315 GPH. What size marine tank is it serving?

> Ans: 420 GAL

8.5.4 Find how many and what diameter counter-current skimmers are required in a 60 gallon marine tank. Assume the water is exchanged every 12 hours and $R_B = 10$.

> Ans: 4″ diameter, or
> two 3″ diameter

8.5.5 What is the diameter of a marine co-current skimmer so that two water exchanges pass through a 400 gallon freshwater system every day? Assume $R_B = 10$. (Hint: an equation must be used.)

> Ans: 8.82″ exact,
> or four 4″ skimmers,
> or two 6″ skimmers,
> or one 9″ skimmer

8.6 REFERENCE

8.6.1 P.R. Escobal, "How to Select the Proper Size Ultraviolet Sterilizer", *Freshwater and Marine Aquarium Magazine,* December 1993

9 Theory Of Protein Skimmers: Laws and Operation

I do not suppose there is anyone in this room who has not occasionally blown a common soap bubble, and while admiring the perfection of its form, and marvelous brilliancy of its colours, wondered how it is that such a magnificent object can be so easily produced. I hope we shall see, there is more in a common bubble that those who have only played with them generally imagine.

Sir Charles Vernon Boys

9.1 THE WAY SKIMMERS FUNCTION

Chapter 8 introduced the fundamental concepts and laws applicable to protein skimmers. Since skimmers contribute greatly to general aquarium management, a theory which explains their operation is mandatory. The laws stated in Chapter 8 will not be repeated, but they will be examined in detail. This second indenture look at skimmer operation will shed considerable light as to the manner in which they function and what parameters need to be selected for proper operation.

As mentioned in the previous chapter, the basic parameters are the skimmer diameter, length, flowrate and bombardment rate. It will be proven that the ratio of water dwell time (the duration the water spends in the skimmer) to bubble rise time (the duration air spends in the skimmer) is independent of skimmer length. This rather bizarre physical phenomenon can be restated as follows. The bombardment of the ascending air bubbles upon the descending water does not depend on the skimmer length (height), but, in fact the bombardment rate depends only on the adopted value of the tank turn time, the number of net gallons in the tank, and the skimmer diameter. This may be difficult to accept, but the proof follows in another section of this chapter. The discussion here will be limited to counter-current skimmers.

9.2 THE SPLIT LOOP CONNECTION

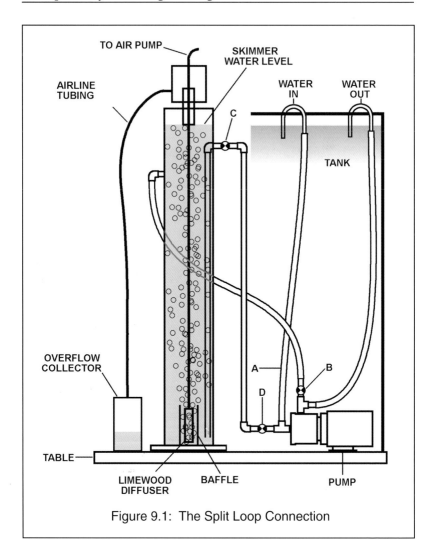

Figure 9.1: The Split Loop Connection

For proper skimmer operation the water level in a skimmer needs to be adjusted carefully so that it just touches the bottom of the bubble collection tube. Maintenance of this precise level is critical. To accomplish this, a split loop connection should be employed upon installation. Figure 9.1 illustrates the split loop connection.

Water is extracted from the tank via flex-line **A**. The pump adds water into the skimmer using a flex-line whose internal flowrate is controlled by valve **B**. Valve **C** is not really needed because of valve **D**, but it is a great aid for fine adjustment of the water level in the skimmer. What does all this do? It ensures that whatever the pump introduces into the skimmer it also removes, regardless of any variation in pump rotational speed. Note that as the line voltage fluctuates during the day, due to more or less electric appliances coming on or off-line, the flowrate produced by the pump will vary. The split loop dampens out these fluctuations to keep the water level constant inside the skimmer. One could avoid this type of connection if an expensive voltage regulator is used. The only other recourse is to keep adjusting the water level in the skimmer (a rather boring job). Also note that in case of a power failure, the split loop automatically resets itself when power is restored.

9.3   TURN TIME

Since the importance of the turnover formula is fundamental (see Chapter 2) it is restated here. The formula is: (9.1)

$$T = 9.2 \ (G/\dot{F}_0),$$

where T, measured in hours, is the time it will take for all the water in the tank to pass through the skimmer. G is the total net gallons in the tank and $\dot{F}_0$ is the flowrate (GPH) passing through the skimmer; 9.2 is the dimensionless purity coefficient. This formula applies to closed aquatic systems wherein water which has been treated by a device is returned to the tank and mixed with untreated water. The adopted value of the purity coefficient implies that 99.99 percent of the water will be passed through the device (skimmer) in the tank. Hence, for a tank of given size, upon selection of T, say two turns per day ($T = 12$ HRS.), the skimmer flowrate becomes a known parameter, and from this parameter the rest of the analysis follows.

9.4   THE BOMBARDMENT RATE

The Bombardment Rate (Ratio), R, is defined by: (9.2)

$$R_B = t_w/t_a,$$

where t_w and t_a are the water and air dwell times. By selection of T, for a fixed diameter skimmer, R_B can be determined. The larger the value of T selected will in correspondence increase the value of R_B, because t_w increases. Figure (9.2) depicts the physical situation schematically.

What does water stripping mean? Notice in Figure (9.2) that as the water particle is in *descendency* for t_w seconds, the air is in *ascendency* for t_a seconds. Hence by taking R_B as large as possible, it follows that

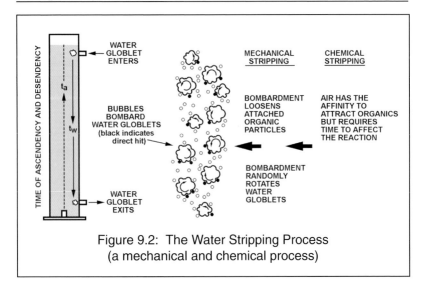

Figure 9.2: The Water Stripping Process
(a mechanical and chemical process)

the water globlets or cluster of water molecules experience more collisions or hits with clean air. The bombardment process mechanically hits the globlets with dynamic forces which cause the attached organics to be pounded off as the globlets randomly rotate. This is somewhat like striking a dusty cushion with a stick. Furthermore, for the chemical stripping action to occur, time is required, i.e., t_w should be of sufficient duration. This can be accomplished by increasing the skimmer length. But if t_w is increased, it will take less time for the bubbles to rise, but as will be seen R_B remains unchanged. Therefore, what is desired is to have R_B be as large as possible per pass, but yet have all the water in the tank be exchanged about two times, i.e., T = 12 hours. This selection, for a tank of fixed gallons, G, will also fix the flowrate Q, (in cubic inches per second) through the skimmer.

One might argue that if T is taken to be less than 12 hours, i.e., the flowrate is increased, the value of R_B will drop but the water will travel through the skimmer more times so that the total number of hits of bubbles upon water globlet will be the same. This is *not* correct. The total number of air hits or sweeps for any selection of T is given by (9.3)

$$\text{TOTAL HITS} = T/t_a.$$

For example, in 12 hours or 43200 seconds, if t_a = 6 seconds, 7,200 hits will occur. Hence, for time T = T_1, e.g., T_1 = 12 hours, the total number of hits is equal to T_1/t_{a1}. Now take T = T_2 to be less than T_1, i.e., increase the flowrate. The total number of hits will then be T_2/t_{a2}. These hits occur in duration T_2, so the equivalent number of hits in duration

T_1 would be obtained by multiplying T_2/t_{a2} by T_1/T_2, namely:

$$\text{(TOTAL HITS)} = (T_2/t_{a2})(T_1/T_2) = T_1/t_{a2}.$$

However, for the larger value of T,

$$\text{(TOTAL HITS)} = T_1/t_{a1}.$$

It is now evident that: when the flowrate through the skimmer is increased, i.e., T is made smaller, the total number of hits is smaller because t_{a2} is greater than t_{a1}. Specifically, by increasing the flowrate the water retards the airflow and it takes longer for the bubbles to rise to the surface. *This proves that it is better to have a higher bombardment rate per pass than to have more passes of water through the skimmer at a lower bombardment rate.* It should also be evident that the bombardment rate is greatly reduced in co-current designs because the bubbles are just carried upwards by the water.

At this point a value of R_B needs to be selected. Considering all the trade-offs discussed above and examination of empirical graphical data, it appears that a reasonable value for R_B is about 10, namely the water globlets should be bombarded 10 times with clean air. This is said in light of the fact that an increase of R_B beyond a factor of 10 increases the value of T, which implies less turns per day, and a decrease of R_B below this level implies less total hits per pass. Of course, one is free to pick alternate values for R_B.

Finally, note that the statement of the Seventh Law is more or less obvious. Specifically, if for a given size tank, a large diameter is required, one is free to select a number of skimmers of lesser diameter as long as the cross-sectional areas involved are equivalent. The total flowrate required is the shared by each of the smaller diameter skimmers. Figure 9.3 can now be examined.

By entering Figure (9.3) on the tank net gallon scale and moving vertically to the 12 hour limit line, the diameter of the skimmer required for a given tank is obtained. With this diameter, a bombardment rate of 10 will be realized and two complete water exchanges (turns) will be achieved. By moving downward from the net gallon scale, the corresponding flowrate through the skimmer is also determined (but only for two turns per day). Above each of the diameter lines are listed the number of equivalent smaller diameter skimmers required as substitutes for the selected skimmer diameter, should this diameter model not be manufactured. It may also be less expensive to purchase a number of smaller diameter skimmers required as substitutes for the

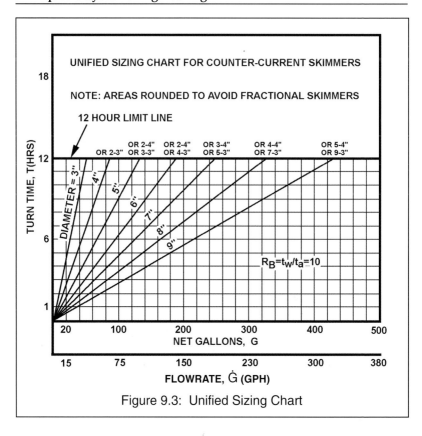

Figure 9.3: Unified Sizing Chart

indicated skimmer diameter. Note the large increase in required skimmer diameter if T is taken less than 12 hours. Finally, select the skimmer length to be as great as possible.

EXAMPLE

Select the proper skimmer and operating parameters for a tank with 100 net gallons.

Enter the horizontal scale (net gallons) at 100 and move upwards. The required diameter is about 4.3″. Since no such skimmer is available, the wise choice here would be to select a four inch skimmer and sacrifice a few hits per pass for the sake of economy, or choose two three-inch skimmers. However, one could also choose to use a four inch and three inch skimmer together. The length of each skimmer should be as long as possible within installation and financial constraints. By moving downward on the 100 gallon line, the flowrate through the skimmer(s) is determined as 75 gallons per hour (total). The flowrate between the skimmers would be shared if more than one is installed. A Flowrater™ device (1.1.11) would be quite useful so as to determine the proper flowrate.

9.5 VOLUME OF AIR

How many bubbles are in a skimmer? This is a difficult question. However, if the answer were known, then the volume of air in the skimmer could be determined. The best attack at answering this question is to establish a theoretical model which approximates the real world system and then to subsequently correct the model by the use of empirical measurement. To this end, consider a top and side

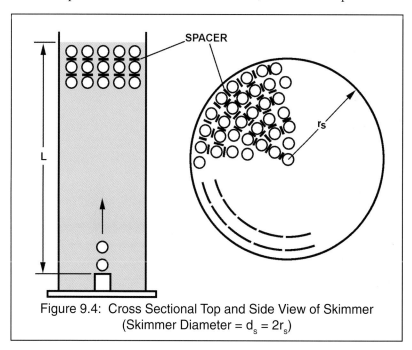

SPACER

L

r_s

Figure 9.4: Cross Sectional Top and Side View of Skimmer
(Skimmer Diameter = d_s = $2r_s$)

view of a skimmer as illustrated in Figure (9.4).

Think of the bubbles as if they were ball bearings of diameter d_b constrained to run in a series of concentric tracks whose circumference decreases towards the center of the skimmer. Assume each ball bearing (bubble) is separated by a space, s, both in the circumferential and radial direction. Since the circumference of a circle is equal to $2\pi r$, the center of the outer most track will have a radius equal to r_s, the skimmer radius minus the radius of the bubble, $r_b = d_b/2$. Hence, the circumference of the center of the outermost track is $2\pi(r_s\text{-}r_b)$. The centerline of the second track toward the center has a radius equal to $r_s\text{-}3r_b\text{-}s$ with corresponding circumference $2\pi(r_s\text{-}3r_b\text{-}s)$. The third track has a circumference of $2\pi(r_s\text{-}5r_b\text{-}2s)$, etc. By dividing the circumference of each track centerline by $d_b\text{+}s$, the number of bubbles plus spacers in each track is obtained. The tracks are then summed to obtain the total number of bubbles $\underline{B}^*$:

$$\underline{B}^* = [2\pi(r_s\text{-}r_b)/(d_b\text{+}s)\text{+}2\pi(r_s\text{-}3r_b\text{-}s)/(d_b\text{+}s)\text{+}2\pi(r_s\text{-}5r_b\text{-}2s)/(d_b\text{+}s)\text{+}2\pi(r_s\text{-}7r_b\text{-}3s)/(d_b\text{+}s)\text{+}\cdots$$

or by collecting terms:

$$\underline{B}^* = (2\pi/[d_b\text{+}s])(r_s[1\text{+}1\text{+}1\text{+}\cdots] - r_b[1\text{+}3\text{+}5\text{+}7\text{+}\cdots] - s[1\text{+}2\text{+}3\text{+}\cdots] + \cdots). \quad (9.4)$$

The above three numerical brackets are arithmetic progressions (Ref. 9.11.4 and the Appendix) and can be summed for the number of tracks, N, where N is obtained by noting that $N(d_b\text{+}s)$ must equal r_s. The result is:

$$\underline{B}^* = \pi r_s^2[1\text{-}s/2r_s]/[(d_b\text{+}s)^2].$$

Hence, the total number of bubbles in the first layer is:

$$B^* = \pi r_s^2/[(d_b\text{+}s)^2]. \quad (9.5)$$

The previous result is obtained by taking s/r_s equal to zero due to its insignificant numerical value.

Since the volume of each bubble is $V = \pi d_b^3/6$, it follows that by multiplying B^* by V, the volume of the first layer of bubbles at the top of the skimmer will be obtained. Imagine this layer as a pancake of thickness $d_b\text{+}s$. The total number of these pancakes, M can be obtained by noting that $(d_b\text{+}s)M$ is equal to the height of the water column L. Performing the summation yields the total volume of air in the skimmer, V_a:

$$V_a = \pi^2 r_s^2 d_b^3 L/[6(d_b\text{+}s)^3].$$

However, since the volume of skimmer, V_s, is $\pi r_s^2 L$ it follows that the ratio of volumes is:

$$V_s/V_a = 6[s/d_b\text{+}1]^3/\pi. \quad (9.6)$$

An interesting result is obtained by letting the bubbles all touch each other, i.e., $s = 0$, namely: $V_a = 0.52V_s$, which says that the volume of air in a skimmer can never be greater than about 52 percent of the volume of the skimmer or the bubbles will merge. Experimental measurements are in agreement and indicate that when s is considered (Fourth Law):

$$V_a = 0.16V_s, \quad s/d_b + 1 = 1.5, \tag{9.7}$$

is a reasonable expression for the volume of air in terms of the volume of the skimmer (Fourth Law). This relationship will be required presently. Also note that by dividing V_a by V_b, for $s = 0$ it follows that the total number of bubbles in the skimmer is equal to $\pi r_s^2 L/d_b^3$, e.g., a three inch diameter skimmer with a length of 36 inches and bubble diameter of 1/32 inches, contains 8,338,440 bubbles (in case you were desperate to know).

9.6 BUBBLE RISE TIME IN STILL WATER

Bubbles are rising. A bubble with a given radius, r_b, inside a cylindrical tube filled with non-moving water is subject to two forces, namely, the lift force produced by the difference in the density of air and water:

$$L_b = 4\pi r_b^3 (w_w - w_a)/3, \tag{9.8}$$

and the drag force which results from the friction of the bubbles against the water:

$$D_b = \pi C_D w_w r_b^2 U^2/2g, \tag{9.9}$$

where:

r_b = Radius of the bubble (ft),
w_w = Density of water (lbs/ft^3),
w_a = Density of air (lbs/ft^3),
g = Acceleration of gravity = 32.174 (ft/sec^2),
U = Velocity of bubble relative to water (ft/sec),
C_D = Drag coefficient of bubble (dimensionless),
π = Mathematical constant = 3.1415.

Newton's second law states that the unbalanced force on an object is equal to its mass multiplied by its acceleration, i.e.,

$$L_b - D_b = (W_a/g)d^2D/dt^2, \tag{9.10}$$

where W_a is the weight of the bubble and D, is the bubble depth from the surface. Substitution of the forces yield the second order differential equation:

$$d^2D/dt^2 + b(dD/dt)^2 - a = 0. \tag{9.11}$$

By assuming that a and b are average values, the acceleration term (first term) can be omitted so that the upward velocity of the bubble, U_b, is given by (See Appendix):

$$dD/dt = U_b = [a/b]^{1/2}, \qquad (9.12)$$

where the ratio of a to b is given by:

$$a/b = (8g/3)(r/C_D)[1 - w_a/w_w]. \qquad (9.13)$$

Since the value of air to water density is ever so small, it can be neglected. On the other hand, the bubble radius increases with height as it rises from the bottom due to the absolute pressure difference. By assuming an adiabatic (no heat added) gas law, the value of r as function of depth and bottom radius r_b can be obtained. This relationship can then be inserted into Eq. (9.13), to yield a/b as a function of the depth, and the unknown constant r_b/C_D. By varying the depth from zero to eight feet, $[a/b]^{1/2}$, can be obtained almost exactly as a linear function of the depth. The variation can next be averaged over an eight foot interval. The results (L measured in feet) are:

$$[a/b]^{1/2}{}_{average} = [r_b/C_D]^{1/2}[9.263 + 0.0143L]. \qquad (9.14)$$

Experimental measurements in seven foot tall columns of marine and freshwater permitted the average upward velocities of the bubbles to be obtained. This in turn yielded the values of $[r_b/C_D]^{1/2}$. The values with r_b measured in feet are:

$$[r_b/C_D]^{1/2} = 0.0365 \text{ (Marine)}$$
$$[r_b/C_D]^{1/2} = 0.0935 \text{ (Freshwater)}. \qquad (9.15)$$

Hence, one has:

$$[a/b]^{1/2} = 4.053 + 0.00052L; \text{ Marine,}$$
$$[a/b]^{1/2} = 10.387 + 0.0016L; \text{ Freshwater,} \qquad (9.16)$$

where L is measured in inches and the velocities $U = [a/b]^{1/2}$ are in inches/sec. As may be inferred, the above procedure is the correct method of obtaining the value of the velocity since only average measurements can be obtained. The very small length dependent term can now be ignored.

9.7 DWELL AND RISE TIMES: THE BOMBARDMENT RATIO

The water dwell time in the skimmer by virtue of Eq. (9.7) is given by:

$$t_w = (V_s - V_a)/Q = (V_s/Q)(1-0.16) = (0.84\pi/4)(L/Q)d_s{}^2, \qquad (9.17)$$

where Q is the water flowrate measured in in^3/sec, so that:

$$t_w = 0.66(L/Q)d_s{}^2.$$

The bubble rise time can be obtained by dividing the skimmer length by the relative velocity of the rising bubble, i.e., the still water velocity of rise minus the retarding velocity of the water, specifically:

$$t_a = L/([a/b]^{1/2} - Q/[A_s-A_a]). \tag{9.18}$$

Note that the water velocity is given by dividing the flowrate (Q) in cubic inches per second by the cross-sectional area of the skimmer, A_s, minus the cross-sectional area of the total number of bubbles. But since by Eq. (9.5) the total number of bubbles in the cross-section is given by B^*, then the product of B^* by the cross sectional area of the bubble, $\pi d_b^2/4$, yields the area of the air column, i.e. by Eq. (9.7):

$$A_s - A_a = (\pi d_s^2/4)[1 - (\pi/4)/(1+s/d_b)^2] = 0.511d_s^2. \tag{9.19}$$

Hence, by use of Eq. (9.16) for marine water:

$$t_a = L/(4.053 - 1.956\ Q/d_s^2). \tag{9.20}$$

Division of t_w/t_a shows that the skimmer length cancels and proves the First Law. The operation yields:

$$R_B = t_w/t_a = 4.53d_s^2(T/G) - 2.19, \tag{9.21}$$

where T is in hours and G is in gallons. For freshwater the constant 4.53 is replaced by 11.61. Note that Q is eliminated by the First Law in the proper units as: $Q(in^3/sec) = 0.5903\ G\ (GAL)/T\ (HRS)$; the 9.2 factor is included.

9.8   REQUIRED AIR FLOWRATE

The air input into a skimmer should be a vigorous, smooth upward blossom of air bubbles. Excessive turbulence should be avoided because it defeats the water stripping process. From theory, because Eq. (9.7) predicts the maximum volume of air that the skimmer can hold at any instant of time, the approximate airpump flowrate, $\dot{F}$, can be simply obtained as:

$$\dot{F} = 0.16V_s/t_a = 0.1256d_s^2LR_B/t_w, \tag{9.22}$$

where if the diameter and length are in inches and the absolute contact time is in seconds, $\dot{F}$ is given in cubic inches per second. Flowrate from a given airpump is best determined by submerging a long tube with one end capped into water so as to remove all the air. The tube is then inverted (full of water) and extracted vertically upwards with the cap on top, until it is nearly out of the water. Insertion of the air line into the tube will now displace the water. Knowledge of the volume of the tube and the time to evacuate the air permits the value of $\dot{F}$ leaving the airpump to be computed by division of the tube volume by the time required to evacuate the tube.

9.9 SUMMARY

The analysis has proven the skimmer laws as applied to counter-current designs. It has been demonstrated that a higher bombardment rate (ratio) with less water passing through the skimmer results in more hits by the bubbles against the water droplets. A compromise bombardment rate was adopted. The results indicate that proper skimmer selection depends on both the length and, the usually neglected skimmer diameter. Increasing the length does not vary the bombardment rate. It is the skimmer diameter which controls this rate. A combination of lesser diameter skimmers can be used in lieu of the indicated diameter obtained from the unified skimmer selection chart. Air flow into a skimmer should not cause excessive turbulence.

9.10 PROBLEMS (Note When Using the Unified Sizing Chart, Round Answers to the Closest Solution)

9.10.1 A skimmer is hooked up with a by-pass line so that the total flow by-passing the skimmer is 300 GPH while the skimmer is fed 60 GPH. A tank containing 80 gallons is to be skimmed twice daily. What is the turnover duration?

Ans: 12 HRS

9.10.2 What size skimmer would be selected in problem 9.10.1?

Ans: 4″ diameter, or two
3″ diameter skimmers

9.10.3 A 200 gallon tank is to be skimmed. What diameter and number of skimmers would be selected for two turns per day? What would be the flowrates?

Ans: 6″ diameter with 150 GPH,
or two 4″ diameter with
75 GPH through each

9.10.4 Four turns per day are desired in a 100 gallon tank. A six inch skimmer is to be used. What is the required flowrate? Remember the bottom flowrate scale in Figure 9.2 only applies for a 12 hour turnover.

Ans: Turn time = 6 HRS
Ans: $\dot{F}_o$ = 153.3 GPH

9.10.5 What diameter skimmer should be selected for a 400 gallon tank? Only one skimmer is to be used. What is the flowrate? How many turns will occur each day?

Ans: 9" diameter
Ans: 300 GPH
Ans: 2

9.11   REFERENCES

9.11.1   P.R. Escobal, "The Time Required to Sterilize a Body of Water with a U.V. Sterilizer." *Freshwater and Marine Aquarium Magazine,* February 1991

9.11.2   P.R. Escobal, "Inside Ultra Violet Sterilizers." *Aquarium Fish Magazine,* January 1993

9.11.3   P.R. Escobal, "How to Select the Proper Size Ultraviolet Sterilizer." *Freshwater and Marine Aquarium Magazine,* December 1993

9.11.4   G.A. Korn and T.M. Korn, *Mathematical Handbook for Scientists and Engineers,* McGraw-Hill, New York 1968

10 Fluid Pumps: Water Moving Devices

You're not a man,
You're a machine.

George Bernard Shaw

10.1 GENERAL DISCUSSION

The use of pumps is central to aquariums and ponds. A pump is the heart of any aquatic system because it provides the water with both kinetic and potential energy. These energies permit the water to be raised to desired locations, force the water through filters and provide water circulation. Rather than discuss pumps from an engineering point of view, an attempt to describe them from practical terms will be undertaken. This will provide the user information as to their design, use and overall cost of operation. As will be seen, this is a prelude to Chapter 11 wherein the actual installation of pumps in operational systems is considered in detail.

10.2 PUMP DESIGN

There are two basic designs. In the first design, a shaft attached axially to a motor carries a permanently attached impeller (fan) on the shaft. The impeller, in turn is enclosed by a housing with a water inlet and exit. This pump is illustrated in Figure 10.1

In this type of pump, usually called the direct drive pump, appeal is made to seals on the shaft which act to contain the water in the impeller cavity. Direct drive pumps suffer from leakage of water through the seals and from excessive heat transfer. In some designs the motor is placed in a sealed container which is filled with oil. The oil, since it has a greater density than water, helps to keep water from leaking through

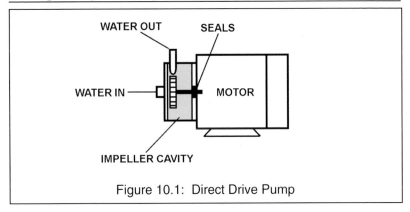

Figure 10.1: Direct Drive Pump

the seals and damaging the electric motor drive. By waterproofing the entire motor and front end (where the impeller is placed) these type of pumps can be made so as to permit underwater operation.

The second type of pump is called a magnetic drive pump. A hollow cylindrical magnet is attached to the motor shaft, this is called the *driver magnet*. An impeller housing is now employed which has a cup that fits axially into the hollow driver magnet. Inside the smaller cup, another magnet which has an impeller attached is placed and held centrally by a shaft which runs axially through the impeller. The smaller magnet is called the *driven magnet*. This type of pump is illustrated in Figure 10.2.

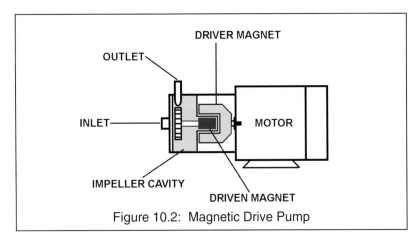

Figure 10.2: Magnetic Drive Pump

As the driver magnet rotates, the lines of magnetic flux capture the small driven magnet and make it spin on a central axis called the front end shaft. The driven magnet which is attached to the impeller will thus spin in a bed of water. Note that the water never touches the large driver magnet and water can never leak into the motor. As a side benefit, heat transfer from the motor to the water will be greatly reduced.

A variation of the magnetic drive pump is to let the axial shaft extend through both sides of the motor drive. This permits placement of a second impeller housing on the other side of the pump. In essence a double sided or headed pump is obtained with two independent pumping heads (two water loops). Hence, one side can be used to run a filter while the other side can run a skimmer, plus an ultraviolet skimmer, etc.

10.3 POWER CONSIDERATIONS

A number of considerable importance is the amperage of the motor which drives the pump paddle wheels or impeller. This number should appear on the pump name plate. It is usually denoted by the symbol I. An index of pump efficiency is the total watts, W, that the pump consumes. Thus one can compare a pump to a light bulb of the same wattage. To obtain the number of watts, W, that a pump consumes is simple, if one has the line voltage, V, i.e.,

$$W = IV.$$

Hence, a pump with an amperage draw of 0.57 amps when plugged into a standard 115 volt wall outlet, roughly would consume:

$$W = 0.57 \times 115 = 65.55 \text{ Watts.}$$

The cost of operation of a given pump is given roughly, Ref. (10.9.1), by:

$$C = (Wtc)/1000, \tag{10.1}$$

where W is the wattage of the pump (watts), t is the duration of operation (HRS) and c is the cost of electricity in kilowatt-hours (Consult your local utility company for kw-h cost).

10.4 THE PRINCIPLE OF PRESSURE INCREASE

Water is delivered to the pump at the inlet or suction port. The impeller imparts energy to the water and forces the fluid through the output port. Therefore, what the pump does is to impart a relative increase in pressure. In other words, if the pressure at the inlet port is equal to p_- and that of the output port is denoted by p_+ then the pump produces a pressure differential of $\Delta p = p_+ - p_-$. Hence, the principle of pressure increase states that pumps only provide a relative increase in pressure equal to the pressure at the outlet port, minus the pressure at the input port.

Usually, manufacturers rate their pumps at a pressure head of one foot, i.e., at a pressure equal to the pressure that a one foot tall column of water would have against the output port; the flowrate is also stated at the one foot benchmark. The manufacturer also states the pump horsepower, however, the rated pump horsepower without an indication of the pump efficiency is not a very useful parameter. Sometimes performance curves are supplied. These are curves of the number of gallons per hour the pump will deliver verses the total height or head that the pump can raise the water. Whether or not the pump can actually achieve the curve indicated values is a question because the pump performance is installation dependent. The true pump performance for a given situation involves the determination of friction losses, pressure drops across filters, etc. (See Chapter 11).

EXAMPLE

A manufacturer states that a pump can deliver eight psi at a one foot head. A pressure gauge at input port reads five psi. (Case 1) What is the pressure at the output port? Suppose the gauge reads less than atmospheric pressure, namely, - 3 psi, again, what is the output pressure (Case 2).

For Case 1:

$$p_+ = \Delta p_+ + p_- = 8 + 5 = 13 \text{ psi.}$$

For Case 2:

$$p_+ = \Delta p_+ + p_- = 8 - 3 = 5 \text{ psi.}$$

How can additional positive pressure exist at the intake port? Since pressure is the product of water density, D, and the height, h, of the water column above the pump intake port ($p = Dh$), it follows that extraction of water from the bottom of the tank provides additional positive pressure. Negative pressures result when a pump drags water toward the intake (suction) port and must overcome friction losses. These conditions are illustrated in Figure 10.3.

Hence in Figure 10.3 the output pressure at the pump spout would be equal to 8 psi + 7 x 62.4/144 psi - 2 psi = 9 psi. Obviously as the pump pushes the water up to position A, it will loose the pressure gain provided by the tank and water in the flexline. Note that the pressure at the bottom of a wide pond is the same as the pressure in a thin pipe whose vertical length is equal to the depth of the pond, i.e., the diameter

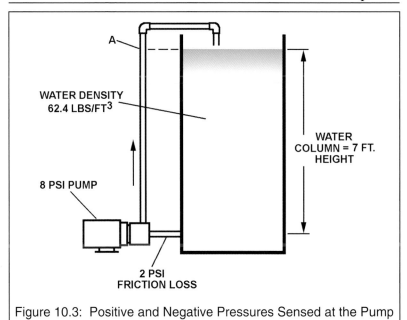

Figure 10.3: Positive and Negative Pressures Sensed at the Pump Intake Port

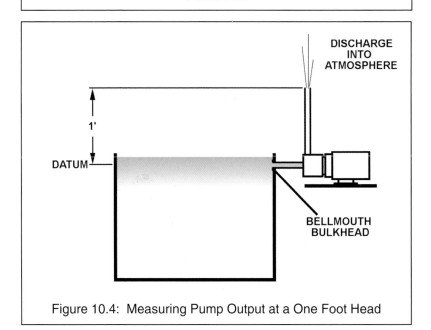

Figure 10.4: Measuring Pump Output at a One Foot Head

of a vertical pipe has no influence as to the pressure at the bottom of the pipe.

To obtain the flowrate for a given pump at, say, a one foot head, appeal is made to Figure 10.4.

Since the pump intake is just slightly below the water level the pressure on the pump inlet can be taken as equal to zero. The pump outlet is extended with pipe of the same diameter to one foot above the datum.

10.5 PUMPS IN SERIES

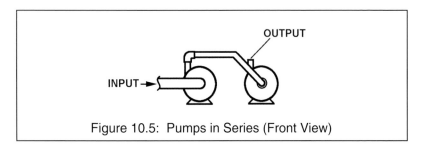

Figure 10.5: Pumps in Series (Front View)

Section 10.4 demonstrated that pumps only provide a relative increase in pressure. Figure 10.5 illustrates two pumps connected in series.

Suppose pump 1 has an input pressure of five psi and can develop a relative pressure of eight psi. It therefore outputs water at 13 psi. But if this water is fed into the intake of pump 2, the pressure will be raised by the relative pressure of pump 2, e.g., if pump 2 has a relative pressure equal to pump 1, namely eight psi, then the new pressure at the output of pump 2 will be 5 + 8 + 8 = 29 psi. Elevated pressures are often desired for the purpose of raising water to higher elevations. However, one must keep in mind that the pump seals, basically the "O" rings can only resist an upper pressure limit and the seals might buckle if three or four pumps are connected in series.

10.6 PUMPS IN PARALLEL

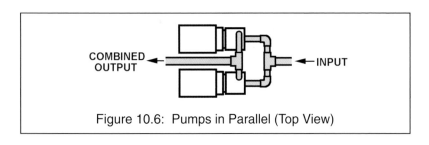

Figure 10.6: Pumps in Parallel (Top View)

Suppose the design objectives just require a greater flowrate. Figure 10.6 shows two pumps connect in parallel.

When pumps are connected in parallel, no increase in pressure is achieved, but more flow is developed. One must be careful not to starve the water flow into the connected system. Thus if the design intake spouts are each of three-fourths inch diameter, the cross-sectional area, A, would be 0.884 in^2 or since the combined area is 2A = $\pi d^2/4$, upon solving for d, the input pipe diameter, d = 1.06 in., i.e., a one inch internal diameter pipe should be used to feed the double parallel hook-up.

The flow out of both pumps could be combined back into a single pipe. Again the rule of areas should be observed so that the output diameter of the combined pipe would be determined by the cross-sectional area of the output spouts.

Usually when pumps are staged in parallel, it is much wiser to deliver two separate lines back to the tank, i.e., to provide two or three separate circulation loops to various ends of the tank.

Pumps in parallel are a welcome solution to the use of one large pump. A pump is a mechanical device and is subject to failure. However, if a tank is run with two smaller pumps (which is usually more economical) the problem of total recirculation failure is avoided and time is made available to repair the damaged pump while the system is still at 50 percent, etc. operation.

Whether pumps are connected in series, parallel or used singly, if noise reduction is of importance, it is recommended that they be

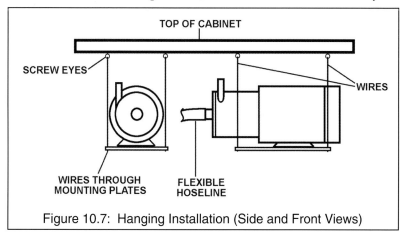

TOP OF CABINET

SCREW EYES

WIRES

WIRES THROUGH MOUNTING PLATES   FLEXIBLE HOSELINE

Figure 10.7: Hanging Installation (Side and Front Views)

suspended by wires. This is called the *hanging installation* as illustrated in Figure 10.7.

This is especially important if the pump(s) are to be placed in a cabinet. Hanging the pumps will prevent vibration and virtually reduce resonance effects to zero. The wires can usually be attached to the metal pump mounting plate. A short flexible hose should be used both at the pump inlet and outlet to further dampen the vibration.

10.7 SUMMARY

Pumps have been discussed from a practical point of view. It has been noted that both direct and magnetic drive pumps are available. The magnetic drive pumps have the advantage of no water leakage into the electric drive which powers the impeller, and of cool running operation. The cost to run a pump has been outlined. Relative pressure increases provided by pumps has been explained. Pumps can be connected in series to increase pressure and in parallel to increase flow. Use of two small pumps in lieu of one large pump has been recommended both from an economical and reliability point of view.

10.8   PROBLEMS

10.8.1 Why can't water enter the electric motor of a magnetic drive pump?

10.8.2 Why is it better to use two small pumps instead of one large pump?

10.8.3 Three pumps are to be connected in series. The inlet port of pump 1 senses a pressure of -5 psi. Each pump produces a relative pressure increase of 10 psi. What is the output pressure of the combined system?

Ans: 25 psi

10.8.4 Three pumps are connected in parallel. If each pump can deliver 500 GPH, what is the combined output of the three pumps? Assume the connection fittings reduce the output by 10 percent. Suppose the pump outputs are not recombined but flow to three separate locations within the tank. Assume the input connections reduce the output by five percent.

Ans: 1350 GPH
Ans: 1425 GPH

10.9   REFERENCE

10.9.1 *Handbook of Electronic Tables and Formulas*, Howard W. Sams & Co. Ed. 5, Indianapolis, Indiana, 1989

11 Installation Hydraulics:
Aquarium Fluid Mechanics

It is quite a three pipe problem.

Sir Arthur Conan Doyle

11.1 FACTORS OF IMPORTANCE

Water is siphoned from the aquarium by a pump. Water is driven by the pump to an aquarium life support system. Water is returned to the aquarium. Quite a three pipe problem. One of paramount importance for proper installation of any aquatic system. Water is flowing through a pipe. How much pressure will the pump expend to push the water through? The water hits a series of elbows and connectors plus a few valves, so that even more pressure is required. A sudden enlargement in pipe diameter occurs implying even more work for the pump. More and more frictional losses occur. What size pump must be chosen for the particular installation under consideration? This is the topic discussed in this chapter.

Any aquatic installation uses PVC pipe and clear flexline to connect a desired system. Apart from the pipe, fittings of all kinds are used. Water flowing through pipelines loses pressure due to frictional factors. Fittings also consume energy in deflecting the water. Modern installations rely heavily on the use of PVC pipe because it is extremely smooth and does not deteriorate with time. PVC fittings are used almost exclusively. Furthermore, connection of pipe fittings is accomplished easily with PVC cement. For these reasons the discussion herein is limited to installations utilizing plastic pipe, fittings and smooth clear flexline.

The classic calculation of frictional loss involves water velocity, kinematic water viscosity, Reynolds number, etc. The calculations become cumbersome. It will be shown that for water it is possible to avoid all these parameters and express the results in terms of the flowrate in the pipe and the cross-sectional area of the pipe.

It would be wise for the reader to understand that in many cases frictional loss cannot be ignored. This is especially true in the selection of a proper pump to power up a given system. Actually, the pump rating or pump curves usually specified by a manufacturer are only an extremely rough indication of proper system performance. Pump selection is installation dependent on frictional losses, i.e., the pump may not adequately perform in a given situation.

As will be seen, the attack of this important problem will be handled in three steps. The first step involves the generation of a detailed drawing of the system installation. All pipes, fittings, filters and elevations of subsystem components above the pump level (datum) should be clearly indicated. The second step is to determine all frictional losses from graphs and tables. Placing all the losses in a table will be helpful. The final third step involves the application of Bernoulli's equation.

11.2   FRICTIONAL LOSSES IN PIPES

The Darcy equation, Ref. (11.9.1), states that the head loss, h_f, (1ft head = 0.4321 lbs/in^2) in a pipe of length, L, and diameter, D, is given by:

$$h_f = k_f [L/D] V^2/2g,$$

where k_f is a friction factor, V is the water velocity in the pipe, and g is the acceleration of gravity = 32.174 ft/sec^2. Since the flowrate in the pipe is the product of the cross-sectional area of the pipe and the velocity, one can easily transform the previous equation to read:

$$h_f = k_f [L/D] b \dot{G}^2/D^4, \tag{11.1}$$

where the flowrate, $\dot{G}$, is measured in gallons per hour, L is measured in feet, D, is measured in inches, and b = 7.2035 x 10^{-7}. This form of the pipe friction loss equation is much more convenient for calculation of pipe losses. By a similar transformation, i.e., elimination of V and the Reynolds number, Ref. (11.9.1), it is possible to generate Figure 11.1.

The figure permits the user to enter the horizontal scale with the flowrate in the pipe, rise vertically and intersect with the pipe diameter

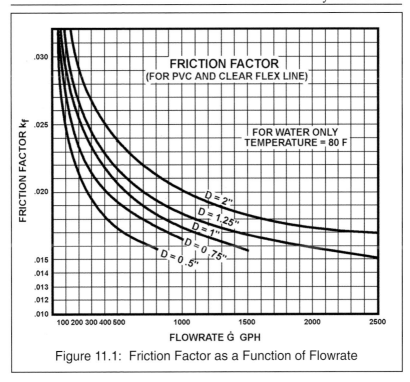

Figure 11.1: Friction Factor as a Function of Flowrate

curve in question and read k_f from the vertical scale. The data comes from Ref. (11.9.1), (11.9.2), and was chosen on the conservative side.

EXAMPLE: Pipe Friction Loss

What are the frictional losses in a straight 100' run of 3/4" PVC pipe carrying 500 GPH?

Enter Figure 11.1 at 500 GPH, intersect the D = 0.75" diameter curve and read 0.0192 as the value for k_f. Next calculate L/D = 100'/(0.75"/12) = 1600. Note that L/D must have consistent units. Finally compute:

$$h_f = 0.0192 \times 1600 \times 7.2035 \times 10^{-7} \times 500^2/0.75^4$$
$$= 17.48' \text{ or } 17.48' \times 0.4321 = 7.5 \text{ psi.}$$

As can be seen the loss is not trivial.

To bring the rest of the analysis into conformity, the loss factor for pipe will be defined as the product:

$$k = k_f \, (L/D), \qquad (11.2)$$

where L is usually measured in feet so that if D is in inches, a conversion to feet is required.

11.3 LOSS DUE TO PIPE, FITTINGS, VALVES AND OTHER CAUSES

This section is quite simple. From actual measurements, the losses which need to be accounted for are collected in Tables 11.1 through 11.6. The values listed are conservative and extracted from Ref. (11.9.1), (11.9.2).

TABLE 11.1

Coefficient k for Minor Losses (Fittings)

Fitting	k (Dimensionless)
Elbow	0.9
Elbow (45°)	0.44
Connector	0.1
Tee	1.8
Return bend "J" tube	2.1
Gate (Ball) valve (open)	0.2
Globe valve	10.0
Long bends	0.4
Nozzle	0.1
Check valve (open)	3.0
Flowrater	0.5

TABLE 11.2

Coefficient k for Entrance to Pipe
From Large Body of Water

Type	k (Dimensionless)
Square Edge — G→	0.5
Re-entrant — G→	1.0
Bell Mouth — G→	0.1

TABLE 11.3

Coefficient k for Sudden Contraction

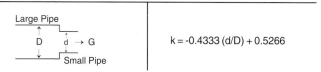

$$k = -0.4333 \, (d/D) + 0.5266$$

TABLE 11.4

Coefficient k for Sudden Enlargement

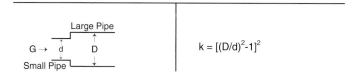

$$k = [(D/d)^2 - 1]^2$$

TABLE 11.5

Coefficient k for Submerged Exit

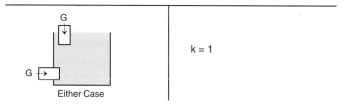

$$k = 1$$

TABLE 11.6

Coefficient k for Long Pipe (L) of Diameter D

For Flow $\hat{G}$ in Pipe use Fig. 11.1 to Obtain k_f

$k = k_f \, (L/D)$; L, D in same units

For any installation these approximate values of k will serve to estimate the frictional budget that must be overcome by the pump(s). The sum of all the k values required for the application of Bernoulli's equation between any two points (but not necessarily the entire system) should be collected conveniently in a table such as illustrated below.

FRICTION LOSS BUDGET

LOSS	OPERATION	k
Elbow = 0.9	X Number of Elbows	Total k
Connectors = 0.1	X Number of Connectors	Total k
Enlargement (D/d) =	$[(D/d)^2-1]^2$	Value of k
Entry = 1	NONE	1
Friction L/D	From Fig. 11.1 for $\dot{G}$ =	
	k_f X (L/D) =	Value of k
	K =	Sum of k

The importance of the k coefficient is that by definition the product of k and $b\dot{G}^2/D^4$ yields the frictional head or pressure loss. The total loss is obtained by use of K = sum of all k. This will be explained further in sections to come.

11.4   MODIFIED BERNOULLI EQUATION

The Bernoulli equation represents an energy balance. At any given station the total energy due to pressure (or flow) and that of kinetic and potential energy can be expressed in terms feet of "head," namely, pressure head, p/w, velocity head, $V^2/2g$, and elevation head, Z. More specifically:

$$H = p/w + V^2/2g + Z, \qquad (11.3)$$

where p is the pressure, w the specific weight of the fluid (water = 62.22 lb/ft^3; at aquarium temperatures). V is the fluid velocity, g is the acceleration of gravity (32.174 ft/sec^2), and Z is the elevation of the fluid above some reference line (datum).

Since energy is always conserved, one can equate H at station one to H at station two and obtain a relation between pressure, velocity and elevation at these two stations. This is not a strong enough relation because friction losses occur as water flows through pipes, pumps can add energy, and turbines can extract energy. Hence for steady flow between two stations, it is necessary to write:

$$H_1 + H_p - H_f - H_e = H_2, \qquad (11.4)$$

where H_p is the energy (head) added, e.g., pump head, H_f is the friction loss and H_e is the head loss due to other sources, e.g., turbines (usually absent). *This equation must always be written in the direction of water flow, i.e., from station one to station two.*

Since, as mentioned earlier, there is an equivalence between $V^2/2g$ and $b\dot{G}^2/D^4$ (see the Darcy equation), the general modified Bernoulli equation can be written as:

$$ap_1 + b\dot{G}^2/D^4{}_1 + Z_1 + H_p - H_f - H_e = ap_2 + b\dot{G}^2/D^4{}_2 + Z_2, \qquad (11.5)$$

where the units are as follows:

p (pressure)	$= LBS/in^2$,
$\dot{G}$ (flowrate)	$= GPH$,
D (pipe diameter)	$= in$,
Z (elevation)	$= ft$,
H (energy heads)	$= ft$,
H_f (friction head)	$= b\dot{G}^2 (K_1/D_1{}^4 + K_2/D_2{}^4) = ft$,
	$= bK\dot{G}^2/D^4$, if $D_1 = D_2$,

with the conversion constants:

$$a = 2.3144 \; ; \; b = 7.2035 \times 10^{-7} \; ; \; 10^{-7} = 1/10000000.$$

Note that if the equation is applied in a pipe of equal diameter, i.e., if station one is a pipe of the same diameter as that of station two, then $D_1 = D_2$ and the second term on each side of the equation cancel. Furthermore, Z_1 is usually taken at the lowest elevation peculiar to the problem so that $Z_1 = 0$.

An important application of Eq. (11.5) was first proposed by Henri Pitot, Ref. (11.9.3). Pitot devised an instrument as illustrated in Figure 11.2.

Basically, this device consists of a hollow bent tube inserted into a short length of pipe so that the bent end points directly at the flowing fluid; a pressure gauge is attached externally. The Pitot tube can be used to measure the fluid pressure at station one. Station two is a stagnation point, i.e., the point at which the fluid velocity is reduced to zero due to impact.

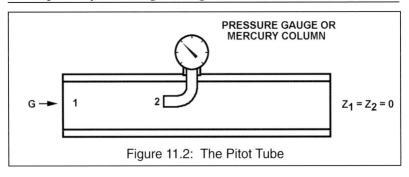

Figure 11.2: The Pitot Tube

EXAMPLE: Determination of Fluid Pressure

What is the pressure in a one inch pipe if the pressure gauge on a Pitot tube reads 10 psi? The flow is 1000 GPH.

Application of Eq. (11.5) between stations one and two (Figure 11.2) yields:

$$ap_1 + b\dot{G}^2/D^4 + 0 + 0 + 0 + 0 = ap_2 + 0 + 0$$

or

$$p_1 = p_2 - (b/a)\ \dot{G}^2/D^4$$
$$p_1 = 10 - [7.2035 \times 10^{-7}/2.3144] \times 1000^2/1^4$$
$$= 10 - 0.311 = 9.68\ \text{psi.}$$

As can be seen, for most aquatic applications the $\dot{G}^2/D^4$ correction term on Pitot's instrument can be ignored, however, note that the fluid pressure is always smaller than what the pressure gauge reads. Construction of a Pitot tube by use of a PVC tee is a simple and inexpensive task. Not only is the instrument important, it must be used in the design of aquatic systems.

EXAMPLE: Selection and Analysis of a Tank/Venturi Skimmer System

A 180 gallon marine tank is to be installed. What diameter skimmer should be selected? How should the skimmer be installed? The tank water level is five feet above the pump inlet port. The pump has a rating of 10 psi.

Since the performance of a venturi skimmer can be approximated by a skimmer of counter-current design, appeal is made to Chapter 8, Figure 8.2. The figure shows that for 180 gallons a six inch diameter skimmer should be selected (or select multiple skimmers whose cross-sectional area sum to the area of the six inch skimmer), and that the flowrate is at least 135 GPH. It could be greater should the venturi not produce enough bubbles. This will ensure all the water in the tank is skimmed twice per day. To this end the tank and skimmer are purchased, under the monetary constraint that the skimmer height will be about five feet.

Step 1
Carefully illustrate the installation, noting that the water level in the skimmer should be above the water level in the tank, in case a power failure should occur. Keep in mind that the initial placement of the skimmer may not work. This is what is to be determined.

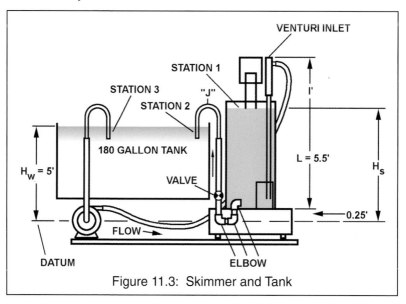

Figure 11.3: Skimmer and Tank

Step 2
The skimmer design has an elbow inside the skimmer at the bottom (to aid in obtaining bubble free water). The water enters this elbow from a large body of water (skimmer water). This will cause a re-entrant friction loss (Table 11.2). There are two more elbows on the outside bottom of the skimmer. These three elbows cause a minor loss (Table 11.1). The control valve causes a minor loss. A sudden enlargement loss (Table 11.4), occurs as the 1/2" diameter fittings meet the 3/4" diameter flexline. Pipe friction occurs in the six foot long flexline (Table 11.6). As the water enters the "J" tube, a sudden contraction occurs (Tabe 11.3). The curved "J" tube causes a minor loss (Table 11.1). Finally, there is a loss due to a submerged exit (Table 11.5). This may all sound

as complicated as hell, but it's really not. Note that the losses were just identified in order as the water moved from the bottom of the skimmer to the water level in the tank. In summary then:

LOSS	OPERATION	k
Re-entrant = 1	NONE	1.00
Elbow = 0.9	X 3	2.70
Valve (open) = 0.2	NONE	0.20
Sudden Enlargement		
D/d = (3/4)/(1/2) = 1.5	$[(D/d)^2 - 1]^2$	1.56
Friction		
L/D = 6/(0.75/12) = 96	From Fig. 11.1 for $\dot{G}$ = 135	
	k_f = 0.023	
	k = k_f x (L/D) = 96 x 0.023	2.21
Sudden Contraction		
d/D = 0.666	k = - 0.433 (d/D) + 0.526	
	k = - 0.433 x 0.666 + 0.526	0.24
Return Bend		
"J" Tube = 2.1	NONE	2.10
Submerged Exit = 1	NONE	1.00
	K =	11.01

This completes the analysis required for the determination of the total friction loss. All that is required is to proceed in order of flow and select the losses from the tables. The pipe friction loss is a simple calculation.

Step 3

Apply the Bernoulli equation in the direction of flow between station one (Surface of water in the skimmer) and station two (Surface of water in the tank):

$$0 + 0 + H_s + 0 - b \, K \, \dot{G}^2/d^4 - 0 = 0 + 0 + H_w.$$

Note that if one wished to "split hairs" two friction terms would be used, since the diameter of the pipe loss terms is equal to D not d.

Solving for H_s yields:

$$H_s = H_w + b \, K \, \dot{G}^2/d^4$$
$$= 5 + 7.2035 \times 10^{-7} \times 11.01 \times 135^2/0.5^4$$
$$= 7.31 \text{ ft.}$$

The proposed placement of the skimmer will not meet with success. The skimmer water elevation is only 5.5' + 0.25'. Increasing the water elevation in the skimmer by approximately 1.5 feet will make the system function , i.e., raise the skimmer.

Step 4

The venturi will be analyzed next. Since the inlet to the venturi has a diameter of $1/2''$ (d_i = 0.5) as measured from the purchased unit, it follows from Chapter 7 that the throat will be about $1/4$ inch in diameter. Examination of the venturi will, of course, determine the exact value. Note that the inlet to the venturi is now taken as 0.25 + 5.5 + 1.5 + 1 = 8.25 feet above the datum.

Apply Eq. (11.5) in the direction of flow from station three to the inlet of the venturi. Since at the water surface the atmospheric gauge pressure is zero and the water surface is not in motion it follows that:

$$0 + 0 + 5 + 2.3144 \times 10 - 0 - 0 = ap_i + b\dot{G}^2/d_i^4 + 8.25.$$

Note that the venturi inlet port is one foot above H_s and that for simplicity the friction loss has been taken equal to zero (on the pump side).

Solving for the venturi inlet pressure yields:

$$ap_i = 23.14 - 7.2035 \times 10^{-7} \times 135^2/0.5^4 - 8.25 + 5$$
$$= 19.68 \text{ ft}; (8.5 \text{ psi}).$$

The Bernoulli equation can now be applied between the venturi inlet and throat with the understanding (Chapter 7) that a friction loss term equal to 15 percent of the difference between the inlet and throat pressures is unavoidable. Therefore:

$$ap_i + b\dot{G}^2/d_i^4 + 8.25 + 0 - 0.15a(p_i - p_t) - 0 = ap_t + b\dot{G}^2/d_t^4 + 8.25.$$

Note that the elevation of the venturi throat is taken as equal to the venturi inlet (it would probably be $1/2$ inch below the inlet). Transposing and collecting terms:

$$ap_t = - (b/0.85) \dot{G}^2 (1/d_t^4 - 1/d_i^4) + ap_i$$
$$= - (7.2035 \times 10^{-7}/0.85) \times 135^2 \times 240 + 19.68$$
$$= 15.97 \text{ ft}; (6.9 \text{ psi}).$$

Since atmospheric pressure at sea level is 14.7 psi, the differential air rush into the venturi will be 14.7 - 6.9 or approximately 7.8 psi. The venturi will operate quite well.

EXAMPLE: Cellar Pump Installation (The Waterfall Problem)

For proper turnover rate to be obtained, it has been determined that 600 GPH must be delivered to a tank located on the first floor of a house. The pump and sump are located in a cellar. PVC pipe of 3/4 inch internal diameter will be used in the installation. The output spout of the pump under consideration has an internal diameter of 1/2 inch; or always assume this value. What size pump need be selected?

Step 1

This problem involves four distinct steps. The first step is to draw a proper installation diagram.

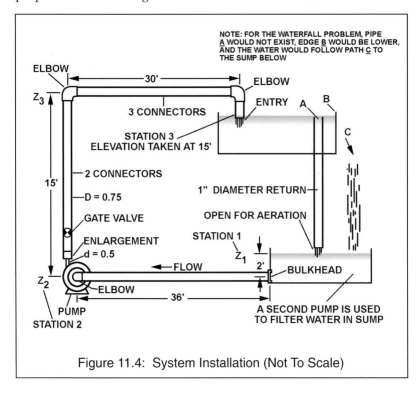

Figure 11.4: System Installation (Not To Scale)

Step 2

This step consists of obtaining the friction losses from station one to the pump inlet. Namely from the friction loss tables:

LOSS	OPERATION	k
Elbow = 0.9	x1	0.90
Bulkhead (bellmouth) = 0.1	NONE	0.10
Friction: L/D = 36/(0.75/12)	From Fig. 11.1 For $\dot{G}$=600	
L/D = 576	k_f = 0.0183	
	k = k_f x (L/D) = 576 x 0.0183	10.54

	K =	11.54

Similarly, the losses from the pump output spout to station three are tabulated, i.e.,:

LOSS	OPERATION	k
Enlargement (D/d) = 1.5	$[(D/d)^2 - 1]^2 = [1.5^2 - 1]^2$	1.56
Gate valve = 0.2	NONE	0.20
Connectors = 0.1	x5	0.50
Elbow = 0.9	x2	1.80
Entry = 1	NONE	1.00
Friction:		
L/D = (15+30)/(0.75/12)	From Fig. 11.1 For $\dot{G}$ = 600	
L/D = 720	k_f = 0.0183	
	k = k_f x (L/D) = 720 x 0.0183	13.20

	K =	18.26

Step 3

Apply the modified Bernoulli equation in the direction of flow taking the datum or reference line so that it passes through the pump inlet (usual standard operating procedure). Start at station one and note that this is not a pipe so that $b\dot{G}/D^4$ or $V^2/2g$ of the water is equal to zero. Likewise the gauge pressure at station one is zero (atmospheric). Then proceed around the circuit to station three. Use the figure to write:

$$0 + 0 + 2 + H_p - H_f - 0 = 0 + 0 + 15.$$

Note that at station three (water surface of upper tank) the pressure and velocity are zero.

The friction head due to the K values from step two and three is given by:

$$H_f = bK\dot{G}^2/D^4 = 7.2035 \times 10^{-7} \times (11.54 + 18.26) \times 600^2/0.75^4$$
$$= 24.424 \text{ ft.}$$

Therefore the Bernoulli equation reads:

$$H_p = 15 - 2 + 24.424 = 37.42 \text{ ft.}$$
$$= 37.42/a = 37.42/2.3144 = 16.17 \text{ psi.}$$

Hence, a pump must be selected that can deliver a pressure head of about 38 ft or 16 psi.

Step 4

The final step involves the determination of the total gallons per hour the pump must deliver at a one foot head. This is the number given by the manufacturer when the pump is sized. To obtain this number for this particular installation will require application of the Bernoulli equation. Appeal is made to Chapter 10, Figure 10.4. The output of a pump usually is stated by the manufacturer at a one foot head. The inlet pressure to the pump when it is rated should also be taken or corrected to zero. Obviously, if the manufacturer were to have generated the flowrate data with any pressure other than zero, this would imply a false value of the true pump pressure rating. The water extraction from the large tank in Figure 10.4 should use a bellmouth bulkhead fitting, wherein $k = 0.1$. Friction loss in the one foot pipe should also be taken into account. Apply Eq. (11.5) between the tank water surface and the pump outlet (Figure 10.4). Note that the velocity of the dropping water in the large tank is negligible and that the outlet pressure is equal to zero (atmospheric). Therefore:

$$0 + 0 + 0 + H_p - bK_p\dot{G}^2/d^4 - 0 = 0 + b\dot{G}^2/d^4 + 1$$

or

$$\dot{G}_1 = d^2[(H_p - 1)/b(K_p + 1)]^{1/2}, \qquad (11.5a)$$

which states that if the required head pressure, output spout diameter, and friction losses are known, the flowrate, $\dot{G}_1$, peculiar to the problem at hand can be determined at a one foot head. To accomplish this the friction factor k_f needs to be determined. Since the flowrate at one foot is not known, but will be greater than the required flowrate of 600 GPH, assume a value of k_f from Figure 11.1, say 0.013 (corresponding to an expected flowrate of about 1200 GPH). The L/D ratio for this problem is $1/(0.5/12) = 24$ and so $k = k_f L/D = 0.312$. To this add the bellmouth bulkhead fitting loss (Figure 10.4) of 0.1 as obtained from Table 11.2. Therefore $K_p = 0.312 + 0.1 = 0.412$. Next apply Eq. (11.5a) with the required head of 37.42 ft:

$$\dot{G}_1 = 0.5^2 \, [(37.24 - 1)/7.2035 \times 10^{-7} \times (1 + 0.412)]^{1/2}$$

$$\dot{G}_1 = 1496 \text{ GPH.}$$

The extrapolated k_f for 1496 is about 0.012 or $k = k_f \, L/D = 0.288$. Repeating the calculation:

$$\dot{G}_1 = 0.5^2 \, [(37.24 - 1)/7.2035 \times 10^{-7} \times (1 + 0.388)]^{1/2}$$

$$\dot{G}_1 = 1525 \text{ GPH.}$$

This value is close enough because another extrapolation of k_f can not be made with precision. Adopt 1600 GPH for the pump output at a one foot head with a pressure of 16 psi as the minimum values of the pump parameters.

11.5 FILTER LOSSES

Filters and other devices, e.g., chemical modules, oxygen reactors, etc. can be analyzed best by the use of Pitot tubes placed forward and aft of the filter. Hence, by observation of the pressure entering and leaving the filter, the pressure difference across the filter $p_1 - p_2$ can be obtained. The flowrate, $\dot{G}$, is usually known from the required turnover duration, along with the pipe diameter. Equation (11.5) can therefore be applied and solved for K which in this case is equal to k:

$$k = [(a/b)(p_1 - p_2)D^4]/\dot{G}^2. \tag{11.6}$$

The friction loss can be determined with a clean filter and then multiplied by 1.5 to yield an average value that compensates for filter clogging. This value of k can now be included in the total friction loss budget. Typical filter values of k are displayed in Figure 11.5 (Ref. 11.9.4).

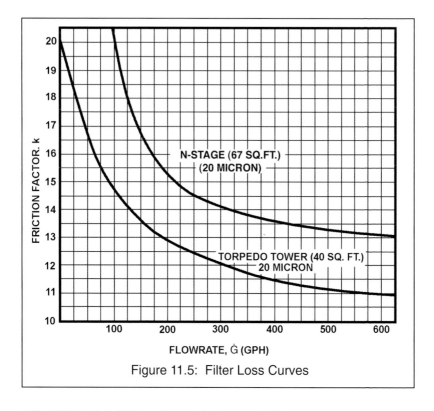

FLOWRATE, Ġ (GPH)

Figure 11.5: Filter Loss Curves

EXAMPLE: Pond Filtration with External Filter

Step 1

The installation diagram is on page 127.

Three quarter inch diameter PVC pipe is to be used throughout. An N-Stage™ filter (67 sq. ft. filtration area) is installed in the pump shed. Station 1 (Z_1) and station 2 (Z_2) are five feet above the pump inlet port. The pump under consideration has a 1/2 inch exit port and a 3/4 inch entry port. For proper turnover of the pond water the flow has been calculated as being equal to 500 GPH. What are the required pump parameters?

Step 2

From Figure (11.5) the value of k (for the filter) at 500 GPH is read off approximately as 13.2 and multiplied by 1.5 for average running conditions. Hence k = 19.8.

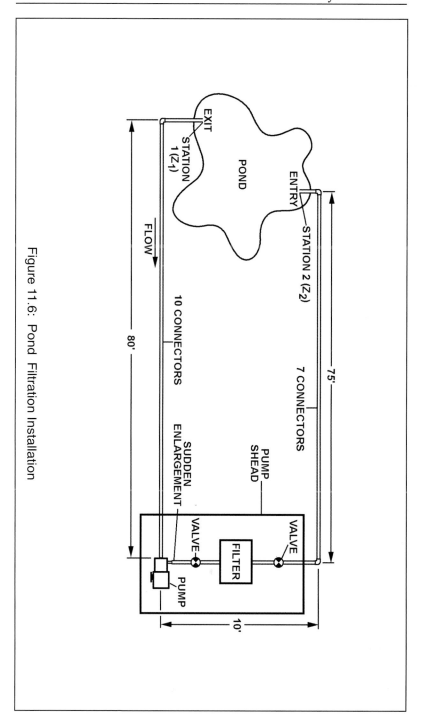

Figure 11.6: Pond Filtration Installation

The friction loss budget from station 1 to the pump inlet port is:

LOSS	OPERATION	k
Connector = 0.1	x 10	1.0
Exit (Re-entrant) = 1	NONE	1.0
Elbow = 0.9	NONE	0.9
Friction L/D = 80/(0.75/12)	From Fig. 11.1 for $\dot{G}$ = 500	
L/D = 1280	k_f = 0.019	
	k x L/D = 0.019 x 1280	24.32
	K =	27.22

Similarly, the friction loss budget from the pump output to the entry point is:

LOSS	OPERATION	k
Sudden enlargement D/d=1.5	$[(D/d)^2-1]^2$	1.56
Gate valve = 0.2	x 2	0.4
Filter = 19.8	NONE	19.8
Elbow = 0.9	x 2	1.8
Connectors = 0.1	x 7	0.7
Submerged exit = 1	NONE	1.0
Friction L/D =		
(75+10)/(0.75/12)	From Fig. 11.1 for $\dot{G}$ = 500	
= 1360	k_f = 0.019	
	k = 0.019 x 1360	25.84
	K =	51.1

Step 3

The flow from station 1 toward station 2, Eq. (11.5), can be analyzed after making the following distinctions. The pressure at station 1 and 2 is equal to zero (assume exit and entry points are only a foot or so below the pond's surface). Note also that the datum is taken such that it passes through the pump inlet so that $Z_1 = Z_2 = $ 5 feet, and that the flowrate and pipe diameter at both stations is the same. Therefore:

$$0 + 0 + 5 + H_p - H_f + 0 = 0 + 0 + 5.$$

Obviously, the elevation heads cancel, since they are equal and therefore, the required head pressure is equal to:

$$H_p = H_f = bK\dot{G}^2/D^4$$
$$= 7.2035 \times 10^{-7} \times (27.22 + 51.1) \times 500^2/0.75^4$$
$$= 44.58 \text{ ft.}$$
$$= 44.58/a = 44.58/2.3144 = 19.26 \text{ psi.}$$

Note that this problem *cannot be solved* unless friction terms are determined, i.e., $H_p = 0$ would be the result. A pump or combination of pumps capable of delivering 19 psi needs to be selected.

Step 4

To obtain the standard flowrate at one foot, apply Eq. (11.5a). Since one would expect the flowrate to be greater than the required 500 GPH, assume a flowrate of 800 GPH or from Figure 11.1 a value of $k_f = 0.0155$. Since $d = 0.5"$, $L/d = 1/(0.5/12) = 24$ and $k = 0.372$. Add the bellmouth loss (Figure 10.4) of 0.1 to obtain $K = 0.372 + 0.1 = 0.472$. Since the required head is 44.58 ft.:

$$\dot{G}_1 = 0.5^2[(44.58 - 1)/7.2035 \times 10^{-7} x(1 + 0.472)]^{1/2}$$
$$\dot{G}_1 = 1602.72 \text{ GPH.}$$

This value is higher than the assumed 800 GPH. Return to Figure 11.1 and extrapolate to obtain $k_f = 0.012 \times 24 = 0.288$. Add the bellmouth loss so that $k_p = 0.388$. The new value of $\dot{G}_1$ is:

$$\dot{G}_1 = 0.5 [(44.58 - 1)/7.2035 \times 10^{-7} x(1 + 0.388)]^{1/2}$$
$$\dot{G}_1 = 1651 \text{ GPH.}$$

This is close enough. Adopt the pump parameters as 20 psi and 1700 GPH.

The analysis is important not only because the pump parameters become known, but because it also indicates that a problem might exist. Since the diameter of the N-Stage™ filter is about eight inches, the top lid area, A, is $\pi D^2/4 = 50 \text{ in}^2$. This value multiplied by the required pressure, p, of 19 psi implies an upward force, F, on the lid of about 955 LBS ($F = pA$). N-Stage™ specifies a maximum working pressure of 25 psi, or 1250 pounds. Torpedo Filters™ are rated at 40 psi, but if selected the analysis should be repeated.

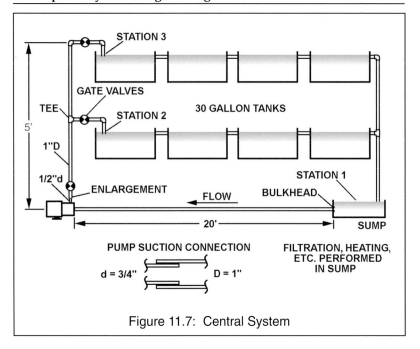

Figure 11.7: Central System

EXAMPLE: A Central System

Step 1

The installation diagram is illustrated above.

As an aside, suppose that the above recirculation of system is to exchange all the water every two hours. There are a total of 240 gallons of water in the system. Forget about the sump volume. The analysis developed in Chapter 2 applies. Note that freshwater is being returned to the tank and mixed with water which is yet to be filtered. Since the turnover rate, T (in hours) is given by:

$$T = 9.2 \, (G/\dot{G}),$$

where G is the total system gallons and $\dot{G}$ is the flowrate (GPH), it follows that by setting $T = 2$ HRS, $G = 240$ gallons that $\dot{G} = 1100$ GPH. Hence, the system flowrate (for recirculation) would be taken as this number.

Step 2

Following the lead of the other examples, the friction budget from station 1 to the pump suction port is:

LOSS	OPERATION	k
Entrance (Bellmouth) = 0.1	NONE	0.1
Connector = 0.1	x 2	0.2
Gate valve = 0.2	NONE	0.2
Contraction = -0.4333(d/D)		
+ 0.5266		
d/D = (3/4)/1 = 0.75	-0.4333 x 0.75 + 0.5266	0.2
Friction L/D = 20/(1/12)	From Fig. 11.1 for $\dot{G}$ = 1100	
= 240	k_f = 0.0168	
	k = 0.0168 x 240	4.0
	K =	4.7

Similarly, the combined friction budget from the pump output to the upper tanks (station 3) is collected as:

LOSS	OPERATION	k
Sudden Enlargement D/d=2	$[(D/d)^2-1]^2$	9.0
Gate valve = 0.2	x 3	0.6
Tee = 1.8	NONE	1.8
Submerged exit = 1	x 2	2.0
Elbow = 0.9	x 3	2.7
Friction L/D = 7/(1/12)	From Fig. 11.1 for $\dot{G}$ = 1100	
= 84	k_f = 0.0168	
	k = 0.0168 x 84	1.41
	K =	17.51

Step 3

Apply the Bernoulli equation in the direction of flow from station 1 to station 3. Assume that the gate valve used to regulate the flow at station 2 is closed. Note that at station 1 (surface of water in sump) p_1 = 0, i.e., station 1 is at atmospheric pressure. Since the level of water in the sump is steady, the velocity head at the surface is zero ($b\dot{G}^2/D^4 = V^2/2g = 0$). Similarly the term $b\dot{G}^2/D$ vanishes at the water level of the tank in the top tier. Hence:

$$0 + 0 + 0 + H_p - H_f - 0 = 0 + 0 + 5$$

or

$$H_p = H_f + 5.$$

Compute H_f inclusive of all friction losses even though the station 2 gate valve is closed. The system will be sized to deliver the full 1100

GPH to the top tank. Thus when the gate valve to the bottom tanks is open, 550 GPH can be removed with confidence that 550 GPH will still reach the upper tier.

Calculate:

$$H_p = bK\dot{G}^2/D^4 + 5 = 7.2035 \times 10^{-7} \times (4.7 + 17.51) \times 1100^2/1^4 + 5$$
$$= 24.36 \text{ ft}$$
$$= 24.36/2.3144 = 10.52 \text{ psi.}$$

Hence, a pump or combination of pumps capable of producing a pressure of about 10 psi needs to be selected.

Step 4

Since the required flowrate is 1100 GPH, assume that the flowrate at a one foot head will be 1500 GPH. Then from Figure (11.1) by extrapolation, $k_f = 0.012$, $L/D = 1/(0.5/12) = 24$ and $k = 0.288$. To this add the bellmouth loss (Figure 10.4) as obtained from Table 11.2 so that $K = 0.388$. Since the required head pressure is 24.36 ft., Eq. (11.5a) yields:

$$\dot{G}_1 = 0.5^2[(24.36 - 1)/7.2035 \times 10^{-7} \times (1 + 0.388)]^{1/2}$$
$$\dot{G}_1 = 1208 \text{ GPH.}$$

For this value of $\dot{G}$, Figure (11.1) yields a value of $k_f = 0.014$ so that $k = k_f L/D = 0.336$. Addition of the Bellmouth loss (Figure 10.4) results in $K = 0.436$ and so:

$$\dot{G}_1 = 0.5^2[(24.36 - 1)/7.2035 \times 10^{-7} \times (1 + 0.436)]^{1/2}$$
$$\dot{G}_1 = 1188 \text{ GPH.}$$

This value of $\dot{G}$ is almost equal to the value in the first trial, so adopt the pump parameters as 11-12 psi with a flow of 1200 GPH.

11.6 PIPE SIZE SELECTION

One should note that for a given installation, the selection of the diameter of the pipe to be used may not be obvious. However, if the flowrate which is required, i.e., $\dot{G}$ and the pump pressure is known, namely p, then Eq. (11.5) can be used to determine the required diameter. By supplying Eq. (11.5) with the $\dot{G}$, p_1 and p_2 (usually equal to zero) an equation in D, the pipe diameter results. Note that K also contains D, but this is still an equation in the unknown parameter D. By trial and error or standard iteration methods, solution of the equation will yield the value of D. This type of analysis becomes important for large flowrates. In summary, one needs to estimate the pipe diameter, perform the analysis and then check to see if the assumed pipe diameter was correct.

11.7 SUMMARY

Analysis of proposed installations can be performed by the use of Bernoulli's equation. Once the proper installation diagram is drawn the friction factors are selected easily from tables and graphs. The sum of all the friction factors permits calculation of the total frictional budget to be performed. It is wise to select the total friction head on the conservative side. The Bernoulli equation should always be written in the direction of flow. Atmospheric pressure will read zero on a pressure gauge. The water velocity or flowrate at the surface of a tank or pond is usually equal to zero. It is convenient to take the reference line or datum so that it passes through and parallel to the pump input port so as to make all the elevation heads positive. By means of the installation diagram, the total energy of the system can be expressed from station 1 to station 2 or station 3, etc., with due consideration of pump, friction, and turbine heads. This energy relationship can be used to determine the pump pressure peculiar to the proposed installation. Application of the Bernoulli equation a second time will yield the required flowrate the pump needs to supply at one foot of head. Many problems have no solution if the friction head loss is ignored.

11.8 PROBLEMS

11.8.1 What are the frictional losses in psi in a straight 100 foot run of one inch PVC pipe carrying 1000 GPH which returns to the point of origin (an extra 100 ft.) by reversing itself via two 90° elbows?

Ans: 13.25 psi

11.8.2 A step ladder type connection of 90° elbows is hooked together with no pipe between the elbows. How many elbows will it take until the pressure of a 10 psi pump is exhausted? The 3/4 inch elbows carry a flow of 500 GPH.

Ans: 45 to 46 elbows

11.8.3 Two Pitot tubes are placed forward and aft of a Torpedo Tower™ filter using 3/4 inch diameter pipe. The pressure difference is six psi. What is the flowrate in GPH? (Hint: an iteration will be required.)

Ans: 750 GPH

11.8.4   Repeat the analysis depicted in Figure 11.4 if a filter (N-Stage™) is placed aft of the illustrated gate valve. Should this type of filter be used?

Ans: Pump: 23.43 psi
Flowrate: 1824 GPH

11.8.5   Repeat the analysis depicted in Figure 11.6 if a Torpedo Tower™ filter is added to the existing filter in the pump shed. Assume two more valves are added.

11.8.6   Add a third tier of tanks to the central system illustrated in Figure 11.7 (one more valve is needed). What are the system requirements?

11.9   REFERENCES

11.9.1   G.N. Cox and F.J. Germano, *Fluid Mechanics*, D. Van Nostrand Co., New York, 1941

11.9.2   Toro Technical Data, *Irrigation Technical Data*, Publications Division, Lafayette, Calif.

11.9.3   H.Pitot, *"Description of a Machine for Measuring the Velocity of Flowing Water and the Speed of Vessels,"* Member Academy of Science, Paris 1732

11.9.4   Filtronics, P.O. Box 2457, Oxnard, California 93033

12 Aquarium Thermodynamics: Heat Transfer

You know my methods, apply them.

Sir Arthur Conan Doyle

12.1 INTRODUCTION TO HEAT ANALYSIS

What is heat? How is it measured? What laws govern its transmission? What size heater is required for a given size aquarium? These questions are addressed in this chapter from an analytic point of view. Definitions of the necessary variables are stated and simple analytic expressions are obtained which permit the user to precisely determine the optimum heater size or wattage required to heat an aquarium.

The solution of heat related problems involves certain fundamental laws, specifically called the laws of thermodynamics. In order to set the analysis on a firm foundation these laws will be stated. Next, the explicit formula developed in this chapter will be stated. This formula permits the number of watts required to heat a tank to be determined inclusive of all heat loss occurring through the aquarium walls. Numerical examples of this type of calculation follow immediately after the statement of the *Wattage Equation*.

The remainder of the chapter shows the manner in which the Wattage Equation is obtained. The analysis is performed as simply as possible but does involve one step using integral calculus. If the reader accepts this one operation, the derivation will be evident. On the other hand, the reader can skip the entire analysis and just use the stated formula. Nevertheless, an attempt at reading the material will enhance the reader's understanding of the thermal balance which occurs in aquariums and the methods required to determine the heat flux lost through tank walls. Should the derivation of the fundamental equations be skipped, the examples will be valuable in understanding the correct method of utilizing the Wattage Equation. A complete thermal analysis of a large tank system is presented at the close of this chapter, along with a second example which shows how to determine heat requirements for central systems.

It will be seen that glass tanks require about 5 times as much heat input as do acrylic tanks, and that careful insulation can reduce losses by factors ranging between two and 22. Further conclusions and recommendations are noted, namely, that variable wattage heaters would be of benefit, and that the aquarium tank manufacturers would greatly assist the end user by heat rating their aquariums.

Even though the method of computing thermal losses through glass or acrylic panels is well established, the heat loss coefficients are difficult to locate. These coefficients are collected and presented in tables in this chapter. The method of equivalent areas in which one single area is used in lieu of the area of each independent wall is an innovation. Furthermore, the development of a single equation which determines how many hours will be required to heat a tank to the desired temperature is developed herein for the first time.

This chapter follows the structure of the previous chapters in that after the introduction, the results are stated first. An example follows to clarify the manner in which the equations are used. A graph will then be presented which will prove to be useful in heater selection.

12.2   HEATER TECHNOLOGY

The simplest of all heater systems consist of heaters placed inside the aquarium which are either clamped in place or positioned via suction cups to the tank wall. The semi-submersible heaters are usually preferred to the fully submersible type for reasons of serviceability. The high technology heaters which have both a separate temperature control and temperature sensing probe that is not located on the heater body are of prime choice. Location of the controller away from the heater makes operation easy and a much accurate water temperature can be monitored via the remote probe. The new technology also has heaters that are fail safe from the point of view that they will cease to heat should the water temperature rise beyond the set limit, i.e., the fish can not be "cooked." Furthermore, the use of silicon controlled rectifier circuits do away with arced points and ensure a long lifetime.

The next level of sophistication in heater usage involves the employment of heater modules. These devices are used to place the heater outside the tank. The better designed modules have a port which permits insertion of the remote heater sensing probe. By splicing these modules in-line, the entire system can be located anywhere underneath the tank.

The latest technology uses the remote temperature controller and sensing probe in conjunction with a flat paper thin laminate containing embedded heating strips. The laminated pad is placed in contact with the bottom of the tank. This technology is excellent from the point of view of clutter elimination and cuts all heat loss which might occur through the tank bottom.

12.3   THERMODYNAMICS OF THE AQUARIUM

Heat is random disorganized motion of individual atoms. The more an object is heated, the greater is the random movement of the atoms and so is its temperature, which is just a measure of this molecular activity. This form of energy obeys certain laws:

The **Zeroth Law** of Thermodynamics states that:

If body number one is in thermal equilibrium with body two, and body two is in thermal equilibrium with body three, then if body one and three are placed in contact, no transfer of heat occurs between them.

The **First Law** of Thermodynamics states that:

Energy can neither be created or destroyed so that the energy into a system, plus the energy stored in the system is equal to the energy out of a system, plus the energy remaining in the system.

The **Second Law** of Thermodynamics states that:

It is impossible to construct a device which, operating in cycle, will produce no effect other than the transfer of heat from a body at low temperature to a body at a higher temperature.

Simply, these laws say that: all bodies tend to come to a mutual temperature, energy can only be transformed, and heat always flows from hot bodies to cold bodies. By accepting these laws, it is possible to completely analyze heat requirements within the domain of the aquarium.

12.4   DEFINITIONS REQUIRED FOR ANALYSIS

Heat is measured in *calories*. One calorie is the heat required to raise the temperature of one *gram* (1/28th ounce) of pure water, one degree *centigrade*, C°, or the equivalent amount of degrees Fahrenheit, F°, where:

$$F° = (9/5)C° + 32°, \; \Delta F° = (9/5)\Delta C°. \tag{12.1}$$

The rate of heat transfer can be specified in calories per second, c/sec, or in watts. A watt is not actually an electrical term, even though bulbs are rated in watts. The relationship between watts, W, and calories is given as:

$$W = 0.23889 \text{ x calories/sec.} \tag{12.2}$$

Most aquarium heaters are rated in watts, which means that the manufacturer is stating the number of calories per second that can be output by the heater.

Also note that:

$$1 \text{ pound} = 16 \text{ ounces} = 453.6 \text{ grams (gm),} \tag{12.3}$$
$$1 \text{ inch} = 2.54 \text{ centimeters (cm),}$$

and that in the metric system of units:

$$1 \text{ cubic centimeter (cm}^3) = 1 \text{ gram of water(gm).}$$

Since tanks will be measured to obtain their volume, the weight of the water in grams will be obtained with great ease in this system.

12.5   APPLICATION OF THE LAWS OF THERMODYNAMICS

Before statement of the Wattage Equation, it will be of benefit to understand exactly the physics involved when the tank is to be heated. Suppose a tank has been filled with water and has been standing in a room with an ambient temperature, T_a. By the Zeroth Law, the water in the tank will come into temperature equilibrium with the room temperature, so will the retaining walls, hood and the unplugged heater hanging in the tank. Let the heater be turned on. Heat flows from the heater into the water, from the water into the tank walls and from the walls into the room. As long as more heat is supplied than what is lost leaking into the room, the tank temperature will rise. The First Law now states:

Heat supplied by heater + heat in water when heater is turned on + heat in retaining walls when heater is turned on = heat lost to room + heat to raise water to desired

temperature + heat to raise retaining walls to the desired temperature.

The symbol for heat is usually taken as, Q, so that in symbolic form the First Law states:

$$Q_H = Q_L + Q_W + Q_R,$$

where the subscripts respectively stand for heater, loss, water, retaining walls.

It becomes obvious that more energy is required up-front because the water and the walls must be heated at the same time that losses need to be overcome. But once the desired temperature is reached, the stored energy in the walls and water remains constant and only losses need to be made up on a continuing timeline.

12.6   THE WATTAGE EQUATION

What size heater is required for a tank of given geometric size? The answer in watts, W, is:

$$W = 0.3371 \; kA\Delta T/(rd), \tag{12.5}$$

which will take time, t (hours):

$$t = 0.00003685 \; pG\Delta T/W, \tag{12.6}$$

to heat the water from room temperature T_a to the desired final temperature T_f, with:

r = 0.90 or a lower value taken from Table 12.4,
p = Heat correction coefficient corresponding to r taken from Table 12.4, (r = 0.90, p = 2.56),
k = Coefficient of conductivity taken from Table 12.2 (k = 0.002 for glass; k = 0.0004 for acrylic),
A = Total area of tank panels through which heat escapes, (in^2),
ΔT= T_f-T_a; Maximum desired final temperature minus room temperature, (F°),
d = Thickness of walls (glass or acrylic), (in),
G = 1.1 (g_w + sg_r),
g_w = Weight of the water in the tank (gm),
g_r = Weight of the retaining panels, (gm),
s = Specific heat of retaining panels (Table 12.3).

As will be clarified in the actual derivation of these equations, the parameter r is chosen more or less at will, as long as it is less than unity, but must be taken so that the wattage will be minimized while the overall time to heat the tank is of reasonable duration. Thus, the Wattage Equation is a *conditional* equation having numerous solutions but only one reasonable solution as dictated by the duration adopted as acceptable in actually heating the tank.

EXAMPLE: Heater Selection

What size heater will be required for a rectangular acrylic tank with 3/8 inch thick plates resting on a 3/4″ thick wood table (with a 1/8 inch thick top plate) which has dimensions of length 36 inches, height 18 inches, depth 12 inches, if the ambient room temperature is on average equal to 68°F but the user wishes to heat the tank to a maximum temperature of 82°F (assume the water level is two inches below the top of the tank)?

Rather than obscure the use on the Wattage Equation, let it be assumed that a precalculation has produced values of $A = 3564$ in^2, $G = 131080.28$ gm. These values will be obtained in an example following the section on geometric properties of tanks, but note that d is the thickness of the tank walls; the value of A will include top and bottom plate thickness different from those of the walls.

Since the tank is acrylic $k = 0.0004$ and $\Delta T = T_f - T_a = 82° - 68° = 14°F$, while $d = 3/8$".

By Eq. (12.5), using the suggested values of $r = 0.90$, $p = 2.56$, it follows that:

$$
\begin{aligned}
W &= 0.337 \ kA\Delta T/(rd) \\
&= 0.337 \times 0.0004 \times 3564 \times 14/(0.90 \times 3/8) \\
&= 19.93 \text{ watts,}
\end{aligned}
$$

which will take:

$$
\begin{aligned}
T &= 0.00003685 \ pG\Delta T/W \\
&= 0.00003685 \times 2.56 \times 131080.28 \times 14/19.93 \\
&= 8.69 \text{ hours}
\end{aligned}
$$

to heat the water to 82°F. Obviously a 19.93 watt heater does not exist and a 25 watt heater would be selected. Note that if the tank were constructed out of glass instead of acrylic, the value of k is five times larger so that:

$$
W = 19.93 \times 5 = 99.65,
$$

which would imply that a heater or combination of heaters totaling, say, 100 watts, should be used. As an aside, remember that r and the corresponding value of p can be taken smaller should the value of T prove to be too large.

12.7 APPROXIMATE HEATING REQUIREMENTS

Use of the Wattage Equation is simple. The theory and computation of the necessary parameters is by the very nature of this problem more complicated. It may be beneficial for the reader now to skip the theory and examine the two examples presented at the end of this paper. This will focus on the chain of calculations which are required. After examination of these examples, the details peculiar to the inputs can then be undertaken. For those readers that just wish to obtain a quick estimate of the minimum heating requirements, Figure 12.1 is presented now. This figure was generated using adopted but more or less established geometric dimensions of rectangular tanks. The bottom of the tanks are assumed to be insulated in the manner to be discussed presently.

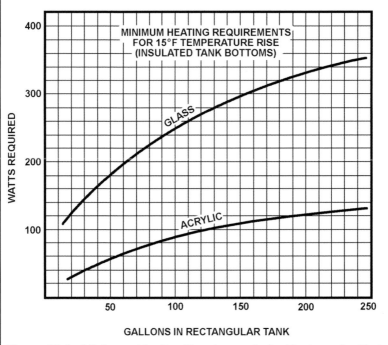

Figure 12.1: Minimum Heating Requirements for Rectangular Tank (For a 30° rise in temperature, multiply by 2, etc.)

12.8   GEOMETRIC AND DYNAMIC PROPERTIES OF TANKS

12.8.1   AREAS AND EQUIVALENT AREAS

Heat calculations involve the areas of the retaining walls plus the top and bottom of the tank, and the total area depends on the geometric shape. If all retaining walls are of the same thickness, then the areas, A, of the most common geometric tank shapes are obtained with the use on Figure 12.2.

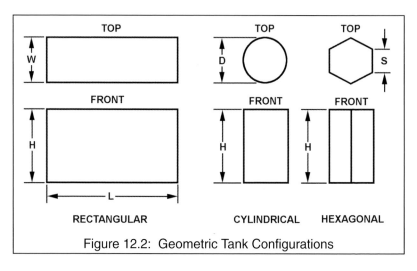

Figure 12.2: Geometric Tank Configurations

From the figure, the following total areas can be obtained:

RECTANGULAR
$$A = 2HL + 2HW + m_T WL + m_B m_C WL, \tag{12.7}$$

CYLINDRICAL
$$A = 3.14DH + m_T 0.785D^2 + m_B m_C 0.785D^2, \tag{12.8}$$

HEXAGONAL
$$A = 6HS + m_T 2.41S^2 + m_B m_C 2.41S^2, \tag{12.9}$$

where the factors m_T and m_B are equivalency coefficients relating to the top (m_T) and bottom (m_B). These equivalency coefficients are only equal to unity ($m_T = m_B = 1$) if the retaining walls are of the same thickness and are constructed of the same material. Usually the top vapor barrier (hood) is of a thinner material and the bottom of the tank will be insulated or rest on a thick wood base. To make calculation simpler and relate everything to a common thickness, m can be defined by the ratios:

$$m_T \; ; \; m_B = \text{thickness of walls/thickness of top or bottom.} \quad (12.10)$$

Similarly, if a different material or insulation is used on the bottom (see Table 12.2), the following ratio can be defined:

$$m_C = \text{coefficient of conductivity of bottom/coefficient of conductivity of walls.} \quad (12.11)$$

All that these coefficients do is adjust the top and bottom areas so that the main formulas (Eq. 12.5) and (12.6) can be applied with d taken as thickness of the walls and k taken as the coefficient of conductivity of the walls. They adjust the true areas into equivalent areas that yield the same numerical values. If these coefficients are not used, then the Wattage Equation must be applied separately for each retaining wall which is of different thickness or is insulated differently. The total watts is then obtained by addition.

12.8.2 VOLUME AND WEIGHT OF WATER

Referring again to Figure 12.2 volumes can be written as:

RECTANGULAR

$$V = LWH^* \quad (12.12)$$

CYLINDRICAL

$$V = 0.785D^2H^*, \quad (12.13)$$

HEXAGONAL

$$V = 2.41S^2H^*, \quad (12.14)$$

where H^* is the height of the water in the tank (not the height of the tank).

To determine the weight of the water, which is needed for heat calculations is easy because in the metric system, one cubic centimeter of water weighs one gram. Hence, the total weight of the water is determined from the volume as:

$$g_w = 16.387V, \quad (12.15)$$

where

$$g_w = \text{weight of water (grams),}$$
$$V \; = \text{Volume of tank water (in}^3\text{).}$$

12.8.3 WEIGHT OF TANK

Since heat is required to raise the tank retaining walls to the desired temperature, the weight of these walls will also be required. The volume of each panel is obtained as the area of the panel multiplied by the thickness of the panel. But Eqs. (12.7), (12.8) and (12.9) define the areas. Hence, assuming that all the retaining walls except the top and bottom are of equal thickness (m_T and m_B take care of the top and bottom thickness):

RECTANGULAR

$$V_r = (2HL + 2HW + WL/m_T + WL/m_B)d \qquad (12.16)$$

CYLINDRICAL

$$V_r = (3.14DH + 0.785D^2/m_T + 0.785D^2/m_B)d \qquad (12.17)$$

HEXAGONAL

$$V_r = (6HS + 2.41S^2/m_T + 2.41S^2/m_B)d. \qquad (12.18)$$

Note that m_C has been taken as equal to one in volume computations. These volumes, if converted to cubic centimeters, would give the weight of the retaining walls as if they were made out of water, but these walls weigh more than water. The weight of a substance compared to the weight of water is called the specific gravity, S, of the material (Table 12.1).

TABLE 12.1

Specific Gravity (S)

Water	1.00
Glass	2.53
Acrylic	1.19

Therefore, by use of Table 12.1, the weight of the retaining walls is:

$$g_r = 16.387\ SV_r, \qquad (12.19)$$

where

g_r = Weight of retaining walls (grams),
V_r = Volume of retaining walls (in^3),
S = Specific gravity.

Note that (1 pound = 453.59 grams). If you do not wish to do this calculation, just weigh the tank and top, then convert to grams. Of course, this is cheating.

EXAMPLE: Area and Weight

For the tank described in the previous example, determine the effective area, weight of the water and weight of the retaining walls, in order to provide the input parameters required for use of the Wattage Equation.

Write: L = 36", H = 18", W = 12" and determine the top area equivalency coefficient:

m_T = thickness of walls/thickness of top lid = (3/8) / (1/8) = 3.

Since the tank bottom plate is 3/8 inch thick, the bottom equivalency coefficient is:

m_B = thickness of walls/thickness of bottom = (3/8) / (3/8) = 1.

Since the bottom of the tank sits on a wood table, the wood surface controls the heat loss, so that from Table 12.2:

m_C = coefficient conductivity of bottom/coefficient conductivity of walls
  = .0005/.0004 = 1.25.

Since the tank is rectangular, select Eq. (12.7):

A = 2HL + 2HW + m_TWL + $m_B m_C$WL
  = 2x18x36 + 2x18x12 + 3x12x36 + 1x1.25x12x36
  = 3564 in^2.

The volume of the tank water is obtained from Eq. (12.12), i.e.:

V = LWH* = 36x12x(18-2) = 6912 in^3,

where only the height of the water is considered, so that the weight of the water in grams (Eq. 12.15) is:

g_w = 16.387V = 16.387x6912 = 113266.94gm, (249 LBS).

To determine the weight of the retaining walls plus the top and bottom plates, select Eq. (12.16) and notice that it assumes that convection heats both the top and bottom plates to the same temperature as the water. The bottom plate sits on a wood surface, but the wood surface does not enter into the calculation of the tank weight. Actually, for weight calculations if the base is the same thickness as the walls, then m_B = 1 and the volume formula is:

$$V_r = (2HL + 2WH + WL/m_T + WL)d$$
$$= (2 \times 18 \times 36 + 2 \times 12 \times 18 + 12 \times 36/3 + 12 \times 36) \times 3/8$$
$$= 864 \text{ in}^3,$$

which upon selection of the specific gravity of the material from Table 12.1 yields the weight of the retaining surfaces (Eq. 12.19) as:

$$g_r = 16.387 SV_r = 16.387 \times 1.19 \times 864 = 16848.45 \text{ gms.}$$

The parameter G, which will be discussed presently can now be determined by use of Table 12.3, which defines the value of s (the specific heat) in the next equation:

$$G = 1.1 (g_w + sg_r)$$
$$= 1.1 \times (113266.94 + 0.35 \times 16848.45) = 131080.28 \text{ gm.}$$

Again, G is a convenient input parameter which is yet to be defined but the object of this example was to show how g_w and g_r are determined. The G equation follows in Section 12.10.

12.9   HEAT LOSS

If an aquarium is filled with water, the water will be in contact with the glass or acrylic panels at the same time that the panels are in contact with the ambient air of the room housing the aquarium. By the Zeroth Law, the water, panels and air, will all come to equilibrium and no heat transfer will occur. This is called the initial state of the system. When the heater is placed into the tank, it also will meld to the initial state. When it is turned on, the Third Law implies that heat will now flow into the water (from the hot to the cold body) but the heat will also flow through the panels and into the room. It can be shown that the heat transfer through a given material is determined by, Ref. (12.12.1):

$$Q_L = \alpha \, kA\Delta T \, t/d, \tag{12.20}$$

where

Q_L = Heat transmitted through a given panel (calories),
α = Unit conversion factor (equal to 2.54 if $A = \text{in}^2$, $\Delta T = C°$,
      $t = \sec$, $d = \text{in}$),
k = Coefficient of conductivity (cal/[cm x sec x C°]),
ΔT = Temperature difference between water and room (C°),
t = Duration that process continues (sec),
d = Thickness of panel (in).

The coefficient of conductivity as used in Eq. (12.20) for various materials is displayed in Table 12.2.

TABLE 12.2

Coefficient of Conductivity
k = cal/(cm x sec x C°)

Glass	0.002
Acrylic	0.0004
Wood	0.0005
Felt	0.00009

Note from Table 12.2 that if all parameters are the same, a glass tank will have five times more heat loss than an acrylic tank. If the tank retaining walls are not to be viewed, the use of felt will be a great help in reduction of thermal loss. When felt is wrapped around the surfaces, the insulated glass or acrylic walls will come into equilibrium with the tank water and therefore the value of k for heat loss calculations can be taken as 0.00009, i.e., for glass tanks heat loss can be reduced by a factor of 22. Obviously the watt savings over a year are substantial. The bottom of tanks, even though they might rest on thick wood surfaces should be insulated. For purposes of heat loss calculations this will always be assumed. When the lights are turned off, heat also flows through the top of the tank. It is assumed that all tanks have a vapor protection plate over the top surface area of the tank. The mechanism of heat transference through tank tops is more complicated since the air space above the water and below the tank top plate is warmed by the water and the rising warm air leaks out of the top tank seams. But an air space is a good insulator, especially if it is a dead air space. Since air is usually added to an aquarium, this creates an additional complication. Furthermore, there are additional air pockets created by the hoods which cover the lights. To model the exact mechanics of tank hoods and vapor barriers thus becomes a complicated business. To simplify this situation, a reasonable compromise is to take the area of the top surface to be just what it is, correct it for thickness, and ignore whatever insulation properties this barrier might have. A conservative approach is adopted. Heat losses in flex lines, etc., can also be determined. The losses in flex lines, etc., could be calculated and indeed they should be if water is pumped over long distances, but for the analysis herein, this complication is not justified. As will be seen, it is necessary to pick a coefficient for the entire system and the line losses just become absorbed in this more generalized coefficient.

Equation (12.20), when t is taken as one second actually defines the rate of change of heat or watts due to loss. This is commonly denoted in calculus as $\dot{Q}$, a Q with an overhead dot, i.e., the time rate of change of heat (See Appendix). But since heaters are rated in watts, which is easily converted to calories per second, one can easily see that the minimum size heater (watts) required to just offset the losses occasioned by the glass or acrylic panels, is given by:

$$W_o = 0.23889 \ (\alpha kA\Delta T/d). \tag{12.21}$$

A heater of less wattage than that predicted by Eq. (12.21), will not even maintain the water at the selected upper temperature. The value of ΔT, i.e., the temperature difference, will always be a compromise, but one will not often have temperatures above 88° or below 58° unless the house or apartment central heating system fails in the middle of winter (in which case an electric space heater would be welcome by both you and your fish). Hence, a reasonable compromise is to choose ΔT to be about 30°. It is interesting to note the reduction in heat loss that occurs when the tank is wrapped in felt, i.e., blankets, should a long power failure occur.

This section has thus determined the theoretical minimum heater wattage required just to sustain the desired upper temperature. It must be realized, however, that this number of watts will never be sufficient to raise the water temperature from the initial state to the final state. The "why?" evoked by the last statement will be discussed presently.

12.10   TANK THERMODYNAMICS

The first law of thermodynamics mentions the energy stored in the system. In the previous section, it was tacitly assumed that the water was already at the desired upper temperature, i.e., it has stored energy relative to the energy that it possessed at the initial state. It was necessary to consider only the loss factors.

The number of calories required to raise g grams of water (the same number of cubic centimeters) through ΔT degrees centigrade, is given through the definition of the calorie as:

$$Q_w = sg\Delta T,$$

where s is a number called the *specific heat* of the material (see Table 12.3, and g is the weight of the material.

Hence, this value of Q will define the stored energy of the water and retaining walls of an aquarium relative to the initial state. To be more exact, the total heat Q_T is:

$$Q_T = (g_w + sg_r) \ \Delta T, \tag{12.22}$$

TABLE 12.3

Specific Heat(s)

Substance	Value
Water	1.00
Glass	0.21
Acrylic	0.35

where g_w is the total number of grams of water and g_r is the total number of grams of retaining wall material (roughly equal to the empty weight of the tank). For compactness, let the value of the coefficient be defined as G, namely,

$$G = g_w + sg_r.$$

As has been seen in examples, this value can always be determined from the physical make-up of the tank. Furthermore, since gravel, rocks, etc. are also in the tank, a good rule is to increase G by 10% so that:

$$G = 1.1(g_w + sg_r).$$

To raise the water temperature, a heater is activated. The heat provided by the heater, Q_H, is simply the product of the heater wattage and the duration of time, t, the heater is on, namely,

$$Q_H = (W/f)t, \tag{12.24}$$

where f is the factor that converts watts to calories per second ($f = 0.23889$). Since the heat required to raise the water and tank walls by the temperature difference, ΔT, degrees centigrade is given by Eq. (12.22) as:

$$Q_T = G\Delta T, \tag{12.25}$$

while the lost heat is determined via Eq. (12.20) by:

$$Q_L = \alpha k A \Delta T t / d, \tag{12.26}$$

it follows at once from the laws of thermodynamics that:

$$Q_H = Q_T + Q_L. \tag{12.27}$$

In this equation Q_L must be correctly identified. Remember that Eq. (12.20) applies to a constant temperature difference between the water and the room. It is obvious that $Q_L = 0$ at the initial state since the water and room are at the same temperature, so that at $t = 0$, when the heater is activated for a minute, the water temperature will rise and ΔT will also rise by a small amount. Hence, unless the tank has reached the upper stable temperature which is desired, the value of ΔT changes as a function of time. The differential (small) amount of heat loss in a differential (small) amount of time is denoted in calculus by placing the letter d in front of the variables in question, therefore:

$$dQ_L = (\alpha k A \Delta T/d)dt.$$

Note that dQ_L and dt are just symbols and have nothing to do with d, the wall thickness. To obtain the total heat lost over the time required to reach the desired temperature, all the differential quantities must be summed. The summation process of these quantities as they get smaller and smaller is called integration (See the Appendix) and is denoted in the integral calculus by an elongated s, i.e.,

$$\int dQ_L = \int (\alpha k A/d)\Delta T dt.$$

The left side of this equation is easily summed since the total heat loss is the sum of all small heat losses which occur as the temperature rises degree by degree. Furthermore, in any sum a constant non-varying term may be factored (See the Appendix) so that:

$$Q_L = (\alpha k A/d)\int \Delta T dt. \tag{12.28}$$

The complete heat balance can thus be written by substitution of Eqs. (12.24) and (12.28) into Eq. (12.27) as:

$$(W/f)t = G\Delta T + c\int \Delta T dt, \tag{12.29}$$

where

$$c = \alpha \, kA/d.$$

To evaluate the integral in Eq. (12.29), a method of successive approximations can be employed along with a change in the variable of integration. The successive approximation involves neglecting losses on the first approximation (c=0) and solving the equation. This provides a second approximation which picks up a portion of the losses. A third approximation, and so forth, improves the results. The equation can thus be solved in an infinite series. Without going into details, the result is:

$$t = (fG\Delta T/W)[1 + (W_o/W)/2 + (W_o/W)^2/3 \\ + (W_o/W)^3/4 + \cdots + (W_o/W)^n/(n+1)], \tag{12.30}$$

where n is the total number terms carried in the series after the 1. In this equation, t represents the total duration in seconds that will elapse since the time the heater is turned on at the initial state, i.e., $\Delta T = 0$, until the temperature reaches the desired temperature.

A look at Eq. (12.30) shows that the term $fG\Delta T/W$ is the time required to heat the tank water with no heat loss. The infinite series in the brackets represents the heat losses. Not all infinite series converge into a finite number, however Abel's test Ref. (12.13.5) when applied to this series proves that this series does converge if the ratio W/W_o is less than unity. The results are displayed in Table 12.4, where p is defined as the value of the series of the heat correction coefficient for a given value of r.

The value of p was calculated with a computer using in excess of 100 terms; the convergence is very slow as r approaches unity.

TABLE 12.4

Heat Correction Coefficient

$r = W_o/W$	p
1.00	INFINITE
.99	4.64
.95	3.15
.90	2.56
.85	2.23
.80	2.01
.75	1.85
.70	1.72
.65	1.62
.60	1.53
.55	1.45
.50	1.39

With this understanding, Eq. (12.30) can now be written as:

$$t = pfG\Delta T/W. \tag{12.31}$$

It is this equation that must be used to determine the heating requirements or the size heater(s) that need to be selected for a given system. Since the time, t is not usually a critical parameter, unless it is desired to heat a tank quickly, in which case addition of warm water in lieu of tap water would solve this problem, the value of t is arbitrary. To compensate for flex line heat losses and modeling errors, let a value of r between 0.9 - 0.85 be adopted. The time to heat the tank is now known.

EXAMPLE: Heat Analysis of a Central System

A store owner has just installed a bank of 20 tanks. Each tank is 24 inches long, 14 inches in height and 12 inches in depth and is covered with a 1/8 inch glass lid. Tanks are placed in a row with sides touching. They are constructed out of 1/4 inch thick glass plate and are placed on 1/4 inch thick felt on a shelving board 3/4 inch thick with supports. At night the store temperature can fall to 55° but the owner wishes to keep his tanks at 78°F. What size heaters are required?

ANALYSIS

Since the tanks are touching, just think of all the tanks as if they were one long tank. The side walls which are touching will feed heat to each other and come to equilibrium. Hence the equivalent tank would be:

$$L = 20 \times 24", \ H = 14", \ W = 12".$$

For this long tank the equivalency coefficients for the top and bottom are:

m_T = thickness wall/thickness top = (1/4)(1/8) = 2,

m_B = thickness wall/thickness bottom = (1/4)(1/4) = 1,

m_C = conductivity bottom/conductivity wall = 0.00009/0.002

$\quad$ = 0.045.

Select Eq. (12.7) to compute the equivalent area:

$A = 2HL + 2HW + m_T WL + m_B m_C WL$

$\quad = 2 \times 14 \times 480 + 2 \times 14 \times 12 + 2 \times 12 \times 480$

$\qquad + 1 \times 0.045 \times 12 \times 480$

$\quad = 25555 \ in^2.$

Use the Wattage Equation (Eq. 11.5), noting k for glass is equal to 0.002:

$W = 0.3371 \ kA\Delta T/(rd)$

$W = 0.3371 \times .002 \times 25555 \times (78-55)/(0.9 \times 1/4)$

$\quad = 1761.2.$

This analysis shows that at least five 350 watt heaters need to be used: preferably six.

EXAMPLE: Heat Analysis of a Large Tank

A large acrylic tank filled within three inches of the top with a length, height and width of 96 inches, 24 inches, and 18 inches, is to be installed. It is manufactured out of 1/2 inch acrylic plate and has a top vapor plate with a thickness of 1/4 inch. It sits on a wooden stand with a thickness of one inch. A sump filled within six inches of the top with length 36 inches, height 18 inches, and width 18 inches, sits directly below the tank. It is manufactured throughout with 3/8 inch thick acrylic and has a 1/8 inch thick vapor plate on top. It sits on the floor on top of a 1/4 inch felt pad. The normal room temperature is 70°F but at night temperatures can drop to 55°F. How many watts will be needed to maintain the tank at a maximum of 84°F?

ANALYSIS

For the tank select

$$L = 96", H = 24", W = 18", d = 1/2",$$
$$k = 0.0004 \text{ (for tank)}, k = 0.0005 \text{ (for base)}.$$

For the tank area, first determine the equivalency coefficients (Eqs. 12.10 and 12.11)

$$m_T = \text{thickness wall/thickness top} = (1/2)/(1/4) = 2,$$
$$m_B = \text{thickness wall/thickness bottom} = (1/2)/(1/2) = 1,$$
$$m_C = \text{conductivity bottom wood stand/conductivity wall}$$
$$= 0.0005/0.0004 = 1.25.$$

Use Eq. (12.7):

$$A = 2HL + 2HW + m_T WL + m_B m_C WL$$
$$= 2 \times 24 \times 96 + 2 \times 24 \times 18 + 2 \times 18 \times 96$$
$$+ 1 \times 1.25 \times 18 \times 96$$
$$= 11088 \text{ in}^2.$$

For the sump select:

$$L = 36", H = 18", W = 18", d = 3/8"$$
$$k = 0.0004 \text{ (for sump walls)}, k = 0.00009 \text{ (for sump bottom)}.$$

For the sump area, determine the equivalency coefficients:

$$m_T = (3/8)/(1/8) = 3,$$
$$m_B = (3/8)/(3/8) = 1,$$
$$m_C = 0.00009/0.0004 = 0.225.$$

Again select Eq. (12.7)

$$A = 2 \times 18 \times 36 + 2 \times 18 \times 18 + 3 \times 18 \times 36 + 1 \times 0.255 \times 18 \times 36$$
$$= 4053.8 \text{ in}^2.$$

Do not add the areas. Remember the tank and sump walls are of different thickness. If they were the same thickness, you could add the areas. Here you have a choice, the wattage required for the tank and sump can be calculated separately (see below) or an equivalency coefficient can be used on the sump area to adjust it fictitiously (it looses more heat through the thinner walls, but the bottom is insulated with felt). This does simplify the calculations. The corrected sump area A_c would be:

$$m = \text{thickness tank wall/thickness sump wall}$$
$$= (1/2)/(3/8) = 1.33$$
$$A_c = mA = 1.33 \times 4053.8 = 5405.1.$$

Now the total equivalent area can be obtained by addition:

$$A = 11088 + 5405.1 = 16493.1.$$

Finally use the Wattage Equation (Eq. 12.5):

$$W = 0.3371 \times kA\Delta T/(rd)$$
$$= 0.3371 \times 0.0004 \times 16493.1 \times (84 - 55)/(0.9 \times 1/2)$$
$$= 143.27,$$

or a 150 watt heater would be selected. If the wattage were calculated using just the tank area, the result would be 96.35 watts. A second application of the Wattage Equation for the sump would yield 46.93 watts which upon addition totals to 143.27 watts.

Note that the extra data on the height of the water would only be used if the volume of water were to be determined for use in the calculation of the time it would take to heat the tank.

12.11 SUMMARY

An equation is available to precisely determine the watt budget required to heat a tank. A complementary equation permits determination of the length of time that will pass before the tank reaches the desired temperature. Equivalent area is used to simplify the calculations. Hence, instead of applying the Wattage Equation for each tank panel separately, an equivalent area can be introduced so that only a single application of the Wattage Equation is required. It was demonstrated that to reach the desired target temperature, a coefficient ranging below 0.9 needs to be selected and input into the Wattage Equation. This coefficient shows that the Wattage Equation is a conditional equation which depends on the length of time the user wishes to allow for the tank to reach the target temperature. Insulation of tanks results in a profound reduction of the wattage required to heat a tank. The difference between heating glass or acrylic tanks varies by a factor of five.

12.12.1 PROBLEMS

12.12.1   What are the three laws of thermodynamics? Which law dictates heat balance?

12.12.2   Determine the heater size (watts) for a glass tank that measures 12″ x 24″ x 60″ (WHL) if the room temperature is 55°F and the tank is to be kept at 70°F. Assume the bottom of the tank is well insulated (with felt) and that the tank walls and bottom are 3/8″ thick. The cover plate is 1/8″ thick.

Ans: 169.25 watts

12.12.3   What is the weight of the water in the tank described in Problem 12.12.2?

Ans: 624 LBS

12.12.4   What is the weight of the retaining panels and top in the tank described in Problem 12.12.2?

Ans: 151.4 LBS

12.12.5   How long will it take to make the water rise from 55°F to 70°F in the tank described in Problem 12.11.2?

Ans: 2.74 HRS

12.12.6   Two acrylic tanks are placed together side-by-side so they touch (lengthwise). The tanks are 14″x28″x80″ (WHL). At night the room temperature can drop to 55°F.; the tank temperatures are to be kept at 77°F. Assuming the tank bottoms are insulated with felt. What size heaters should be selected? The tanks have retaining walls 1/2 inch thick and cover plates 1/4 inch thick; the bottom plate is 3/4 inch thick.

Ans: Two 50 watt heaters

12.12.7 Add an acrylic sump under the tanks described in Problem 12.12.6 which measures 12"x12"x36" (WHL) with an insulated felt bottom, and a 1/16 inch acrylic cover plate. Assume the retaining walls and bottom are 1/4 inches thick. What are the additional heat requirements in watts?

Ans: Add one more
50 watt heater

12.12.8 What are the advantages of using equivalent areas? Solve Problem 12.12.6 without equivalent areas.

12.12.9 Prove the law of equivalent areas.

12.13 REFERENCES

12.13.1 F.A. Saunders and P. Kirkpatrick, *College Physics,* Henry Holt and Co., Ed. 4, New York, 1953

12.13.2 K.R. Atkins, *Physics,* John Wiley and Sons, New York, 1967

12.13.3 H.A. Everett, *Thermodynamics,* D. Van Nostrand Co., New York, 1941

12.13.4 C.F. Warner, *Thermodynamics Fundamentals,* Littlefield, Adams and Co., Ames, Iowa, 1957

12.13.5 G.A. Korn and T.M. Korn, *Mathematical Handbook for Scientist and Engineers,* McGraw-Hill, New York, 1968

13 Sterilization By Use Of Ozone: Correct Airflow Requirements

Why Think? Why Not Try The Experiment?

John Hunter

13.1 OZONE

It was in the year 1785 when Van Marum smelled an odor similar to very dilute chlorine. About 55 years later Schöbien demonstrated that this odor belonged to a distinct gas to which he gave the name ozone (from the Greek "to smell"). He discovered a number of ways to obtain this gas. A satisfactory way of preparing ozone, O_3, was to pass an electric discharge through oxygen. However, significant amounts of ozone can be obtained when ultraviolet radiation at the proper wave length is exposed to air. This procedure has been used commercially to obtain ozone. Compared to oxygen, ozone is a much more active oxidizing element. It is used commercially as a bleach and to deodorize air and water. Certain bacterial organisms fall easy prey to the high germicidal activity of O_3. Less than one PPM (one part per million) will completely sterilize and clarify water if it contains phenol or iron and magnesium salts. Algae and some fungus growths resistant to chlorine are highly susceptible to ozone. Due to its high oxidizing potential, the American Medical Association, and other health organizations recommend that extended safe ozone exposure levels for humans should be about one part in ten million.

For aquarium and pond applications, ozone can be safely used in a reactor wherein the water is sterilized and excess ozone is filtered through carbon. Any noticeable smell of ozone should be attended to by shut-down of the ozone producing unit or replacement of the carbon filters. A good carbon filter will last a long time. Furthermore, contact of the U.V. rays on a person's eyes should be avoided at all times. There is no hazard in the use of ozone if it is handled correctly. Fire, handled incorrectly, would be far more dangerous.

The benefits of ozone sterilization are many. It controls aquatic parasites, ammonia, nitrate, nitrite, bacterial diseases and algae. Maintenance time, odor and the use of chemicals are all reduced by the use of ozone. In opposition, water clarity, biological system strength, and tank bio-load capacity are increased by its use. Ozone does not alter the pH of water.

In this chapter only the ultraviolet generation of ozone will be examined. This is because the output of the gas can be easily controlled, and the U.V. method of generation produces *pure particle free ozone*.

Chapter 16 will define the necessary inputs to actually run ozone reactors.

13.2   THE OZONE GENERATOR

It will be demonstrated herein that the production of ozone or the output rating (usually stated in parts per million, PPM or milligrams per hour) is *absolutely and totally meaningless* if the input flow of air to the generator is not specified. If a manufacturer does not give this information, it is a sure indication that the unit will not function as advertised. By adjustment of the air input one can completely control the amount of ozone that is produced. The other option to control the ozone production is mechanical in nature.

A moveable sleeve can be fitted over the bulb within the reactor which effectively, by adjustment, lengthens or shortens the bulb or better said, the arc length of the bulb. Certainly, it is more economical to just cut down the air pump flowrate, use less power, and achieve the desired output from the generator. Only an air valve is needed to obtain this great flexibility.

It is very important to note that the transformation of oxygen to ozone requires that the airflow be as dry as possible. It is imperative that a prefilter which desiccates the air be used between the air pump and the ozone generator. The efficiency of the transformation falls dramatically if moist air enters the generator.

As may be obvious, the oxygen supplied to the reactor comes from the atmosphere. Hence, one must realize that whatever the required air flowrate into the generator must be to yield the desired output, only 21 percent of the oxygen will be available from the provided air.

It is repeated, that any statement as to the rated output of an ozone generator, i.e., a closed cylindical tube containing an ultraviolet bulb into which air is pumped in and out, is *absolutely meaningless* unless the flowrate of air into the generator is specified. Actually, for any kind of generator:

$$14.29 \text{ Air} \rightarrow 2 \text{ O}_3, \tag{13.1}$$

i.e., it takes 14.29 liters of air to produce two liters of ozone under the assumption that the proper energy input is supplied, and as indicated by the arrow that the reaction is complete.

13.3 OZONE LEVELS

Redox, means reduction-oxidation potential. A positive redox potential is an indicator that free oxygen is present; a negative redox potential indicates a lack of free oxygen. A swimming pool chlorine test kit (OTO solution) used as directed (usually six drops in 10cc) will turn yellow if ozone is present; no color indicates a lack of ozone. When a test kit is used, only a faint yellow tint should be seen as an indicator of proper ozone level. If the test indicates more than a slight yellow tint, the ozone level should be decreased.

Natural seawater, when measured with a platium electrode redox (orp) meter has a potential of about 375 millivolts (0.375 volts). If hazardous conditions due to accumulated organics are present, a redox level below 200 millivolts is usually indicated.

Ozone by the process of oxidation clarifies water because it attacks dissolved organics, bacteria and small organic particles. Therefore, ozone increases the redox level or potential.

13.4 EMPIRICAL DATA

Since there are quite a number of variables to consider in the determination of the output from a given diameter and length generator it is wise to obtain data from a reputable company; Ref. (13.9.1). This data can then be used to verify the analytic theory of ozone generation developed herein. The analytic theory can then be used to predict the ozone output of any other generator under design consideration. The data, courtesy Ref. (13.9.1) is on the following page.

As can be clearly seen as airflow is increased, the PPM of O_3 rise to a maximum at 6331 and then decrease. The mass output steadily increases and tapers off at about 23.8 LPM. It is obvious from the data that increasing the airflow raises the mass output to any desired value (until it tapers to a maximum value), but the concentration of ozone decreases. So what does rating an ozone generator in milligrams per hour mean?

TABLE 13.1

Adopted Standard
Ozone Generator with a 34.5 Watt Bulb in a
Reactor 2" Diameter with a Length of 12"

LPM = Liters per Minute; PPM = Parts per Million

LPM (Air)	PPM (O₃)	Output (Milligrams per Hour)
0.476	5000	56.7
1.429	6162	226.8
2.381	6331	414.5
4.762	5562	728.6
9.524	4587	1181.3
14.286	3687	1447.7
19.048	3565	1840.5
23.810	3281	1990.2

The Input LPM in Ref. (13.9.1) was in O_2; The Output was in LBS/Day

Any number for the mass output can be stated; it just depends on the airflow input. It would seem then, that the important parameter is the concentration, i.e., the PPM output. The reader should think this through and question what the generator under consideration, rated in milligrams per hour, is actually producing in parts per million. Again, the output in milligrams per unit time is *absolute nonsense* without the associated airflow.

Hence, as a general rule, the more air that is input to the generator, the lower will be the concentration of ozone. The output increases to some maximum value because of the greater airflow put through the generator. This will be explained in greater detail shortly.

TABLE 13.2

Properties of Air, Oxygen and Ozone
(at 14.7 psi and 32°F)

gm = Grams, L = Liters
Air: Density = 1.293 gm/L
Oxygen: Density = 1.429 gm/L
Ozone: Density = 2.144 gm/L

Air: Composition by Volume	Composition by Weight
Nitrogen 78%	Nitrogen 75.6%
Oxygen 21%	Oxygen 23.1%
Residual 1%	Residual 1.3%

13.5   PROPERTIES AND CHEMISTRY

13.5.1 PHYSICAL PROPERTIES

Table 13.2 collects the physical properties of interest for air, oxygen and ozone.

This collection of data is of primary importance when attempting to determine the true output of ozone in any generator which is to be designed. However, to understand the operation of any ozone generator, the chemical reactions must also be understood. A brief outline of ozone generation follows.

13.5.2 CHEMICAL REACTIONS

When oxygen transforms to ozone, energy is absorbed. Hence, from Ref. (13.9.2):

$$\text{Oxygen} + 68820 \text{ Calories} = \text{Ozone}, \qquad (13.2)$$

$$3 \text{ O}_2 \;\overset{\rightarrow}{\leftarrow}\; 2 \text{ O}_3.$$

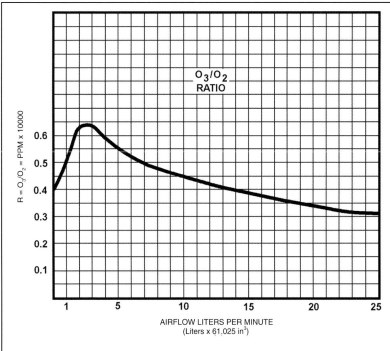

Figure 13.1: Ozone to Oxygen Ratio as A Function of Air Input Rate

The definition of a calorie was discussed in Chapter 12. What is important here is that heat provided by the ultraviolet bulb, at the proper wavelength, input into the reactor or cell is required for the transformation to occur. However, the transformation is reversible. This is evident from the examination of Table 13.1. Notice that at low air rates (where the air spends a longer duration in the generator and thus receives more heat and radiation), less ozone is produced. This reversibility makes prediction of ozone output difficult. By examination of the ratio of ozone (LPM) to that of oxygen (LPM) and the use of Table 13.1, it is possible to generate Fig. (13.1) for what will be called the *standard generator*, as denoted by the subscript s.

The ratio can be used to obtain a formula which closely predicts the empirical results displayed in Table 13.1. The formula is:

$$\dot{O}_3 = 270.144 \ R \ \dot{A}, \tag{13.4}$$

where $\dot{O}_3$ is determined in milligrams per hour, R is a dimensionless ratio obtained from Figure 13.1 and $\dot{A}$ is the air rate input into the generator in liters per minute (LPM).

EXAMPLE

How many milligrams of ozone are produced in the standard generator which has a 34.5 watt bulb housed in a 2" x 12" generator if the airflow is 2.4 LPM?

From Figure (13.1) for $\dot{A}$ = 2.4 LPM, obtain R = 0.64. Next use Eq. (13.4)

$$\dot{O}_3 = 270.144 \times 0.64 \times 2.4$$
$$= 414.9 \ mg/HR.$$

Compare this output to the value in Table 13.1.

13.6   THE GENERAL OZONE EQUATION

Equation (13.4) only applies to the generator described in Table 13.1. A number of other parameters need to be considered. The radiation produced by the bulb decreases inversely as the square of the distance as the diameter of the generator is increased. However, as the diameter is increased, the amount of air in the generator at any given time increases, i.e., the volume increases and so the radiation has more air reaction mass to operate on. The wattage of the bulb is a parameter; it supplies the energy. Finally, if the data of the standard reactor, namely, the data which is embodied in Eq. (13.4) is to be used to predict the ozone production of generators with parameters different than those in Table 13.1, the dwell times of the air in the reactor of the proposed and standard reactor must be equal.

Under the fairly reasonable assumption that the generation of ozone in non-standard reactors will follow the same trends, Eq. (13.4) can be adjusted by scaling the equation up or down depending as to whether a loss or gain of ozone production is expected. This scaling is accomplished by multiplication of Eq. (13.4) by the ratio of the parameters of the standard to non-standard (proposed) generator.

For example, the radiation loss would imply a $1/r^2$ correction from the axial bulb filament to the reactor wall, i.e.,

$$c_1 = r_s^2/r^2,$$

where in correction c_1, r_s is the radius of the standard generator and r is the radius of the new generator.

Since a larger radius implies a greater volume of air in the non-standard generator and the volume is given by $\pi r^2 L$ where L is the length of the new generator:

$$c_2 = (\pi r^2 L/\pi \, r_s^2 L_s) = (r/r_s)^2 (L/L_s).$$

The wattage correction is just the ratio of the new to old bulb watt rating, W_s, i.e.,

$$c_3 = W/W_s.$$

Finally, a correction for the dissipation of the radiation due to its travel through non perfectly dry air can be modeled by use of a reasonable dissipation constant p^* that reduces to unity for the standard generator. A value 6″ - 8″ will be adopted. Such a function can be constructed as:

$$c_4 = 1 - (r-r_s)/p^*.$$

Multiplication of Eq. (13.4) by the product $c_1 c_2 c_3 c_4$ yields:

$$\dot{O} = 270.144[LW/L_s W_s][1 - (r-r_s)/6]R\dot{A}, \tag{13.5}$$

or by insertion of the standard parameters:

$$\dot{O}_3 = 0.6525[1 - (r-1)/6]LWR\dot{A}, \tag{13.6}$$

where all lengths are in inches, W is measured in watts, $\dot{A}$ is input in liters per minute (L x 61.025 = in^3) and $\dot{O}_3$ is output in mg/HR.

EXAMPLE

Air is input into a three inch diameter generator at 10 LPM (610 in^3/min). The generator length is 10 inches. A bulb with a power of 16 watts is to be used. What is the mass ozone output?

First enter Figure (13.1) with $\dot{A}$ = 10 LPM and read R = 0.45 then just use Eq. (13.6), namely:

$$\dot{O}_3 = 0.6525 \times [1 - (1.5 - 1)/6] \times 10 \times 16 \times 0.45 \times 10$$
$$= 0.6525 \times 0.916 \times 720 = 430.3 \text{ mg/HR.}$$

EXAMPLE

Increase the airflow to 19 LPM in the previous example. What is the mass ozone output? First enter Figure (13.1) with 19 LPM and obtain R = 0.35 by Eq. (13.6):

$$\dot{O}_3 = 0.6525 \times 0.916 \times 10 \times 16 \times 0.35 \times 19 = 635.9 \text{ mg/HR.}$$

As can be seen from the previous example, increasing the airflow just raises the mass output. However, by so doing, the value of R declines. The structure of Figure (13.1) shows that the decline in the value of R is modest, but as departure from the crest of the graph (point of maximum PPM output), the PPM of ozone production decreases.

13.7 SUMMARY

Use of ozone in aquarium management has many benefits. Empirical data and the properties of air and ozone permitted the ratio of ozone to oxygen to be obtained as a function of airflow input into an adopted standard generator. Consideration of radiation loss and volume, as the diameter of any proposed new generator is increased, provided scaling factors that must be applied to the equation specific to the output of the standard generator. An additional correction factor for bulb wattage variations was introduced along with a dissipation function. All these correction factors gave rise to a more general equation that can be used to predict the output of any generator, not too far removed in physical dimension from the standard adopted generator. The operations determined the proper airflow to be used in the general equation. It was noted that rating a generator without specifying the air flow is *absolutely meaningless.* Only ultraviolet radiation was examined as an ozone source because ozone output is easy to control and provides ultra pure ozone. Finally, it was stated that the airflow should be chosen so as to have an acceptable mass output, but not at the expense of lowering the parts per million of ozone that are produced.

13.8 PROBLEMS

13.8.1 Describe two methods of producing ozone.

13.8.2 How many parts per million of ozone are needed for complete sterilization of water?

13.8.3 Describe two methods for controlling the output of ozone generators.

13.8.4 Why is ozone generation difficult to predict?

13.8.5 What does the crest in the graph displayed in Figure (13.1) signify?

13.8.6 Determine the ozone mass output in the standard generator if the airflow input is 5 LPM.

Ans: 743 mg/HR

13.8.7 Discuss generally the scaling factors needed to correct the standard prediction formula.

13.8.8 A six inch diameter generator with a length of 34 inches is to be constructed. It holds a bulb with a watt rating of 34.5. If 6 LPM are to be supplied as input, what is the associated output?

Ans: 1653.2 mg/HR

13.8.9 Is a three inch diameter ozone generator better in mass output than a two inch diameter ozone generator?

13.9 REFERENCES

13.9.1 Jetlight Company, Inc., "Ozone Generators," Laguna Hills, Calif.

13.9.2 M.C. Sneed, J.L. Maynard, R.C. Brasted, *General College Chemistry*, D. Van Nostrand Co., Princeton, N.J., 1956

13.9.3 G.L. Clark, G.G. Hawley, *The Encyclopedia of Chemistry,* Ed. 2, Van Nostrand Reinhold Co., New York, N.Y., 1966

14 Systems Integration: Applications

In questions of science, the authority of a thousand is not worth the humble reasoning of a single individual.

Galileo Galilei

14.1 A BRIEF REVIEW

The previous chapters of this book have investigated many aquarium devices and the required turnover durations which enable the devices to function correctly. The analysis may have seemed complicated, but as will be seen herein, application of these methods is straight forward.

It would seem that the best approach to applying the theories introduced in each chapter can best be handled by examples which show how each of the individual chapters can be applied to specific aquarium installations under consideration. One can be certain that some analysis prior to purchase of suitable equipment is almost mandatory. What size pump should be purchased? How many watts of heat are needed? How about selection of the proper size sterilizer and protein skimmer, etc.?

It will be shown that one need not spend hours in the correct selection of components. Indeed, the graphical approach to component selection is very rapid. Furthermore, one need not be overly precise, but some heed to the scientific approach will be of great benefit—not only from the point of view of correctly operating the equipment—but from the monetary savings to be accrued by using only the amount of power required to correctly operate the system.

14.2 ANALYSIS OF A PROPOSED INSTALLATION

Suppose a large system is to be installed. Usually these systems are placed into a wall or room divider so that all the equipment is not visible. The first step is to carefully draw a skematic of the system. As an example, consider Figure 14.1. The figure displays a large acrylic tank with a sump underneath. It will be assumed that the tank is insulated as well as possible. It will be filled with water within three inches of the top of the tank. The tank dimensions are L = 96", H = 24", W = 18". Dimensions of the sump are L = 36", H = 18", W = 18", but it will only be filled to a height of 12 inches.

14.2.1 NET GALLONS IN TANK

From Chapter 3, Table 3.2, the number of gallons in the tank and sump are:

$$G = 0.0043 \times H \times L \times W. \qquad (14.1)$$

So the number of gallons in the tank is:

$$G_T = 0.0043 \times (24" - 3") \times 96" \times 18" = 156.0$$

while the sump holds the following number of gallons:

$$G_S = 0.0043 \times (18" - 6") \times 36" \times 18" = 33.43.$$

The total amount of water can therefore be taken as **189.43 GAL or 190 GAL.**

It is best to round up this value for the amount of water in the filter, skimmer, reactor, etc. A value of 200 gallons is a good choice. This value is important when medications need to be added to the tank, i.e., it should reflect the net gallons contained in the entire system.

14.2.2 STERILIZER SELECTION

Chapter 4, Table 4.1, displays the target organisms. If complete sterilization is desired, a zap dose of 100,000 microwatt-sec/cm^2 can be selected. This dose will eliminate even protozoans. The flowrate that must pass through an optimum three inch diameter sterilizer is now determined via Figure (4.5) by entering the vertical (ordinate) axis at the adopted zap dose of 100,000. It would seem logical to select a 64 watt sterilizer with a corresponding flowrate of 166 GPH. This will ensure that all the water in the tank passes through the sterilizer twice per day. This is why the flowrate in the sterilizer line of Figure (14.1) is to be adjusted by a valve and the use of a Flowrater™ to be 166 GPH. The sterilizer analysis is now complete.

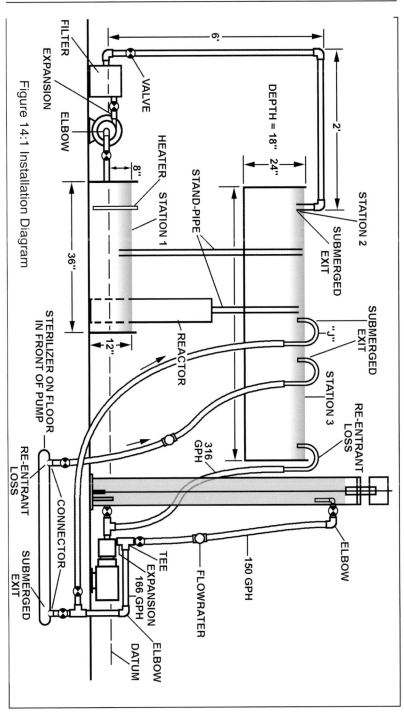

Figure 14:1 Installation Diagram

14.2.3 SKIMMER SELECTION

Since the total net gallons contained in the tank, plus sump, has been adopted as 200 gallons, appeal can now be made to Chapter 8, Figure (8.2). Assume the installation is for a marine tank. Then for 200 gallons, a six inch diameter counter current-skimmer should be selected. Of course, two smaller diameter skimmers can be used as long as the cross-sectional areas of the smaller skimmers sum to the cross-sectional area of the six inch skimmer.

From Figure (8.2), the flowrate is taken as 150 GPH. The skimmer length (height) is to be taken as long as is possible. The water level in the skimmer should be close to or above the tank water level. Obviously, the skimmer would be positioned out of sight behind the tank. This completes the skimmer selection for the proposed installation. A split loop connection is indicated.

14.2.4 HEATER SELECTION

From Chapter 12, Figure (12.1), the heating requirements for a 200 gallon acrylic tank system can be read off at once. Apparently a 125 watt heater will suffice. Actually, due to heat losses in pipes, etc., this number can be increased by a factor of 1.5, so that a heater of about 200 watts should be selected. Note that it is placed in the sump. The heater wattage is now known. A more detailed heat transfer examination of this type of system can be found in the last example of Chapter 12.

14.2.5 TURNOVER FLOWRATE

It is usually accepted that two or three turns per day of mechanical filtration is an acceptable water purification rate. Assume that three turns per day will be performed. Then from Chapter 3, Figure (3.1), yields for $T = 8$ hours (3 turns/day) about 310 GPH as the acceptable average flowrate for the 200 gallon system. Keep in mind that filtration turnover has nothing to do with the circulation (non-filtered) water exchanges in the tank. Low cost powerheads should also be added to the system to satisfy circulation demands. One or two 300 GPH powerheads should suffice.

14.2.6 PUMP SELECTION (Filter Side)

To select the pump which runs the filter, there is no recourse but to apply Bernoulli's equation as described in Chapter 11, by Eq. (11.5). To this end the friction losses must be determined. The friction budget is displayed on the next page.

FRICTION LOSS BUDGET
(Filter Side)

LOSS	OPERATION	k
Elbow (Table 11.1) = 0.9	X4	3.6
Submerged Exit (Table 11.5) = 1	NONE	1.0
Valves (Table 11.1) = 0.2	X3	0.6
Sump Bulkhead (Table 11.2) Bellmouth = 0.1	NONE	0.1
Sudden Enlargement (Table 11.4) Pump Spout = 1/2" Pipe = 3/4" $D/d = (3/4)/(1/2) = 1.5$	$[(D/d)^2-1[^2$	1.56
Filter Loss (Figure 11.5) At 310 GPH = 14	X1.5	21.0
Friction (Pipe)(Table 11.6) $[L/D = [6+2]/(0.75/12)$ $= 128$	From Figure 11.1 For $\dot{G} = 310$ $k_f = 0.0213$ $k = k_f[L/D] = 128 \times 0.0213$	2.7
	$K =$	30.56

Next, apply Eq. (11.5), i.e.,

$$ap_1 + b\dot{G}^2/D_1^4 + Z_1 + H_p - H_f - H_e = ap_2 + b\dot{G}^2/D_2^4 + Z_2$$

between station 1 and station 2 in the direction of flow, namely:

$$0 + 0 + (8/12) + H_p - bK\dot{G}^2/D^4 - 0 = 0 + 0 + 6,$$

where since $D_1 = D_2 = D$:

$$bK\dot{G}^2/D^4 = 7.2035 \times 10^{-7} \times 30.56 \times 310^2/0.75^4$$
$$= 6.69 \text{ ft.}$$

Therefore:

$$H_p = 6 - (8/12) + 6.69 = 12.02 \text{ ft}$$
$$= 12.02/2.3144 = 5.2 \text{ psi.}$$

Since the flowrate of most pumps is stated at a one foot head, Eq. (11a) applies. At a one foot head, one would expect a higher flowrate from the pump. Assume 600 GPH. From Figure (11.1), $k_f = 0.0165$, $L/d = 1/(0.5/12) = 24$ so that $k = k_f L/d = 0.396$. To this value of k, add the bellmouth bulkhead loss (Figure 10.4) as obtained from Table 11.1 so that $K_p = 0.496$. Then:

$$\dot{G}_1 = d^2[(H_p - 1)/b(K_p + 1)]^{1/2}$$
$$= 0.5^2[(12.02 - 1)/7.2035 \times 10^{-7} \times (1 + 0.496)]^{1/2}$$
$$= 799 \text{ GPH}.$$

This value is greater than the assumed 600 GPH. From Figure (11.1) for 799 GPH (d = 0.5) k_f = 0.0155 so that k = k_fL/d = 0.372. The new value of K_p = 0.372 + 0.1 = 0.472, and:

$$\dot{G}_1 = 0.5^2[(12.02 - 1)/7.2035 \times 10^{-7} (1 + 0.472)]^{1/2},$$

$$\dot{G}_1 = 805 \text{ GPH}.$$

There is very little variation in the second estimation of $\dot{G}$, so the lower limit pump parameters can be adopted as six psi with a flowrate of 800 GPH at a one foot head.

14.2.7   PUMP SELECTION (Skimmer Side)

The power requirements for the skimmer and sterilizer are quite different. A skimmer has been selected so that the water level in the skimmer and tank is approximately the same (or the skimmer has been elevated to make it so). A split loop is employed in the installation (Chapter 9, Section 9.2). The sterilizer sits on the floor next to the skimmer (The U.V. could be suspended by wires under the tank.). It is assumed that 3/4 inch diameter PVC pipe or flexline is used throughout.

The important point is to note that water flows from station 3 (tank water level) and returns to the same station (approximately). Any pressure increase as the water flows down, is lost as the water returns to the upper water level. The pressure requirements on the pump are only due to friction loss. Start the friction analysis with the entry "J" tube.

Apply the Bernoulli equation from station 3 (water surface) in the direction of flow toward the pump and return to the same station:

$$0 + 0 + 6 + H_p - bK\dot{G}/D^4 - 0 = 0 + 0 + 6.$$

Select an average flowrate through the complete system, i.e., $\dot{G}$ = (316 + 150 + 166)/3 = 210.6 GPH. Then, from the Friction Loss Budget (next page), since K = 35.14:

$$bK\dot{G}^2/D^4 = 7.2035 \times 10^{-7} \times 35.14 \times 210.6^2/0.75^4 = 3.55 \text{ ft}.$$

Solve for H_p, namely:

$$H_p = bK\dot{G}^2/D^4 = 3.55 \text{ ft.}$$
$$= 3.55/2.3144 = 1.53 \text{ psi.}$$

As can be seen, the pressure requirements are quite low. There is no actual resistance except for the friction factors. These factors are approximations to the actual losses in the system. To be certain of not having an underpowered system K could be increased by 10 percent. the important point is that: One should identify all the friction factors and then multiply by the "safety factor."

FRICTION LOSS BUDGET
(Skimmer Side)

LOSS	OPERATION	k
Re-entrant (Table 11.2) = 1 (Tank)	NONE	1.0
Submerged exit (Table 11.5) = 1 (Tank)	X2	2.0
Tee (Table 11.1) = 1.8	X2	3.6
Valves (Table 11.1) = 0.2		
Slighted Closed = 0.4	X5	2.0
Elbow (Table 11.1) = 0.9	X3	2.7
Enlargement (Table 11.4) (Pump)		
Pump Spout = 1/2"		
Pipe = 3/4"		
D/d = 1.5	$[D/d-1]^2$	1.56
Flowrater (Table 11.1) = 0.5	X2	1.0
Connectors (U.V.) (Table 11.1) = 0.1	X2	0.2
Submerged Exit (U.V.) Table 11.5 = 1.0	NONE	1.0
Entrance (Table 11.2) (U.V. Out)		
Re-entrant = 1	NONE	1.0
Submerged Exit (Table 11.5)		
(Skimmer Top)	NONE	1.0
Entrance (Table 11.2)		
(Skimmer to Pump)		
Re-entrant = 1.0	NONE	1.0
Return Bend "J" Tube (Table 11.1) = 2.1	X3	6.3
Pipe (Table 11.6)		
Assume 4 Lengths of 7'	From Figure 11.1 for $\dot{G}$ = 316	
L/D = 7/(0.75/12)(Suction Line)	k_f = 0.0213	
= 112	k_f X L/D =	2.38
L/D = 21/(0.75/12) (Return Lines)	From Figure 11.1 for $\dot{G}$ = 158	
= 336	(150 + 166)/2 = 158	
	k_f = 0.025	
	k_f X L/D =	8.4
	K =	35.14

To obtain the pump flowrate at a one foot head Eq. (11a) is recalled:

$$\dot{G}_1 = d^2 \, [(H_p - 1)/b(K_p + 1)]^{1/2}.$$

At a one foot head, the flowrate should be higher than 316 GPH. Assume 600 GPH (overkill). Then from Figure 11.1 for a pump spout diameter of 0.5 inch, $k_f = 0.0165$. Since $L/d = 1/(0.5/12) = 24$, $k = k_f L/d = 0.0165 \times 24 = 0.396$. The bellmouth loss (Figure 10.4) is obtained from Table 11.1 and added to k so that $K_p = 0.396 + 0.1 = 0.496$. The required head is 3.55 ft. so that:

$$\dot{G}_1 = 0.5^2 [(3.55 - 1)/7.2035 \times 10^{-7} \times (1 + 0.496)]^{1/2},$$

$$\dot{G}_1 = 377 \text{ GPH}.$$

This value is lower than expected. For a second trial, Figure (11.1) yields $k_f = 0.0183$ so that $k = 0.0183 \times 24 = 0.439$ and $K_p = 0.439 + 0.1 = 0.539$. Therefore:

$$\dot{G}_1 = 0.5^2 [(3.45 - 1)/7.2035 \times 10^{-7} \times (1 + .539)]^{1/2}$$

$$\dot{G}_1 = 371.6.$$

The standard pump parameters are now taken as two to three psi with a flowrate of about 400 GPH. With these low values a wise choice would be to run the skimmer and sterilizer with an inexpensive powerhead placed in the sump.

14.2.8 SYSTEM COMMENTS

Note that the water running down the stand-pipe into the bio-tower need not be analyzed; this sub-system functions solely by gravity. The stand-pipe, which is slit at the top to allow water—not fish—to drain into the bio-tower, should have a valve to control the duration of water contact. For complete safety, a second stand-pipe should be installed which is slightly higher than the first. Should the bio-tower clog, the second stand-pipe would come into action and prevent overflow of the tank.

Finally, note that the skimmer side circulation loop with its flowrate of 316 GPH provides for a turnover duration of:

$$T = 9.2 \, G/\dot{F}_o$$

$$= 12.75 \times 200/310 = 8.22 \text{ HRS}.$$

The skimmer loop which has a constant resistance loss, uses the turnover flormula developed in Chapter 2, (Eq. 2.1), whereas the filter loop uses the turnover formula developed in Chapter 3, (Eq. 3.7), because the filter produces ever increasing resistance.

14.3 CENTRAL SYSTEM ANALYSIS

There are many ways to connect central systems. These systems consist of a number of tanks which share the same water. They are mainly used in retail outlets and hatcheries, but an advanced hobbyist might also want to consider use of such systems. A system designed along these lines is illustrated in Figure 14.2.

The system consists of two teirs of four 30 gallon tanks and a 50 gallon sump. Each tank has a 1-1/4 inch diameter stand-pipe extending upwards to maintain the desired water level in the tank. The stand-pipe exits the bottom of the tank and acts as a drain. Each drain is connected to a horizontal pipe of large diameter (1-1/4"). The upper valve is used to adjust the flow into each tank (each tank has a 1/2 inch diameter feed line); the lower valve can be used to isolate an individual tank (take it out of the system). At times this may be necessary (disease, etc.). In this case, the isolated tank is filtered separately. The 1-1/4" collection pipes are joined to a common pipe that descends into a large bio-tower (1.1.5). From the bio-tower, the water flows into a sump. The heaters are placed in the sump. Water is extracted from the sump, passed through a filter and subsequently returned to the sump (this constitutes an independent filtration loop with pump P_2). Pump P_1, with outport spout diameter of 3/8 inch diameter, extracts water from the sump and raises it to a 3/4 inch diameter overhead main feed line. The water passes through an ultraviolet sterilizer on its upward journey. This second loop is the circulation system. For most purposes the circulation loop is free of devices which cause the flowrate in this loop to vary. Remember, the filter, which clogs as a function of time, is independent from the constantly operating circulation loop.

14.3.1 TOTAL GALLONS OF WATER IN THE SYSTEM

In this system, the amount of water contained in the pipes is negligible. However, in large systems this may not be the true. For this reason, the amount of water in the pipes will be determined.

There are eight feeder lines of 1/2 inch diameter, with a combined length of 20 feet. From Chapter 3, Table 3.2, the number of gallons in the small feeder lines is:

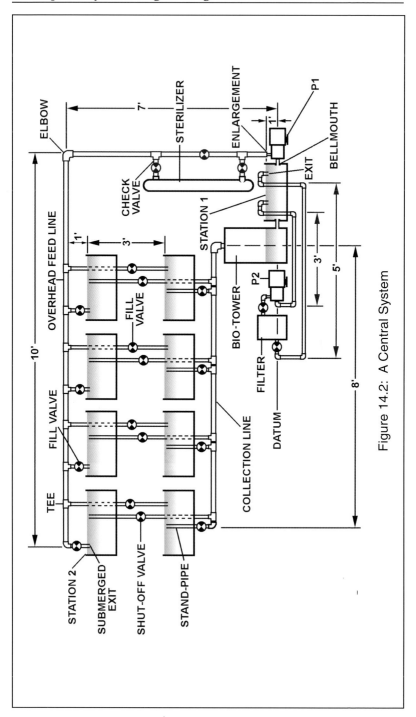

Figure 14.2: A Central System

$G_{0.5} = 0.0034 \times L \times D^2 = 0.0034 \times 20 \times 12 \times 0.5^2 = 0.204$ GAL.

Note the conversion of L to inches. Similarly, the 3/4 inch main feed lines have a combined length of 17 feet so that:

$G_{0.75} = 0.0034 \times L \times D^2 = 0.0034 \times 17 \times 12 \times 0.75^2 = 0.390$ GAL.

The collection line (1-1/4" drain line) below both rows of tanks may not be totally full of water, but assume that it is, so that:

$G_{1.25} = 0.0034 \times 8 \times 12 \times 1.25^2 = 0.510$ GAL.

Since the bio-tower contains 15 gallons and each tank holds 30 gallons, with the sump contributing another 50 gallons, the total number of gallons in the system is:

$G = 8 \times 30 + 15 + 50 + 0.2 + 0.39 + 0.51 = 306$ GAL.

This number can be adjusted if the net gallons in each tank is less than 30.

14.3.2 CIRCULATION

From Chapter 2, Eq. (2.1) holds, namely:

$$T = 9.2 \, G/\dot{F}_o$$

or

$$\dot{F}_o = 9.2 \, G/T.$$

The selection of T, the number of hours it takes for 99.99 percent of the water to pass through the sump is, of course, arbitrary, but four hours is certainly a reasonable choice. This choice implies $24/4 = 6$ complete turns per day. Therefore:

$$\dot{F}_o = 9.2 \times 306/4 = 703.8 \cong 704 \text{ GPH.}$$

The control valves should be set to deliver $704/8 = 88$ GPH to each tank. A Flowrater™ with a flexible lead that can be attached to each 1/2 inch feeder line will be very useful to set the control valves so as to achieve the proper flowrates.

14.3.3 FILTRATION

The independent filtration loop is controlled by Eq. (3.7) of Chapter 3:

$$T_{ave} = 12.75 \; G/\dot{F}_o.$$

This relationship expresses the turnover duration with increasing resistance. Particulate filtration turnover times are also a matter of choice, but even in crowded systems four turns (T = 6 HRS) per day should suffice. Remember this has nothing to do with the circulation flow. To this end:

$$\dot{F}_o = 12.75 \; G/T_{ave} = 12.75 \times 306/6 = 650 \; GPH.$$

Note that the total number of water turnovers due to filtration and circulation total 10 per day.

14.3.4 ULTRAVIOLET STERILIZATION

From the discussion set forth in Chapter 4 (Figure 4.5) it would be wise to select a zap dose of at least 50,000 microwatt-sec/cm^2. Enter Figure 4.5 at 306 gallons and move vertically upward until a value of 50,000 is reached or exceeded. This implies selection of a 64 watt sterilizer. A corresponding flowrate of about 225 GPH is also obtained from the figure. This will ensure that the entire system water passes twice a day through the U.V. The flowrate could be made slower to increase the zap dosage.

14.3.5 HEATING REQUIREMENTS

Since the glass tanks in each teir are almost touching each other and have been well insulated, each teir can be thought of as one long tank containing 120 gallons. To protect against a 30° temperature drop, appeal is made to Chapter 12, Figure 12.1. To prevent a 15° drop, the figure yields heater requirements of 270 watts or for a 30° drop 540 watts. This requirement is for one teir. For two teirs, 1080 watts would be required, plus another 180 watts for the 50 gallon sump. In total, 1260 watts will be required to protect the system against the rather large 30° drop in temperature. Five 300 watt heaters placed in the sump should protect the fish on a cold winter night. Obviously, the heaters will not supply heat continuously.

14.3.6 PUMP REQUIREMENTS (P_1)

For the circulation loop, the friction losses from the sump to the surface of each tank need to be determined. Proceeding in order from station 1 (the sump water surface) one has:

FRICTION LOSS BUDGET

LOSS	OPERATION	k
Bellmouth (Table 11.2) = 0.1	NONE	0.10
Sudden Enlargement (Table 11.4)		
Pump Spout To Pipe		
D = 3/4", d = 3/8"	$k = [(D/d)^2 - 1]^2$	9.00
Tee (U.V.) (Table 11.1) = 1.8	X2	3.60
Elbow (U.V) Table 11.1) = 0.9	X4	3.60
Valve (U.V.) (Table 11.1)		
Partially Closed = 0.4	X3	1.20
Check Valve (Table 11.1) = 3.0	NONE	3.00
Valve (Tanks) (Table 11.1)		
Partially Closed = 0.4	X8	3.20
Tee (Tanks) (Table 11.1) = 1.8	X8	14.40
Sudden Contraction (Table 11.3)		
d/D = 0.5" /0.75" = 0.666	(-0.4333(d/D) + 0.5265) X 8	1.90
Submerged Exit (Tanks)		
(Table 11.5) = 1	X8	8.00
Friction (Pipe) (Table 11.6)	From Figure 11.1 For $\dot{G}$ = 704	
L/D = (10 + 7)/(0.75/12)	k_f = .0176	
= 272	$k = k_f$ (L/D) = 272 X .0176	4.79
Friction (1/2 pipe) (Table 11.6)	From Figure 11.1 For $\dot{G}$ = 88	
L/D = 20/(0.5/12)	k_f = .0245	
= 480	$k = k_f$ (L/D) = 480 X 0.0245	11.76
	K =	64.55

Apply the Bernoulli Equation (Chapter 11) in the direction of flow from station 1 (sump water surface) to station 2 (water surface of furthermost left tank on top teir);

$$0 + 0 + 1 + H_p - bK\dot{G}^2/D^4 - 0 = 0 + 0 + 6,$$

or

$$H_p = 5 + 7.2035 \times 10^{-7} \times 64.55 \times 704^2/0.75^4$$

$$= 77.83 \text{ ft.} = 77.83/2.3144 \cong 34 \text{ psi.}$$

As can be seen, the pressure requirements are high. They can be reduced by using a one inch diameter pipe for the main feed line instead of the adopted 3/4 inch line. Note that $0.75^4 = 0.316$ and it is the division by this value which is increasing the value of H_p, the required pumphead, in the previous equation. For a one inch pipe, the values in the previous table change, namely:

$$\text{Sudden Contraction} = 2.48$$
$$\text{Sudden Enlargement} = 37.34$$
$$\text{Friction (main feeder)} = 3.83.$$

Deletion of the 3/4 inch diameter values, i.e., 1.90, 9.0, 4.79 and insertion of the one inch diameter values yield K = 92.51 so that

$$H_p = 5 + 7.2035 \times 10^{-7} \times 92.51 \times 704^2/1^4$$
$$= 38.02 \text{ ft.} = 16.43 \text{ psi.}$$

This is a more reasonable value. A one inch diameter line should be selected for the main feeder line. To determine the circulation pump parameter (flowrate) at a one foot head, Eq. (11.5a) is recalled. Substitution of the basic parameters results in:

$$\dot{G}_1 = d^2 [(H_p - 1)/b (K_p + 1)]^{1/2}$$
$$= (3/8)^2[(38.02 - 1)/7.235 \times 10^{-7}(0.58 + 1)]^{1/2}$$
$$= 802 \text{ GPH,}$$

where K_p is obtained by entering Figure 11.1 for the required flowrate of 704 GPH and reading off (by extrapolation) $k_f = 0.015$ so that $k = k_f$ (L/D) = 1/[(3/8)/12] = 12.0.375 = 32. Therefore, k = 0.015 x 32 = 0.48, to which is added the minor loss due to the bellmouth fitting (See Figure 10.4). The bellmouth loss is 0.1 so that $K_p = 0.48 + 0.1 = 0.58$.

The value of G_1, could be refined by entering Figure 11.1 with a value of 802 GPH, but the extrapolation required does not justify this added calculation. Adopt the circulation pump parameters as 16-17 psi with a flowrate of 800 GPH at a one foot head.

14.3.7   PUMP REQUIREMENTS (P_2)

The 3/4 inch diameter filter loop friction loss budget follows on the next page.

Apply the Bernoulli Equation in the direction of flow from station 1 to station 1 (return):

$$0 + 0 + 1 + H_p - bK\dot{G}^2/D^4 - 0 = 0 + 0 + 1,$$

or

$$H_p = bK\dot{G}^2/D^4 = 7.2035 \times 10^{-7} \times 43.1 \times 650^2/0.75^4,$$
$$= 41.46 \text{ ft.} = 41.46/2.3144 = 17.91 \text{ psi.}$$

FRICTION LOSS BUDGET

LOSS	OPERATION	k
Elbow (Table 11.9)	X11	9.9
Valve (Open) (Table 11.9) = 0.2	X 2	0.4
Entrance (Re-entrant) (Table 11.2) = 1.0	NONE	1.0
Exit (Table 11.5)	NONE	1.0
Sudden Enlargement Pump Spout To Pipe D = 3/4", d = 3/8"	$K = [(D/d)^2-1]^2$	9.0
Filter (Assume N-Stage); $\dot{G}$ = 650 GPH From Fig. 11.5 k = 13	X 1.5	19.5
Friction (Pipe) (Table 11.6) L/D = (3 + 5)/(0.75/12) = 128	From Figure 11.1 for $\dot{G}$ = 650 k_f = 0.018 k = k_f(L/D) = 128 X 0.018	2.3
	K =	43.1

Finally, the flow at a one foot head is given by Eq. (11.5a). Since for an assumed flow of 800 GPH (pump spout = 3/8" diameter) k_f = 0.0145, it follows that $k = k_f(L/D) = 0.0145 \times 1 \times 12/(3/8) = 0.464$. To this add the bellmouth loss of 0.1 (Figure 10.4) so that K_p = 0.564. Application of Eq. (11.5a) yields:

$$\dot{G}_1 = 0.375^2[40.46/7.2035 \times 10^{-7}(1 + 0.564)]^{1/2},$$

$$= 843 \text{ GPH}.$$

A pump capable of providing about 18 psi with a flow of 850 GPH at a one foot head would be adopted for the filter loop.

14.3.8 SYSTEM COMMENTS

The central system depicted in Figure 14.2 used two separate pumps. Should the filtration pump (P_2) fail, circulation will still be maintained via pump (P_1). Note, the correct design enables one to take any tank out of the system by the use of the valves. This is an important feature should a given tank need to be medicated or conditioned separately. As an added safety feature, the bio-tower should have an overflow drain near the top which leads directly to the sump. Should it clog, no overflow will occur. Furthermore, note that the U.V. is installed with a by-pass connection which will provide the correct flow of water through the sterilizer.

14.4 SUMMARY

Two large systems have been analyzed in this chapter. The importance of drawing a proper installation diagram has been stressed. This diagram should show even the most minute elements of the installation. As shown, the selection of most components can be performed very rapidly via the graphical approach developed in Chapters 2 through 13. The selection of the pump requirements needs be done analytically, but once the friction budgets are established, the analysis is straight forward.

14.5 PROBLEMS

14.5.1 Design your own central system. Use as many tanks as you wish. Include a skimmer and ozone generator.

14.5.2 Suppose you were given the job of designing a central system consisting of 40 thirty gallon tanks. How would you handle the installation?

14.5.3 How can three bio-towers, each with a different function, be added to the central system discussed in this chapter?

14.5.4 Add an ozone generator to the system displayed in Figure 14.1.

14.6 REFRENCES

14.6.1 Chapter 2 through 13.

15 Tank Bio-Load: Fluidized Beds

The fleas we know have other fleas
upon their backs to bite'm
And these in turn have other fleas
and so ad infinitum.

Unknown

15.1 SYSTEM COMMENTS

An existing tank can only hold a predetermined number of fish. But this number can be increased by use of fluidized or fluidic beds or trickle filters. What is a fluidized bed? What advantages does it have over a trickle filter? And for that matter, what is a trickle filter?

A fluidized bed is a reactor into which a fine sand is introduced and water is made to lift and coat the sand with a laminar layer of water. The water suspended grains of sand expose their individual surface area. This area is miniscule but the number of grains is vast and the total surface area which is exposed is very large. On the extensive area defined by *ad infinitum* bumps on top of bumps beneficial bacteria are cultured. The greater the total area the higher will be the bio-load capacity of the tank, namely, many more fish can be placed in the tank. The nitrifying aerobic bacteria (aerobes that live only in the presence of oxygen) will feed and prosper and in due process convert toxic substances such as ammonia and nitrite to nitrates (which are plant nutrients), or better said to nontoxic substances. This process occurs before the water is returned to the tank. High oxygen levels assist this chemical transformation. The efficiency of this change is much quicker in a fluidized bed than in a trickle or undergravel filter because of this high oxygen level. The oxygen these aerobes consume comes from the tank water but if desired oxygen can be boosted by an air pump.

The trickle filter functions in much the same manner but the fact is that for the same capacity the trickle filter has to be much larger. This is due to the smaller surface area. These numbers will be quantified shortly. A second drawback to the trickle filter is that the aerobes grow on the bio-balls and progressively produce a bacterial crust which fills the crags peculiar to the bio-balls and inhibits to some degree or another the oxygen from feeding the aerobes. Hence, it would need to be cleaned. In opposition, the constant bombardment of the grains of sand in a fluidized bed will shear off thickened clusters or colonies of aerobes, i.e., the fluidized bed is self-cleaning, so it has a definite advantage in this respect. The only disadvantage in a fluidized bed device is the suffocation of the aerobes which can occur if the bed lays dormant for an extended duration. But to some degree this is also true for trickle filters. As can be seen a fluidized bed, with its large surface area is quite a useful device. It is also beautiful to look at, so much so that many hobbyists display the bed in lieu of hiding it under the tank cabinet.

Once placed in motion, the fluidized bed is usually kept in constant operation. It is an integral part of the full circulation philosophy adopted in this book. Filters need not be run constantly, sterilizers obey the same rules of non-continuous operation, as do ozone generators. But a fluidized bed should always be in motion. The fluidized bed is an important device that supplies the tank with an extended area upon which beneficial bacteria can grow and thrive. Cessation of operation can prove to be fatal to the beneficial bacteria because this action deprives them of the life giving oxygen upon which they thrive. Short durations of less than 12 hours of non-operation are not fatal to the bacteria or better said, have minimal consequences upon their health.

In summary, a fluidized bed should be run with an independent or dedicated pump which is in continuous operation. Water is extracted from the tank via flexlines, run into the bed and returned to the tank. The flowrate is adjusted so that the upper sand surface of the bed is in constant undulation, but is not great enough to suspend the sand and have it be suctioned forward and thus returned to the tank.

The intent of this chapter is to provide a scientific rational wherein the importance of the filter bed peculiar to any given tank plus the added benefit of auxiliary devices such as fluidized or fluidic beds is identified and thus answer to the questions: How many fish can be placed in a tank of given dimensions or conversely what size tank is needed to house a given population?

To answer these questions requires a quantitative knowledge of the available surface area provided by the filter bed, and as might be expected, the flowrate of the water that brings life sustaining oxygen to the aerobes who live on this area. If these parameters are specified and a reasonable estimate of the amount of pollution produced by the fish plus that of feeding is also known, then a mechanism for estimation of total fish population can be constructed. As will be seen the unified theory, developed herein for the first time, yields the required mechanism.

Please note that graphical data is provided so that most of the mathematics can be avoided. The reader can rest assured that the author will in no sense be slighted if at this point a rapid leap to Figure 15.4 is executed. The intervening material is there so that the results which are obtained can be substantiated. From this juncture, graphical data permits the reader to proceed without the use of, what some might call, ominous looking equations, but the equations are there as proof of what otherwise would just be assertions. Remember, assertions always can be made but to prove the assertions is a different matter.

15.2 PARAMETERS OF FUNDAMENTAL IMPORTANCE

The outstanding feature of a fluidized bed is the large surface area provided by the aggregate of sand particles. If this area is determined then the resulting value can be used as an index of the bio-load capacity of a given aquatic system. So how is this area to be determined? There are three basic parameters required to answer this question. The first is the number of grains of sand contained in the filter bed or reactor and the second is the surface area of each grain of sand. Upon multiplication of these parameters, the total surface area will become known. The third compound parameter is the size and shape of each grain of sand, and as may be obvious it needs be known prior to the determination of the first two parameters.

15.3 SAND SIZE AND SHAPE

How is sand graded with respect to uniformity? It is just passed through two screens composed of square windows of two different sizes, i.e., there is a *large* screen of U_b by U_b millimeters and a *small* screen of size U_s by U_s. The irregular shaped sand or quartz (SiO_2) of size smaller than U_b x U_b but bigger that U_s x U_s becomes trapped between both screens; larger particles are held back by the top U_b screen while smaller particles fall through the U_s screen. Hence, the sand siphoned off between the screens is an average graded sand between U_b and U_s millimeters. The values of U_b and U_s can be adopted as desired but for the fluidized beds it seems reasonable to take U_b = 0.35 and U_s = 0.25 millimeters (These values multiplied by 39.37/1000 will yield these limits in inches). The average size will therefore be equal to (0.35 + 0.25)/2 = 0.3 millimeters. Sand much larger that this will be more difficult to "float" within the reactor while smaller diameter grains will be suspended in the water and have a tendency to be siphoned back into the tank.

For purposes of determination of the number of grains of sand contained within the reactor it will be assumed that these grains of sand are spherical. This assumption is not sacrilegious from a statistical point of view. Apart from the fact that the grains of sand do tend to sphericity because of the constant collision process, the near infinite number of random projections and depressions peculiar to the sand grains will tend to average out and yield a spherical but fictitious grain. This is not the case when the surface area of each grain is to be determined. Also note that sand self compacts, i.e., is virtually non-compressible, so that in the absence of water a vertical column of sand is devoid of any air pockets save those produced by the touching spheroids. It is interesting to note that for fine sand 1 cubic foot weighs about 100 pounds.

15.4   NUMBER OF SAND GRAINS

Section 9.5 showed that the number of bubbles, N, in a protein skimmer is given by:

$$N = \pi r_s^2 L_s/(d_b+s)^3, \qquad (15.1)$$

where π = 3.1415, r_s is the radius of the skimmer, L_s is the height of the water column, d_b is the diameter of the bubble and s is the spacer between each bubble, i.e., the fluid layer buffer. It is not a great leap to associate r_s with the radius of the reactor, r_r, L_s with the height of the sand column without water movement, L_r, d_b with the diameter of the sand grain, d_g, and to let s = 0. The parameter s is taken equal to zero because to estimate the number of grains of sand no fluid layer is involved. Note that if L_r is measured prior to the addition of water and remeasured once water is added and the reactor is in operation, then s can be computed via Eq. (15.1) so as to determine the laminar fluid envelope about each grain.

EXAMPLE

How many sand grains of 0.3 millimeter average diameter are contained in an 8 inch diameter reactor which contains a 10 inch column of sand which has settled in motionless water?

Use of Eq. (15.1) with d_g = 0.3 x 39.37/1000 = 0.011811" with s=0 yields:

$N = \pi r_r^2 L_r/(d_g + s)^3 = 3.1415 \times 4^2 \times 10/0.011811^3 = 305,077,267$, or about 305 million grains of sand!

15.5 SAND SHAPE

If the shape of the sand grain were to be assumed as spherical, a true picture of the surface area would not be obtained. This is said in light of the fact that a sand grain surface is composed of many *bumps*, i.e., indentations and protrusions with random distribution and height. Think of the grain as a miniature golf ball with semispherical indentations but also with an equal number of similarly shaped projections. Why spherical indentations or projections? Certainly the surface characteristics are jagged not spheroidal. Think of the process of arriving at spherical surface indentations or protrusions this way. There are a vast number of sand grains and the footprint of these projections would statistically average out, e.g., pick any shape footprint such as triangular, elliptical, polygonal, etc. and rotate it from grain to grain. The average will be circular. Next average the height of say 1/3 of the lowest indentations, the height of 1/3 of the medium indentations, and finally the height of the remaining third of the tallest indentations or protrusions. Why this tricotomy? The value of 1/3 is arbitrary but on a statistical basis there would be more low protrusions, less medium and even less high value protrusions; just like mountains. Connection of this profile of indentations/protrusions would yield approximately a semispherical form. In summary, it is assumed that the grain of sand can be statistically modeled by adoption of a mean spheroidal shape upon which much smaller semispheroidal projections and indentations, call them *bumps*, are superimposed along the mean surface. But how many bumps are to be superimposed on the surface, and how many footprints do these bumps have? This number is

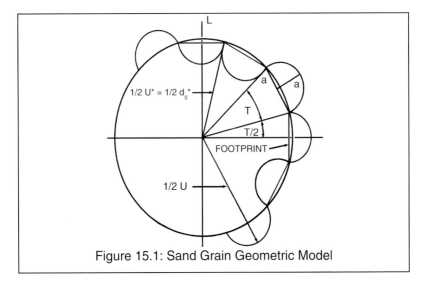

Figure 15.1: Sand Grain Geometric Model

unknown and must be adopted as an operating parameter which as will be seen can be averaged out at a later stage of analysis. To this end consider Figure (15.1).

The figure represents a model of the sand grain with indentations/ projections or bumps in a cross-sectional equatorial plane. The footprint diameter is 2a while the angle it subtends is T. The radius of the grain is $d_g^*/2$; this is yet to be determined. For a totally general model it is possible to let M, the total number of equatorial footprints be any number (in the Figure M = 12). Hence, a chain of touching circles of diameter 2a dominate the equatorial plane. To simplify the analysis let M be chosen so that it is divisible by 4. Now think of Figure (15.1) as a latitudinal slice through the grain. It is evident that there are N = M/4 footprints in this plane, or that N chains of circles can be placed perpendicular to the equator in the upper quadrant of the grain. Note that the two halves of the footprint peculiar to the model count as one. The equatorial chain consists of only semicircles.

The central angle T is just equal to $2\pi/M$ or $360°/M$. If a hemispherical bump were placed on the smooth surface of a grain of sand it would be larger in diameter that the screen dimensions U_b or U_s and the diameter would need be reduced so that the bumpy grain can pass through the sifting screens. Examination of Figure 15.1 and defining the reduced diameter as $U^* = d_g^*$, shows that:

$$U_b{}^*\cos T/2 + U_b{}^*\sin T/2 = U_b \qquad (15.2a)$$

$$U_s{}^*\cos T/2 + U_s{}^*\sin T/2 = U_s, \qquad (15.2b)$$

where for emphasis $U_b{}^*$, $U_s{}^*$ denote the reduced diameters. Therefore, the average grain diameter for surface area calculations is just:

$$U^* = (U_b + U_s)/2(\cos T/2 + \sin T/2). \qquad (15.3)$$

Note that to obtain the number of grains in a given volume the average individual grain size is $(U_b + U_s)/2$ not U^*.

15.6 MODEL FOR SURFACE AREA CALCULATION

By the use of calculus it is easy to show that the surface area of a sphere is $\pi(U^*)^2$. If hemispheres of radius a are dotted on the mean surface of the sand grain, they add the surface areas inherent to their shape but rob the footprints total surface area. The shape of the curved area of each footprint is a three dimensional lune (cap) whose surface area can be shown to be:

$$S = \pi(U^*)^2[1 - \cos T/2]/2, \quad 0 \le T \le 180°.$$

Since $a = (U^*/2)\sin T/2$, the surface area, S_c, of a circular footprint is just the area of the circle or

$$S_c = \pi(U^* \sin T/2)^2/4.$$

Keeping in mind that S is the surface area of the spherical cap and S_c is the surface area of the flat circular area under the cap, the ratio of S_c to S by definition ($\equiv$)is:

$$c \equiv S_c/S = 1/2(\sin^2 T/2)/[1 - \cos T/2],$$

or in terms of the equatorial footprints, using $T = 2/M$,

$$c = S_c/S = 1/2(\sin^2 \pi/M)/[1 - \cos \pi/M]. \qquad (15.4)$$

The analysis that follows will use S_c in lieu of S for the surface area robbed by each bump. As M becomes greater and greater the limit of S_c to S goes over to the undefined form $0/0$ since $\sin^2 / = 0$ and $\cos / = 1$. However use of l'Hopital's rule shows that the true limit of this expression is equal to unity, as well it should. For low values of M the correction c is easily applied, as well it will.

Figure 15.2 depicts a cross-sectional view of the sand grain with its *ad infinitum flea* series of bumps.

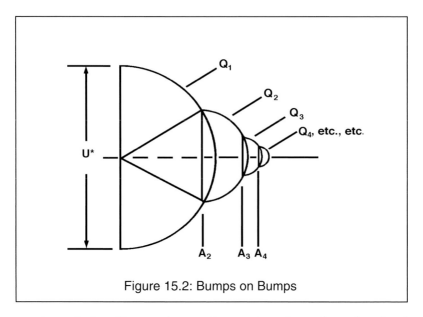

Figure 15.2: Bumps on Bumps

As each tier of bumps is superimposed on the surface of grain of diameter U^* it can be demonstrated that the total surface area is given by:

$$S_g = [1 + (\pi/g + \pi^2/2g^2 + \pi^3/4g^3 + ...)(1/2 - 1/4c)]\pi(U^*)^2, \quad (15.5)$$

where g is the ratio of all the footprints obtained by simply dividing the spherical surface area of the smooth grain by the footprint diameters A_2^2 or A_3^2, etc., to the integer footprints that actually fit, i.e., to F as will be determined in Section 15.7; the value of c is obtained from Eq. (15.4). For those readers interested in how Eq. (15.5) is obtained it will be helpful to note that in Figure (15.2) the footprint diameters are given by:

$$A_2 = 2a, A_3 = A_2^2/U^*, A_4 = A_2^3/(U^*)^2, \text{ etc.;}$$

The surface areas are obtained as:

$$Q = \pi(U^*)^2, Q_2 = 1/2A_2^2\pi, Q_3 = 1/2 A_2^4\pi/(U^*)^2, Q_4 = 1/2 A_2^6\pi/(U^*)^4, \text{ etc.}$$

The footprint values are:

$$N_1 = Q_1/A_2^2g, N_2 = 1/2 \pi(U^*)^2/A_2^2g, N_3 = N_2, \text{ etc.,}$$

while the areas of the footprints of the superimposed bumps are:

$$B_1 = \pi A_2^2/4c, B_2 = \pi A_2^4/4c, B_3 = \pi A_2^6/4c, \text{ etc.}$$

15.7   EXACT NUMBER OF FOOTPRINTS

The circumference of any horizontal circle parallel to the equator of the sand grain is:

$$\pi \ U^* \cos I \cdot T,$$

e.g., if $I = 0$ the circumference is measured in the equator and equal to $\pi \ U^*$ by virtue of the fact that $\cos(I \cdot 0) = 1$. However, as the same size circular footprints are placed at increasing latitude they will consume more arc length about this circumference. This arc length needs to be determined. The footprint angle, z, subtended at any latitude is given by[1] $z = 2 \sin^{-1}(a/U^* \cos T \cdot I)$, where $U^* \cos T \cdot I$ is the distance from the axis of L in Figure (15.1) to the center of the footprint. However, if the arc length is the product of this distance and the subtended angle, it follows that s, the arc length, taken up by each footprint at any given latitude is:

$$s = [(U^*/2) \cos I \cdot T][2 \sin^{-1}(a/U^* \cos I \cdot T)].$$

The number of footprints at any latitude can now be obtained by dividing the circumference at this latitude by s so that:

$$W_I = \pi/\sin^{-1}[\sin(T/2)/\cos I \cdot T]. \tag{15.6}$$

Since the single footprint at the pole ($\cos I \cdot T = 0$) can not be determined because of the mathematical singularity and at the equator only half circles are obtained (see Figure 9.1) the general formula for total number of footprints on a given sphere is:

$$F = 2[M/2 + 1 + \sum_{I=1}^{I=N-1} INT\ (W_I)], \quad N = M/4, \tag{15.7}$$

where the value of W_I is integerized (INT W_I) because partial footprints have no physical meaning; the symbol $\sum$ denotes a sum, namely:

$$\sum INT(W_I) = INT\ (W_1) + INT\ (W_2) + ... + INT\ (W_{N-1}).$$

EXAMPLE

How many footprints can be dotted on the surface of a grain of sand with an average diameter of 0.3 millimeters, for an adopted value of $M = 12$, namely, when exactly 12 footprints are taken about the grain diameter?

1.   Arcsine ($\sin^{-1}$) means: find the angle whose trigonometric sine is a given number. The arcsine function is available on any calculator.

First, the central angle is determined from:

$$T = 2\pi/M = 0.5236 \text{ radians} = 30°,$$

and the corrected diameter obtained via Eq. (15.3):

$$U^* = 0.3/(\cos[0.5236/2] + \sin[0.5236/2]$$
$$= 0.2449.$$

Since $M = 12$, then $N = M/4 = 3$. This means the summation in Eq. (15.7) has two terms, i.e., $I = 1, 2$; therefore:

$$W_1 = /\sin^{-1}([\sin 0.5236/2]/[\cos 0.5236]) = 10.351$$
$$W_2 = /\sin^{-1}([\sin 0.5236/2]/[\cos 1.0472]) = 5.774.$$

Equation (15.7) now yields:

$$F = 2[12/2 + 1 + 10 + 5] = 44 \text{ footprints.}$$

Note that if the grain diameter is any number, the value of F is the same.

15.8 SURFACE AREA CALCULATION

The employment of Eq. (15.5) requires that explicit determination of the parameters g and c. To accomplish this task a computer simulation must be performed wherein g and c are determined as a function of the yet unspecified number of equatorial circles, M, placed about the sand grain. With this input and Eq. (15.7) these parameters become known. The results are displayed in Table 15.1.

TABLE 15.1

Surface Shape Coefficients g and c

Circles M	Coefficient g	Coefficient c
8	1.073	0.9619
12	1.066	0.9830
16	1.058	0.9904
20	1.035	0.9938
24	1.048	0.9957
28	1.027	0.9968
32	1.028	0.9976
36	1.024	0.9981
72	1.013	0.9995
144	1.006	0.9998
400	1.002	0.9999

As can be seen the c coefficient proceeds slowly to unity as M increases. The value of g also proceeds to unity with a slight jitter for low values of M. This jitter is due to the integer truncation inherent to the model. It is interesting to note the vast number of footprints that are generated as M is increased (see Figure (15.3)). For M > 28 the footprints grow as the logarithm of M. Note that Figure (15.3) is graphed on standard logarithmic paper. This paper permits the range of the parameters to be greatly extended.

Armed with the calculated parameters g and c for a selected value of M the value of S_g is given by Eq. (15.5). Actually by dividing Eq. (15.5) by the mean surface area of the grain the surface area expansion coefficient, E, can be written as:

$$E = 1 + (\pi/g + \pi^2/2g^2 + \pi^3/4g^3 + ...) (1/2 - 1/4c), \qquad (15.8)$$

where each term in the geometric series (a series wherein the next term is obtained by multiplication of the last term by a common ratio) represents a tier of bumps. So how many tiers should be used in the

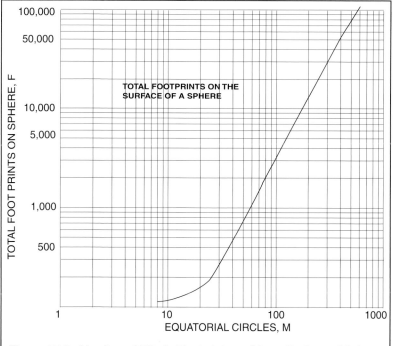

Figure 15.3: Number of Whole Footprints on Mean Surface of Sphere

model? For the adopted mean grain diameter of 0.3 millimeters with M = 32, the footprint diameter would be about 0.22 microns (1 micron = 1/1000 of a millimeter) if three tiers are utilized. This footprint diameter is too low to be effective as a bed upon which the bacteria will rest. It would seem reasonable to adopt only two tiers for this size grain. On the other hand, if the mean grain diameter were, say, 4 millimeters then 3 tiers would yield a footprint diameter of about 2.9 microns (M = 32). These investigations indicate that fine sand (0.3 mm) would best be modeled with two tiers; medium gravel (4 mm) should use a three tier model and coarse pebbles an even higher number of tiers (4 or 5).

What value of M should be used for the number of circles or equatorial footprints? On a statistical basis some grains of sand will be rougher than others. Therefore M can vary from very low to moderate values. High values of M would make the grain surface footprint so

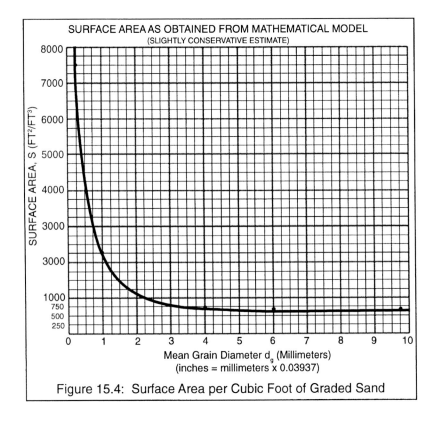

Figure 15.4: Surface Area per Cubic Foot of Graded Sand

small that it would render it ineffective, i.e., so smooth that it would violate physical reality. But some of the tiny mountains dotting the surface will be higher than others. The best compromise is to obtain the value of E with high and low values of M and average the resulting surface areas. The results of this analysis are presented in Figure (15.4), wherein E was computed under these ground rules and S_g, the surface area of the grain, obtained as:

$$S_g = E \, \pi \, (U^*)^2. \tag{15.9}$$

This graph is of central importance because it is required in the next section that deals with the quest for a method to answer the question: How many fish can be placed in a tank of given size? It simply determines the surface area of sand particles per cubic foot or surface density as a function of mean grain diameter. The mean grain diameter is known from data provided with the purchased sand.

15.9 OXIDATION/POLLUTION BALANCE

By attacking waste products with oxygen they can be rendered harmless. This process is called *oxidation*. The *potential* or *oxidizing capacity* of a given filter bed, if it were known, could be equated to the waste by-products of the fish plus the pollution produced by the food introduced into the tank, i.e., *to the inherent pollution potential*. If these two potentials are equal an ecological balance exists and the resulting equations will yield an expression that can be solved for the total bio-mass the tank can safely hold. As will be seen presently, the oxidation potential is a function of surface area of the filter bed and the flowrate into the tank, while the pollution potential depends upon the number of fish, their mass (weight) and input of food.

15.9.1 THE OXIDATION POTENTIAL

In 1966 Hirayama (Ref. [15.13.1]) obtained an expression for the oxidizing potential of a given filter bed. This relationship is also reported in Ref. [15.13.2]. It is a formula that depends upon four parameters, namely: filter bed cross sectional area, water velocity passing through the filter bed, gravel depth, and mean grain diameter. Adopting Hirayama's empirical coefficients a direct algebraic manipulation and units conversion collapses his equation to the two parameter form:

$$O_p = S/(1009.2 + 11.095 \, S/\dot{G}), \tag{15.10}$$

where O_p is the oxidizing potential of the filter bed measured in milligrams per minute, S is the total filter bed surface area (not the cross-sectional area) in square feet, and $\dot{G}$ is the flowrate into the tank in gallons per hour. This equation assumes that water passes through the entire filter bed. Obviously in a fluidized bed this is always realized but in a tank without undergravel plates and where all the water is not forced by suction to pass entirely through the gravel the value of O_p would be greatly reduced. This effect, as will be seen, can be absorbed into S. The previous formula for the oxidizing potential can be applied to each filter bed separately and then each result can be added together to obtain a combined oxidizing potential. For example in a stand-alone tank only one oxidizing potential exists, but add a fluidized bed and two oxidizing potentials are in action. If a second fluidized bed is added then three potentials are present, etc. The total surface area of each filter bed is just given as the product of S_g as obtained from Figure (15.4), and the volume of the filter bed, i.e.,

$$S = k \, S_g \, V, \tag{15.11}$$

where k is coefficient ranging from 0 to 1, S_g is measured in ft^2/ft^3 and V is the volume of the filter bed in ft^3. The coefficient k would be taken as 1 for a fluidized bed since it has 100% total water circulation about each sand grain or for a regular tank with undergravel plates wherein all the water is suctioned through the sand. If no subgravel plates are used the value of k would be reduced to, say 0.25, because only the top few layers of gravel would receive the beneficial oxygen needed for full activity. If there is no gravel then k = 0 and other mechanical devices must eliminate the water pollutants.

Note that for estimation of the tank filter bed required to house a given population, i.e., Eq. (15.10), via Eq. (15.11) is easily solved to yield:

$$V = 1009.2 \, O_p/(1 - 11.095 \, O_p/\dot{G})k \, S_g, \tag{15.10b}$$

where the units are the same as in the two previous equations. Figure (15.5) displays the results graphically.

EXAMPLE

What is the oxidizing potential of an aquarium wall system that displays a tank measuring 34.8" in length, L, 16" in width, W, with a height, H, of 60." A gravel bed of 14.2" in depth, D, consisting of 4 millimeter diameter grains is used. A flowrate, $\dot{G}$, equal to 600 GPH is utilized to suction the water down through the gravel.

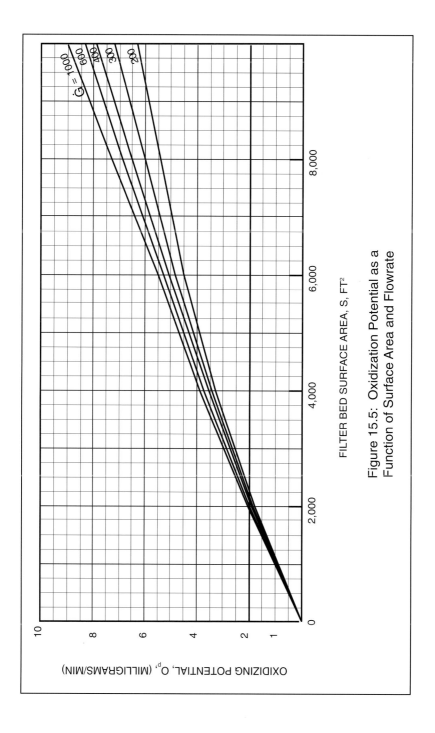

FILTER BED SURFACE AREA, S, FT^2

OXIDIZING POTENTIAL, O$_p$, (MILLIGRAMS/MIN)

Figure 15.5: Oxidization Potential as a
Function of Surface Area and Flowrate

The volume of the filter bed is:

$$V = L \times W \times D = 34.8 \times 16 \times 14.2 = 7906.56 \text{ in}^3$$
$$V = 7906.56/1728 = 4.576 \text{ ft}^3.$$

Next enter Figure (15.4) with d_g = 4mm and read S_g = 750 ft^2/ft^3. The total surface area of the bed, S, is $V \times S_g$ or $kV \times S_g$ but in this case K = 1 and

$$S = 1 \times 4.576 \times 750 = 3432 \text{ ft}^2.$$

Finally, use Eq (15.10) or Figure (15.5) to obtain the oxidizing potential as:

$$O_p = 3432/(1009.2 + 11.095 \times 3432/600)$$
$$= 3.2 \text{ mg/min}.$$

EXAMPLE

Suppose a fluidized bed is to be added to the tank discussed in the previous example. What is the total oxidizing potential? The 8″ diameter fluidized bed has a 10″ high column of 0.3 mm diameter sand and water is pumped in at 300 GPH.

The volume of the fluidic bed is:

$$V = (1/4)\pi\, D^2 L/1728 = 3.1415 \times 8^2 \times 10/(4 \times 1728) = 0.291 \text{ ft}^3.$$

In a fluidized bed k is always equal to 1, and from Figure (15.4) for d_g = 0.3 the surface area per cubic foot S_g = 7250 so that:

$$S = 1 \times 0.291 \times 7250 = 2109 \text{ ft}^2.$$

Equation (15.10) then yields:

$$O_p = 2109/(1009.2 + 11.095 \times 2109/300)$$
$$= 1.94 \text{ mg/min}.$$

The total oxidizing potential is now determined by addition of the individual potentials, i.e.,

$$O_p = 3.2 + 1.94 = 5.14 \text{ mg/min}.$$

15.9.2 THE POLUTION POTENTIAL

The previous section developed an expression for the ability of the filter bed to oxidize waste products. A relationship which permits an estimate of these waste products to be obtained is now required. Acceptance of Hirayama's empirical constants as reported by Spotte,

Ref. (15.13.2), permits the following equation to be brought into focus:

$$P = 0.051f\sum_{j=1}^{j=q}B_j + 0.01\sum_{j=1}^{j=q}B_j^{0.544}, \qquad (15.12)$$

where P is the pollution potential that exists due to the fish and food (mg/min.), f is food to weight ratio fed, B_j is the weight of each fish in grams and q is the total number of fish in the system; as before $\sum$ represents a sum. Please note that Figure (15.6) is provided for those readers not in possession of a calculator that can exponentiate to fractional powers. A reasonable value for f, as suggested by Spotte, is $f = 0.0132$. This is equivalent to saying that a 180 pound man consumes about 2.5 pounds of food daily. Of course, f can be chosen as desired. The weights of the fish peculiar to the system also needs be known.

Some estimates are presented in Table 15.2.

Table 15.2

Fish Weight and Length Data
Weight (grams)/Length (inches)

	Fresh Water			Marine	
Species	Weight	Length	Species	Weight	Length
Hatchet	1.20	1.75	Small Clown	1.2	1.5
Angelfish	1.25	2.00	Damsel	1.4	1.75
Platy	1.35	1.50	Dwarf Flame Angel	4.6	2.5
Ram	1.50	1.75	Dwarf Rusty Angel	7.1	2.38
Gourami	3.85	2.50	Large Clown	14.5	3.13

(For longer lengths just scale the weights)

Equation (15.12) is very easy to use. The summations $\sum$, if deemed mysterious by the reader, just need to be written out.

EXAMPLE

A tank contains 100 two-inch long red platies. What is the pollution potential?

Adopting $f = 0.0132$ and scaling the weight from Table 15.2 yields the weight of each fish as $B_j = (2/1.50) \times 1.35 = 1.8$ grams. Obviously q = 100. Equation (15.12) can now be written as:

$$P = 0.051 \times 0.0132 \sum_{1}^{100} 1.8 + 0.01 \sum_{1}^{100} 1.8^{0.544}.$$

The sums say that there are 100 terms equal to 1.8 and 100 terms equal to 1.8 raised to the fractional power of 0.544, i.e.,

$$\sum_{1}^{100} 1.8 = 1.8 + 1.8 + 1.8 + \ldots = 100 \times 1.8,$$

and by use of a calculator or Figure 15.6, $1.8^{0.544} = 1.38$ so that:

$$\sum 1.8^{0.544} = 1.38 + 1.38 + \ldots = 100 \times 1.38.$$

Hence the pollution potential is:

$$P \quad = 0.051 \times 0.0132 \times 100 \times 1.8 + 0.01 \times 100 \times 1.38$$
$$= 1.498 \text{ mg/min.}$$

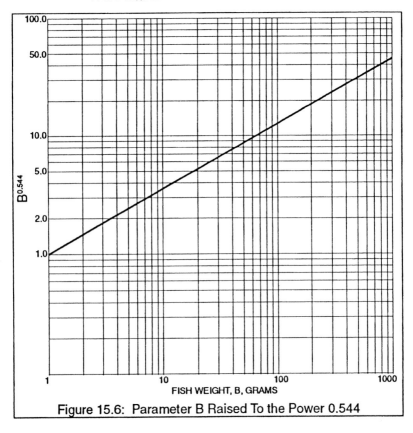

Figure 15.6: Parameter B Raised To the Power 0.544

15.10 THE BIO-LOAD CAPACITY EQUATION

In any static tank Eq. (15.10) yields the oxidizing potential while Eq. (15.12) determines the pollution potential. It is by no means a great leap to realize that the oxidizing potential needs to be greater than or equal to the pollution potential, i.e., $O_p \geq P$. So how many fish can a given tank hold? There are two approaches to this question. The first approach is straight forward. Just take the weight of each fish and compute P via Eq. (15.12) and make sure that O_p is greater than or equal to P. The second approach is to average the weight of all the fish so as to obtain $\bar{B}_j$, the average weight. Specifically, if a tank is to hold fifty Rams and fifty Gourami as listed in Table 15.2, the average weight $\bar{B}$ would be $\bar{B} = (50 \times 1.50 + 50 + 3.85)/(50 + 50) = 2.675$ gm. Since $\bar{B}_j$ is the same number, it an be factored out of the summations of Eq. (15.12) so that:

$$P = 0.051f\bar{B}\sum_{j=1}^{j=q} + 0.01\bar{B}^{0.544}\sum_{j=1}^{j=q}.$$

But the summation from 1 to q, i.e., $1 + 1 + 1 + \ldots = q$, and

$$P = 0.051f\bar{B}q + 0.01\bar{B}^{0.544}q. \tag{15.13}$$

If P is set equal to O_p and this equation is solved for q, then:

$$q = O_p/(0.051f\bar{B} + 0.01\bar{B}^{0.544}). \tag{15.14}$$

This equation determines exactly how many fish, q, a given tank can hold without any additional water purification devices. Specifically, this equation controls the natural ecological balance that must exist in a tank. If f is taken as 0.0132 then:

$$q = 1000\, O_p/(0.673\bar{B} + 10\bar{B}^{0.544)}. \tag{15.15}$$

In closing it should be emphasized that the oxidation potential must always be equal to or greater than the pollution potential. This permits Eq. (15.10b) to be written as:

$$V = 1009.2P/(1 - 11.095P/\dot{G})kS_g, \tag{15.16}$$

and since V is given in cubic feet a conversion to gallons yields:

$$V_G = 7549.34P/(1 - 11.095P/\dot{G})kS_g, \tag{15.16}$$

where the volume of the gravel bed, V_G, is in gallons. It should be obvious that the tank volume must of necessity be larger than V_G, i.e., there must be sufficient water for the fish. How much water? Estimates vary but a reasonable rule of thumb is to assume that 20 to 25% of the tank volume is consumed by the gravel so that:

$$V_T = (5 \text{ to } 4)V_G. \tag{15.17}$$

Specifically, if 10 gallons of gravel make up the filter bed, then a tank that holds 40 to 50 gallons would be selected. Of course it would be better to select an even larger size tank so as to allow for fish growth. Keep in mind that the filter bed size is uniquely determined whereas the amount of water is just taken so as to not crowd the fish. It is the filter bed size that is of importance. The old school of thought estimated fish capacity based on the available air surface area of the tank wherein each fish was assigned an area peculiar to the length of the fish.

EXAMPLE

How many fish can be housed in a tank with an oxidizing potential of 3.2 mg/min. if the average weight of each fish is 3 grams?

Select Eq. (15.15) so that:

$$q = 1000 \times 3.2/(0.675 \times 3 + 10 \times 3^{0.544})$$

$$= 158 \text{ fish weighing 3 grams each.}$$

Note that from Figure 15.6, $3^{0.544} = 1.8$ (approximately). In short, the number of each species can be varied as long as the combined weight does not exceed 3 gm.

EXAMPLE

A marine tank is planned which is to hold 100 fish of which 30% are large clowns 3.5" in length, 40% are Dusty Rust Angels (2.8"), 20% are Damsels (1.75") and 10% are Dwarf Flame Angels (2.25"). The installation will use sub-gravel plates upon which a 7" layer of crushed coral with a mean diameter of 6 mm is to be placed. An existing pump with a flowrate of 400 GPH will pull the water through the gravel via sub-tank filtration. What is the required cross-sectional area of the tank that should be used to house the fish?

First, obtain the weights and lengths from Table 15.2, or the fish supplier. The corrected weights for the new lengths as obtained from Table 15.2 are:

Clown	14.5 x 3.5/3.13 = 16.20 gm
Rusty Angel	7.1 x 2.8/2.38 = 8.35 gm

Damsel   1.4 x 1.75/1.75 = 1.40 gm

Flame Angel   4.6 x 2.25/2.5 = 4.10 gm.

The average weight of the population based on the proposed percentage of each species is:

$$\bar{B} = 16.20 \times 0.3 + 8.35 \times 0.4 + 1.4 \times 0.2 + 4.1 \times 0.1$$
$$= 8.9 \text{ gm.}$$

Adopting f = 0.0132, select Eq. (5.13) and for q = 100 compute the pollution potential P, i.e.,

$$P = 0.051 \times 0.0132 \times 8.9 \times 100 + 0.01 \times 8.9^{0.544} \times 100$$
$$= 3.88 \text{ mg/min.}$$

Enter Figure 15.4 and for the grain size of 6 mm determine the surface area of the sand grain, S_g, as S_g = 500 + 0.8 x 250 = 700 ft^2/ft^3 (Note that 2 squares = 500 plus about 0.8 of the next square). Since for biological balance O_p = P and S = S_gV (k = 1) Eq. (15.16) reads:

$$V = 1009.2 \; P/(S_g - 11.095 \; PS_g/\dot{G})$$
$$= 1009.2 \times 3.88/(700 - 11.095 \times 3.88 \times 700/400)$$
$$= 6.269 \text{ ft}^3.$$

This is the total volume of the filter bed. But since a D = 7″ layer of crushed coral is to be used (7″ = 7/12 = 0. 5833 ft.), it follows that the cross-sectional area of the tank is:

$$A = V/D = 6.269/0.5833 = 10.75 \text{ ft}^2.$$

So as long as the tank length and width equal this number the ecological balance will be obtained, i.e., a tank 72″ in length by 22″ in width which has a cross-sectional area equal to 72 x 22 = 1584 in^2 or 1584/144 = 11 ft^2 will handle the load; so will other tanks of different lengths and widths.

15.11   SUMMARY

Fluidized beds and trickle filters were discussed from a general point of view. The area density, namely the square feet of surface area contained in a cubic foot of sand was determined as a function of mean grain diameter. The mathematical model required the adoption of reasonable shaping parameters based on grain size. By multiplying the area density by the volume of the filter bed, the total surface area of the system was obtained. This surface area along with the flowrate passing through the bed form the basis needed to obtain the oxidizing potential of the filter bed. When this potential is equated to the pollution generated by the fish and the food fed, an equation is obtained that determines the number of fish that can be introduced into a given tank.

15.12 PROBLEMS

15.12.1 What is the surface area density of a grain of sand which passes through a screen with sieve size of 0.45 by 0.55 millimeters?

Ans: $4875 \text{ ft}^2/\text{ft}^3$

15.12.2 A pebble with a relatively large mean diameter is to be analyzed. A four tier model for the grain size is to be used. What is the additional term that should be added to the expansion coefficient given by Eq. (15.8)?

Ans: $\pi^4/8g^4$

15.12.3 What is the oxidizing potential of a tank with a length of 80", width of 18" and height of 22" if a gravel bed 5" in depth composed of 0.25" grains of sand is used. The flowrate pushing the water through the sub-sand filter plates as provided by the powerheads is 300 GPH. The tank contains 138 gallons of water.

Ans: 2.6 mg/min.

15.12.4 A one specie tank of 300 red Platies 2" in length is to be stocked. What is the pollution potential?

Ans: 4.34 mg/min.

15.12.5 Can the tank in problem 15.12.3 accommodate the number of fish to be stocked in exercise 15.12.4? What options are available?

Ans: No.

15.12.6 What diameter cylindrical tank can accommodate 100 2" long Angelfish along with 50 blue Gourami with a length of 4". A filter bed composed of 0.25" diameter gravel 6" deep exists in the tank. The flowrate through the gravel is 500 GPH. Approximately what size tank (gallons) would be selected?

Ans: 42 in.
Ans: 174 gal.

15.12.7 What happens in a tank that has no filter bed? Why do the fish still live. Explain generally.

15.13 REFERENCES

15.13.1 K. Hirayama, "Studies on Water Control by Filtration Through a Sand Bed in a Marine Aquarium with Closed Circulation System," IV, Bull. Jap. Soc. Sci. Fish, 32, 20 - 26

15.13.2 S. Spotte, *Fish and Invertebrate Culture,* John Wiley & Sons, New York, N.Y., 1970.

16 Reactors: Operational Principles

Water, water, everywhere
And all the Boards did shrink;
Water, water, everywhere,
Nor any drop to drink.

S. T. Coleridge

16.1 REACTORS IN GENERAL

For water to be fit for human or fish use, it needs to be treated. This is not to say that water from a pure borne mountain spring can not be consumed or used by freshwater fish, but even the *ne plus ultra* source has been modified by nature. The water has been cascaded over rocks to supply it with oxygen and provide it with minerals. In summary, water needs to be pure, oxygenated and enhanced with additives that provide attainment of some primary objective. The process of water disinfection is obvious. Oxygenation of water removes stagnation and provides living organisms with this fundamental element of life. Enhancement of water with additives is central to marine life so as to provide salt and of paramount importance to freshwater plants whose existance demands carbon dioxide.

On the boundless extent of our planet nature provides this necessary balance of life. In small closed systems this balance cannot be achieved and appeal must be made to auxiliary devices that force this optimal balance provided by nature to come about. These devices are called *reactors*.

Chapter 6 discussed reactors from a general point of view. These reactors are devices that permit necessary additives to be introduced into a closed system such as an aquarium. But what quantity of additives must be supplied to the reactor and even more important in what duration?

207

This chapter will discuss chemical disinfection first, i.e., purification by means of ozone as opposed to ultraviolet disinfection, which as discussed in Chapters 4 and 5, uses irradiation to purify the water. Both approaches are viable and complement each other. The mechanics of oxygenation will follow. Finally, the techniques required to have proper carbon dioxide and calcium levels will be detailed. However, to reach these goals some preliminary principles need to be introduced.

16.1.1 DURATION OF OPERATION AND FLOWRATE

It needs be emphasized that all the net gallons in the tank must pass through the reactor. This statement is not as trite as it sounds because the water treated within the reactor is returned to the tank or pond and is therein mixed with water that has not been treated. As proven in Chapter 2 the duration, T, required for all the untreated water to go through the reactor is given by Eq. (2.10), i.e.,

$$T = 9.2(G/\dot{F}_0),$$

where G is the net gallons contained in the tank and $\dot{F}_0$ is the water flowrate passing through the reactor in gallons per hour. Obviously, for correct reactor operation in duration T, the flowrate through the reactor must be taken as:

$$\dot{F}_0 = \dot{G} = 9.2G/T.$$

The parameter T is selected as in input, e.g., carbon dioxide is to be added to a tank during an T hour interval with the lights on.

16.1.2 INSTALLATION REMARKS

The typical installation of these devices is exactly the same as the sterilizer installation depicted in Figure 2.1 except that the sterilizer is replaced by the reactor. A Flowrater™ placed on the return line out of a given device will be most useful since by the clock and bucket method or the Flowrater™: the flow rate must be known. When ozone is used carbon filters *must* be placed on the degas line. As pointed out in Ref. [16.13.1, Sec. 4-17], "Raw water, after being filtered is passed to an absorber chamber in which ozone...destroys bacteria and pure water without taste or odor results." Therefore if the reactor is operating correctly the effluent should be ozone free. However it would be wise to test for residual ozone in the tank.

For those readers that are kind enough to accept the results of the analysis and care not about the steps which lead to the control equations some options are available. For ozone use proceed to Eq. (16.11). If oxygen addition is the name of the game, go to Eq. (16.17), for carbon dioxide enhancement proceed to Eq. (16.23), and finally for calcium to Eq. (16.28). The examples should clarify the proper use of the pertinent equations.

16.2   THE PERFECT GAS LAWS

Any physics text can be consulted to find the relationship between the pressure, volume and temperature of a gas. These relationships or laws are due to Boyle and Charles, Ref. [16.13.1] and state that the volume of a gas V in cubic feet is:

$$V = wRT/p, \tag{16.1}$$

where w is the weight of the gas in pounds, R is the ideal gas constant, T is the gas temperature in absolute units ($T = °F + 460$; $°F$ = degrees Fahrenheit), p is the gas pressure in absolute units ($p = p_g + 14.7$; p_g is the gauge pressure and 14.7 psi is the atmospheric sea level pressure); all pressures are in pounds per square foot. To use this equation the value of R must be known. Table 16.1 lists the molecular weight of the four main gases of interest.

TABLE 16.1

Molecular Weights of Gases

Gas	Molecular Weight, M
Ozone	48
Oxygen	32
Carbon Dioxide	44
Air	28.95

Since equal volumes of gases under the same conditions contain the same number of molecules (Avogadro's Law), it follows that $R = R_0/M$ where R_0 has been determined as: $R_0 = 1544$ (FT-LB)/(LB-Mole R). A pound mole (LB-Mole) is a quantity of gas equivalent to the molecular weight of the gas expressed in pounds. Equation (16.1) therefore can be expressed as:

$$V = (wR_0/M)T/p, \tag{16.2}$$

where the quantity in the brackets is a constant; call it k.

This gas law is of importance because the gas which is to be supplied to the generator, e.g., air, is at some reference condition (state a), but in the reactor it will be at a different condition (state r). Since by Eq. (16.2)

$Vp/T = k$ upon equating the parameters at the two different states it follows that:

$$p_r V_r/T = p_a V_a/T_a = k,$$

or

$$V_r = (p_a T_r/p_r T_a)V_a. \qquad (16.3)$$

Therefore, to correct any volume of gas the pressure and temperature in the reactor must be known. This data is easy to obtain because the pressure in the reactor, p_r, is given by the pressure gauge, and the temperature, T_r, by the tank thermometer. Remember the units must be absolute so $p_r = p_g + 14.7$ (psi) and $T_r = T(°F) + 460$.

Another important parameter which is fundamental to the analysis herein is the gas density, d. Since density is expressed as weight/volume, the density correction is simply:

$$d_r = (p_r T_a/p_a T_r)d_a. \qquad (16.4)$$

For convenience the correction factors are defined as:

$$C_v = p_a T_r/p_r T_a; \; C_d = (1/C_v). \qquad (16.5)$$

In closing this section note that Table 16.2 displays the densities of the pertinent gases at the reference conditions. These values will be used for the needed corrections to the gas flow equations.

TABLE 16.2

Gas Densities
(68°F, 14.7 psi)

Gas	Density (LB/FT^3)
Ozone	0.12471
Oxygen	0.08313
Carbon Dioxide	0.11500
Air	0.07522

16.3 DEFINITION OF PARTS PER MILLION

A measure of the concentration of one ingredient to the main body that contains this ingredient is denoted in parts per million (PPM). If P denotes the integer value of PPM then, for example:

$$g_g/g_w = LBS_g/LBS_w = P \times 10^{-6} = P/1000000, \qquad (16.6)$$

where g_g are the number of grams of gas contained in g_w grams of water (or number of pounds of gas contained in so many pounds of water). As mentioned in Chapter 13 concentrations of 1 PPM ozone are sufficient for disinfection. Chapter 6 noted that about 10 - 15 PPM carbon dioxide is the target value for plant growth. Fish health requires oxygen to be no lower that 5 PPM, with 10 - 15 PPM accepted as the proper concentration.

The reader is cautioned again that there is a fundamental difference between a lethal and non-lethal concentration of additives. A tank cannot have a concentration of ozone equal to 1 PPM; this would be fatal to the fish. But a tank can have a dissolved oxygen or carbon dioxide level equal to say 10 PPM. What does this mean? It means that disinfection by ozone must be performed within the reactor and subsequently the disinfectant purged from the degas water line prior to returning the water back to the tank. Spotte, Ref. [16.13.3] also makes this statement. Carbon filtration will satisfy the purging requirements. On the other hand, addition of positive health inducing elements need to have a preset level in the tank—a totally different problem. This rather obvious fact must be stressed because improper operation of reactors can cause absolutely fatal results.

16.4 REACTOR SELECTION AND VOLUME

The analysis of this Chapter could have been directed so as to find the actual size, e.g., under the assumption a cylindrical reactor is used, the height and diameter of the reactor. This, however, is not a realistic approach. The user of these reactors will have installation and cost factors that will define these parameters. It therefore shall be assumed that the user will select a reactor, and that the height and diameter of the reactor will be as large as possible. These desired characteristics will increase surface area—which is what is desired. Keep in mind that the larger the diameter of the reactor is, the shorter the reactor can be in height.

If the diameter of the reactor is symbolized by D and the height of the bio-ball column is H then making the substitution of bio-balls for bubbles, the results of Section 9.5 come directly into play. Specifically, the total number of bio-balls the reactor holds is:

$$\pi D^2 H/4d_b^3,$$

where d_b is the diameter of the bio-ball, and H is (for emphasis) the height of the active bio-ball column in the reactor. But since the same space in the empty reactor is $\pi D^2 H/4$ and the volume of a given spheroidal bio-ball is $\pi d_b^3/6$ it follows that the volume available for gas within the reactor is:

$$(\pi D^2 H/4) - (\pi d_b^3/6) \cdot (\pi D^2 H/4 d_b^3),$$

or

$$V_r = \pi D^2 H(1/4 - /24) = 0.3742 D^2 H. \qquad (16.7)$$

Experimental measurements of 1″ diameter bio-balls indicate that each have a volume of about 0.54 in^3; the formula for the volume of a sphere yields 0.52. Therefore, within acceptable limits, Eq. (16.7) holds true. This equation ignores that water cascading over the bio-balls, which will of course further reduce the space available for gas within the reactor. Unless the reactor is very tall this correction is negligible. However, in accordance with Galileo: a cannon ball and a feather, in the absence of air, fall to the ground at the same time. By use of this non-obvious observation, as proven by astronauts on the moon plus empirical measurement to account for the sought-for friction delay in water travel time caused by the bio-balls, it can be demonstrated that:

$$t = H^{1/2}/3, \qquad (16.8)$$

where t is given in seconds and H is input in inches. A knowledge of the flowrate will yield the volume of the water in transit (cascade flow) over the bio-balls. This additional volume can be subtracted from the volume predicted by Eq. (16.7).

16.5 OZONE DISINFECTION WITH REACTOR

16.5.1 MASS FLOWRATE

An equation of central importance to all reactors will now be obtained. To obtain this equation some input needs to be supplied. The basic formula obtained in Chapter 2 is called forth, namely Eq. (2.10). In this chapter the number of net gallons in the tank is denoted by G while $\dot{G}$ is the symbol for the flowrate. If all the water in the tank is to pass through a given reactor N times per day, then T = 24/N hrs, and $\dot{G}$ = 9.2G/T = (9.2/24)GN (GPH). By use of conversion factors and the knowledge that for water 1 cm^3 = 1 gm:

$$\dot{G} = 0.40308 \, GN, \text{ gm/sec}, \qquad (16.9)$$

where G is input in gallons and N is the selected and desired number of complete water exchanges. Use of definition (16.6) and a few more conversion factors yields the mass flowrate (actually weight flowrate)as:

$$\dot{O}_3 = P \times 10^{-6} \times 4.0308 \times 10^{-1} GN \times 3600 \text{ (sec/HR)} \times 1000 \text{ mg/gm}$$
$$= 1.4512 \text{ GNP, mg/HR.} \qquad (16.10)$$

This is the required mass flowrate that the reactor must receive; P = P* is the desired integer PPM.

16.5.2 OZONE GENERATOR AND REQUIRED AIRFLOW

From Eq. (13.6) the ozone generator produces:

$$\dot{O}_3 = 0.6525 \text{ KLWR\.A}, \qquad (16.11)$$

namely, if L is the length of the generator in inches, W denotes the bulb wattage and R is taken from Figure 13.1, then the output $\dot{O}_3$ in mg/HR depends on the airflow input $\dot{A}$ in liters per minute; the constant K (Chapter 13) is:

$$K = 1 - [r - (r-1)/r^*], \qquad (16.11a)$$

where r is the radius of the generator (inches) and r* is the adopted dissipation factor (6″ to 8″).

Equation (16.10) will now be solved for P, i.e.,

$$P = \dot{O}_3/1.4512GN, \qquad (16.12)$$

and the value of $\dot{O}_3$ from Eq. (16.11) inserted into Eq. (16.12). The result is:

$$P = 0.4496 \text{ KLWR\.AC}_v/GN. \qquad (16.13)$$

Note the C_v correction has been introduced, and $\dot{A}$ is in liters per minute.

Examination of Figure 13.1 shows that the maximum ozone PPM, i.e., the crest of the curve corresponds to an R value of about 0.64 and an airflow of 2.5 liters per minute. As a first approximation they can be used in Eq. (16.13), along with the other constants to compute P = P*; if a value of 1 - 1.5 PPM is obtained the reactor parameters are defined. Should this not be the case the value of $\dot{A}$ can be increased and the corresponding value of R obtained from Figure 13.1, etc. Another option is to use a smaller value of N. Why not set P = P*=1 and obtain the required airflow? No go, the value of R is unknown.

Once $\dot{A}$ is obtained it can be converted to in³/min by multiplication with the conversion factor 61.025. Equation (16.7) can now be used to determine the initial degas time, namely:

$$t_g = 6.13 \times 10^{-3} D^2 H / \dot{A}.\qquad(16.14)$$

Note that $\dot{A}$ is input in liters per minute, and t_g is obtained in minutes. Hence, if a reactor full of water is emptied in time t_g the airpump has been correctly set. Be careful to interpret H as the distance from the reactor top to the degas line port.

Since the airflow is difficult to measure it is easier to just vary the airflow from the air pump in order to achieve the degas time predicted by Eq. (16.14), or to obtain the time it takes to empty the reactor of water from the top to the degas port.

EXAMPLE: General Application

The temperature and pressure in a coastal city are 68°F and 14.7 psi. A 100 gallon tank with a water temperature of 80°F is to be totally disinfected 4 times a day by the use of ozone and a reactor which is 8″ in diameter and has a column of bio-balls 15″ high. The 3″ diameter ozone generator has a bulb with a length of 15″ and uses a 34.5 watt bulb. Assume a radiation dissipation distance of 6 inches. The reactor pressure gauge reads 4 psi. What are the operational parameters needed to achieve 1 PPM ozone within the reactor?

The required flowrate of water into the reactor is given by Eq. (2.10), i.e.,

$$\dot{G} = 9.2G/T = 9.2GN/24.$$

Taking $N = 4$ (6 hours) the flowrate is fixed as:

$$\dot{G} = 9.2 \times 100 \times 4/24 = 153.3 \text{ GPH}.$$

The reactor by-pass connection valve is adjusted to this value as determined by a Flowrater™ or by the old clock and bucket method. It might be convenient to compute the pressure/temperature corrections at this point, namely by Eq. (16.5):

$$C_v = 14.7 \times (80°F + 460)/(14.7 + 4) \times (68°F + 460)$$
$$= 0.804.$$

Another useful parameter is the ozone generator parameter KLW, which by Eq. (16.11a) is given by:

$$KLW = (1 - [1.5 - (1.5 - 1)/6])LW$$
$$= 0.9166 \times 15 \times 34.5 = 474.4.$$

Assume operation at the crest of the curve displayed in Figure 13.1, i.e., $\dot{A}$ = 2.5 and R = 0.64. Use Eq. (16.13) and compute:

$$P = 0.4496 \times 474.4 \times 0.64 \times 2.5 \times 0.804/100 \times 4$$
$$= 0.685.$$

Obviously P = P* = 1 has not been attained. As a second attempt select $\dot{A}$ = 4 which from Figure 13.1 corresponds to R = 0.6 so that:

$$P = 0.4496 \times 474.4 \times 0.6 \times 4 \times 0.804/100 \times 4$$
$$= 1.03,$$

so at 4 LPM the desired value of P* is obtained. But 4 LPM = 244 in^3/min., and a rather hefty air pump would need to be used; remember the airflow must be delivered at 4 psi.

A second approach would be to select less water exchanges, e.g., N = 2 (which actually is all that is required). So, returning to the first attempt, a direct computation would yield P = 1.37 and only use an airflow of 2.5 LPM = 152 in^3/min.

The initial degas time for the previous or second approach is obtained from Eq. (16.14), i.e.,

$$t_g = 6.13 \times 10^{-3} \times 8^2 \times 15/2.5$$
$$= 2.35 \text{ min.}$$

Note that for N = 2 the input flowrate will change to:

$$\dot{G} = 9.2GN/24 = 9.2 \times 100 \times 2/24 = 76.6 \text{ GPH.}$$

This is all that is required. Just keep adjusting the water flowrate (should it drop) and the airflow into the reactor. When the reactor degas time is 141 seconds, the system is adjusted. Keep filling the reactor with water, i.e., bleed off all the gas and start the air pump so as to obtain t_g. Note that the reactor backpressure valve should be adjusted so that the reactor pressure is about 1 - 2 psi above the nominal pressure when the water—not air—is running through the reactor: this helps the ozone reaction. When the air is turned on and the reactor begins to cycle, the pressure gauge will swing from a low to a high value. Just use the average pressure to obtain C_v. For exactness t_g may need to be re-calculated.

16.6 OXYGEN ADDITION WITH A REACTOR

For those readers that care not about the theory peculiar to oxygen addition, a jump to Eq. (16.17) should be taken.

16.6.1 OXYGEN SUPPLY RATE

As mentioned previously this is a different problem than that posed by ozone disinfection. Here the goal is to have the tank water at a 10 - 15 PPM dissolved oxygen level. Of course, heavy tank bio-load will require a greater PPM distribution, but excess oxygen is to be avoided. The oxygen comes from the air provided by the air pump (unless pure bottled oxygen is used—a rather hazardous approach). If the air flowrate is denoted by $\dot{A}$ then by virtue of the volume composition of air, 20.99 percent (23.08% by weight) will be oxygen. Therefore, the oxygen flowrate, $\dot{O}_2$, provided by the air pump will just be 0.2099 $\dot{A}$, in say, cubic inches per minute. Since the density, d, of air at room temperature and pressure can be found in Table 16.2 it follows that the product of the density (d = 0.07522 LBS/FT^3) and airflow, $\dot{A}$, in the proper units is the mass (weight) flowrate = 0.2308$\dot{A}$d or:

$$\dot{O}_2 = 6.028 \times 10^{-4} \dot{A} C_d, \quad \text{LBS/HR} \qquad (16.15)$$
$$= 273.43 \dot{A} C_d, \quad \text{mg/HR},$$

where $\dot{A}$ has the units of in^3/min and C_d provides the gas correction provided by Eq. (16.5). Equation (16.15) does not reflect that at any instant of time oxygen is being consumed by the fish and escaping by natural evection. The evection problem is further addressed in Section 16.9. For a given system this is most difficult to model. As will be seen this effect is taken care of best by a use of a correction factor, this will be discussed presently. The dimensionless value of C_d used in Eq. (16.15) relates to the observed tank temperature and reactor pressure as read from the gauge. Note that during the reactor cycle the pressure will vary. Use an average value for the pressure to determine C_d.

16.6.2 PARTS PER MILLION IN TANK

At any instant in time the tank will have a specified number of gallons that have passed through the reactor and become oxygen or gas enriched and the complementary number of gallons that have yet to pass through the reactor. This existing PPM balance can be modeled as a weighted mixture of two quantities at different parts per million. Namely, the weighted mixture P_T of initial PPM, i.e., P_o, and P_e, the PPM at any time t is:

$$P_T = (W_{ox}/W)P_e + [(W - W_{ox})/W]P_o,$$

where W is the total weight of the water in the system and W_{ox} is the weight of the water that has been oxygenated or treated at any time t. This relationship just says that, e.g., if 10 gallons of water have a concentration of 5 PPM while another 20 gallons have 2 PPM then the combined amount of water (30 gallons) will have a total PPM concentration of (10/30) x 5 + (20/30) x 2 or 3 PPM. Collecting terms P_T becomes:

$$P_T = (W_{ox}/W)(P_e - P_o) + P_o. \qquad (16.16)$$

However, at any time after the reactor is engaged:

$$P_e = 10^6 \dot{O}_2 t/W_{ox} + P_o,$$

where $\dot{O}_2$ is given by Eq. (16.15) and Eq. (16.16) becomes:

$$P_T = 10^6(\dot{O}_2/W)t + P_o,$$

or in terms of the tank gallons, G, since the weight is 8.345G

$$P_T - P_o = 72.23 \dot{A} C_d t/G.$$

But when $P_T = P^*$, $t = T$ so that solving for $\dot{A}$ in cubic inches per minute:

$$\dot{A} = 0.0138 f(P^* - P_o)G/C_d T, \qquad (16.17)$$

where, in summary P^* and P_o are the target and initial PPM (integer values), G is the total net gallons in the tank or pond, C_d is the density correction given by Eq. (16.5) in terms of the tank temperature and average reactor pressure and T is the desired duration in hours or T = 24/N to achieve P^* PPM; the factor f will now be discussed.

Since most chemical reactions are incomplete, it is difficult to determine the efficiency and natural losses, f, of the reaction. The factor f is best obtained by obtaining the value of $\dot{A}$ predicted by Eq. (16.17) with $f = 100$ and measurement of the value of the dissolved oxygen at t = T, call it P_M^*. For the computed value of $\dot{A}$, insertion of P_M^* for P^* will then yield f. For air f will be a high value. This value is the calibration parameter of the system.

The available volume for the air in the reactor is given by Eq. (16.17), so it follows that the initial degas time, t_g, will be:

$$t_g = 0.3742 D^2 H/\dot{A}, \qquad (16.18)$$

where the reactor diameter and height of the bio-balls are in inches and via Eq. (16.17) $\dot{A}$ is in in^3/min so that t_g will be determined in minutes. Equation (16.18) is very important because it permits the user to adjust the airflow such that t_g is the value which is predicted. Obviously, without even measuring the airflow the reactor can be adjusted by just observing t_g. It is emphasized that t_g is the time it takes a reactor that is totally filled with water to degas the first time.

EXAMPLE

An 8″ diameter reactor with a bio-ball column of 10″ is to be used to raise the dissolved oxygen in a 100 gallon tank (net gallons) to 12 PPM in 2 hours. At initiation of the process the measured dissolved oxygen is 6 PPM while the tank temperature is 80°F and the observed average reactor pressure is 3 psi. Determine the operational parameters of the process.

The flowrate into the reactor (Section 16.1.1) must be:

$$\dot{G} = 9.2 \times 100/2 = 460 \text{ GPH.}$$

From Eq. (16.5) the density correction factor is:

$$C_d = p_r T_a/p_a T_r = (14.7 + 3)(68 + 460)/(14.7)(80 + 460)$$
$$= 1.177.$$

Select $f = 100$ and use Eq. (16.17):

$$\dot{A} = 0.0138 \times 100 \times (12 - 6) \times 100/1.1771 \times 2$$
$$= 352 \text{ in}^3/min.$$

The initial degas time is next obtained from Eq. (16.18) as:

$$t_g = 0.3742 \times 8^2 \times 10/352 = 0.68 \text{ minutes,}$$

i.e., the reactor should cycle from the no gas to full gas situation in this time.

EXAMPLE

In the previous example after 2 hours the measured value of $P^* = P_M{}^*$ was only 8 PPM and after adjusting the reactor to the previous airflow, the observed average pressure was 2 psi. Correct the reactor parameters.

The new value of C_d is:

$$C_d = (14.7 + 2)(68 + 460)/(14.7)(80 + 460)$$
$$= 1.11.$$

Via Eq. (16.17) f is determined as:

$$f = \dot{A}C_dT/0.0138(P_M{}^* - P_o)G$$
$$= 352 \times 1.11 \times 2/(0.0138[8 - 6] \times 100)$$
$$= 283.$$

The value $\dot{A}$ now can be recomputed:

$$\dot{A} = 0.0138 \times 283 \times (12 - 6) \times 100/1.11 \times 2$$
$$= 1055 \text{ in}^3/\text{min.,}$$

and

$$t_g = 0.3742 \times 8^2 \times 10/1055 = 0.227 \text{ min.}$$

A check at $t = T = 2$ can be performed to see if the target $P^* = 12$ actually is achieved; if not another correction can be made.

These corrections are unavoidable because of reaction inefficiency and also because in time T some of the oxygen will be depleted due to natural evection losses and animal bio-load (See Section 16.9) But once f is determined it will be a fixed system constant. Should the airflow value be unacceptable (too high) T can always be increased.

16.7   EXCEEDING PPM CONCENTRATIONS

It should be self evident that if the gas supply into the reactor is not turned off or scaled down in order to just compensate for natural gas dissipation losses and animal/plant bio-load usage, the target PPM will continue to rise until a gas to water saturation state is reached. A property of any gas is its solubility at the standard atmospheric pressure of 14.7 psi and 68°F. The solubility of these gases is shown in Table 16.3.

TABLE 16.3

Solubility of Gases in a Gallon of Water
(in^3/gal at 68°F and 14.7 psi)

Gas	Solubility	PPM
Ozone (O_3)	9.10	78.7
Oxygen (O_2)	7.16	41.2
Carbon Dioxide (CO_2)	202.79	1617.2

As temperature increases the solubility decreases, while an increased pressure increases solubility. As can be seen from the Table the PPM of the gas in water can reach high levels. This in not fatal for ozone disinfection if the water which exits the reactor is carbon filtered and all the ozone is removed. The proper application of ozone using the fundamental ozone equations never will permit even such high levels of ozone to be attained. On the other hand as long as the gas source is generating the gas, levels up to those indicated in the Table can be attained. Obviously, the source for oxygen or carbon dioxide must be on a timer or at least closely monitored.

In essence there are two facets in this chemical addition problem. The first division is related to the attainment of the proper level of dissolved gas while the second part of the problem relates to station keeping and maintenance of the proper level. For any given tank, once the proper gas level is attained and the source for the gas is turned off, the depletion of the additive can be determined a given number of hours later by direct measurement of the dissolved gas PPM, call it P_d^*, i.e., the PPM measured T_d hours after P^* is achieved at time T. The rate of depletion $\dot{P}_d^*$ is now given by:

$$\dot{P}_d^* = (P^* - P_d^*)/(T_d - T). \qquad (16.19)$$

The value of the required PPM increment ΔP over any duration T^* is now determined as:

$$\Delta P = \dot{P}_d^* T^* - P^*, \qquad (16.20)$$

and the previously developed equations will now yield the station keeping value of the airflow or carbon dioxide gas flow, $\dot{A}_s$, which is required over a continuous timeline, i.e., if control of the desired PPM is to be on a daily basis ($T^* = 24$ HRS) then $P^* - P_o$ in Eq. (16.17) is replaced by ΔP from Eq. (16.20) and the airflow becomes known. Obviously until the operational parameters are well established the PPM levels over the duration T^* need to be monitored.

EXAMPLE

The second example in Section 16.6 determined that an airflow of 1055 in^3/min was required to raise the oxygen level to 12 PPM in 2 hours. The air supply to the reactor was turned off after 2 hours. It was observed that the dissolved oxygen dropped to 7 PPM 4 hours later. What is the station keeping airflow that should be administered over the next 24 hours?

By Eq. (16.19) the depletion PPM is given by:

$$\dot{P}_d^* = (12 - 7)/(4 - 0) = 1.25 \text{ PPM/HR}.$$

So on a daily basis, i.e., T = 24 HRS, the required PPM increment, Eq. (16.20) is:

$$\Delta P = 1.25 \times 24 - 12 = 18.$$

So by Eq. (16.17) with $f = 283$:

$$\dot{A}_s = 0.0138 \times 283 \times 18 \times 100/1.11 \times 24 = 264 \text{ in}^3/\text{min.},$$

while

$$t_g = 0.3742 \times 8^2 \times 10/264 = 0.907 \text{ min.}$$

Therefore adjust the airflow into the reactor to 264 in^3/min. This airflow is now adopted on a continuing timeline during system operation.

16.8   CARBON DIOXIDE ADDITION WITH A REACTOR

Carbon Dioxide reactors differ in operation from their oxygen and ozone cousins in that no degas venting is performed. The degas vent operation is not required because pure CO_2 is introduced from a supply cylinder and appeal is made to the fact that CO_2 is extremely soluble in water. This intrinsic characteristic was displayed in Table 16.3. Note that since a gallon is equal to 231 in^3 and 203 in^3 of CO_2 are soluble in each gallon, the percent solubility is $203/231 = 0.88$ or 88%, and it dissolves quickly to boot.

Another fundamental difference in CO_2 addition verses that of ozone or oxygen is that bio-balls are not required within the reactor. The level surface between the gas and the water, especially at the elevated pressure within the reactor is sufficient for the gas to enter into solution. With this proviso Eq. (16.7) is not valid and the volume within an assumed cylindrical reactor is simply given by:

$$V_r = \pi D^2 H/4, \tag{16.21}$$

where D is the reactor diameter and H is the reactor height identified with the height available for the CO_2 to be injected above the in and out water ports of the reactor. The reactor is of course selected to be as large as possible. The discussion peculiar to Section 16.6.2 still holds so as to account for mixing of carbonated and uncarbonated water but in this case the counterpart of Eq. (16.15) reads:

$$\begin{aligned} (\dot{C}O_2) &= 3.993 \times 10^{-3} \dot{A}_c C_d, \quad \text{LBS/HR}, \\ &= 1811.2 \, \dot{A}_c C_d, \quad \text{mg/HR}, \end{aligned} \tag{16.22}$$

where the subscript c on $\dot{A}$ denotes CO_2 gas flow. Equation (16.17) takes the form:

$$\dot{A}_c = 0.00209 f(P^* - P_o)G/C_d T, \text{ in}^3/\text{min.}, \quad (16.23)$$

with $\dot{A}_c$ in $\text{in}^3/\text{min.}$ Also note that the total volume of CO_2 in T hours, i.e., Eq. (16.23) multiplied by 60T can be divided by the reactor volume to yield the total number of discrete CO_2 injections, M, that need be given, namely:

$$M = 0.1597 f(P^* - P_o)G/C_d D^2 H. \quad (16.24)$$

Hence, the injection of CO_2 can be done on a continuous basis by means of a gas valve adjusted to give a CO_2 gas flow as predicted by Eq. (16.23) or by a discrete number of injections equal to M. Note that the product of M and H, the available reactor height, gives the distance from the top of reactor to the water surface for each injection. Obviously if M is greater than 1 more than a single injection is needed. To adjust the valve so that it produces $\dot{A}_c$ the gas flow must be measured (see exercises 16.12.1 and 16.12.2) and Section 7.6.

In closing, it will be useful to know for how long a CO_2 cylinder that contains W pounds or grams of CO_2 will last. This is easy to determine from Eq. (16.23). The total gas volume is given as before by multiplication of Eq. (16.23) by 60T. This volume multiplied by the corrected density yields the gas weight W_{CO2} as:

$$W_{CO2} = 8.345 \times 10^{-6} f(P^* - P_o)G, \quad \text{LBS} \quad (16.25)$$
$$= 3.785 \times 10^{-3} f(P^* - P_o)G, \quad \text{gms.}$$

Please note that Eq. (16.25) predicts the initial total gas required, but not the prerequisite station keeping gas weight (see Section 16.7). A division of W by W_{CO2} yields the number of possible injections.

EXAMPLE

A 60 gallon (net) tank is to have the dissolved CO_2 raised from 2 PPM to 16 PPM starting at 5 P.M. and ending at midnight (lights on). A reactor with an 8" diameter and usable height of 14" is to be used for CO_2 injection. The average reactor gauge pressure and temperature are 2 psi and 80°F respectively. A 74 gram disposable CO_2 cartridge is to be used for the gas supply. For purposes of discussion f is taken as 1. This is not true because of natural evection during the interval of gas addition. By measurement f is probably closer to a value of 8 - 10. Analyze the system.

The flowrate into the reactor (Section 16.1.1) must be:

$$\dot{G} = 9.2 \times 60/(12 - 5) = 78.8 \text{ GPH.}$$

As a preliminary step obtain the density correction from Eq. (16.5), i.e.,

$$C_d = (14.7 + 2)(68 + 460)/(0 + 14.7)(80 + 460) = 1.11.$$

The number of CO_2 injections is given by Eq. (16.24) as:

$$M = 0.1597 \times 1 \times (16 - 2) \times 60/1.11 \times 8^2 \times 14$$
$$= 0.135,$$

which says that if discrete injections are to be used over a time interval of 12 - 5 = 7 HRS the reactor should be filled once to about 0.135×14 = 1.88 inches from the top (2").

On the other hand if the gas is to be supplied at a constant fixed gas flow over this same interval then by Eq. (16.23):

$$\dot{A}_c = 0.00209 \times 1 \times (16 - 2) \times 60/1.11 \times 7 = 0.226 \text{ in}^3/\text{min}.$$

Specifically, if a needle valve is set to release this amount of CO_2 the target value of P^* will be reached in the desired time interval. See Exercise 16.11.1 and 16.11.2 for a technique as to how the valve can be adjusted to yield the desired airflow.

The number of pounds of CO_2 required over a 7 hour duration is directly given by Eq. (16.25), namely:

$$W_{CO2} = 8.345 \times 10^{-6} \times 1 \times (16 - 2) \times 60 = 0.007 \text{ LBS}$$
$$= 3.785 \times 10^{-3} \times 1 \times (16 - 2) \times 60 = 3.18 \text{ gms.}$$

Initially 3.18 grams will be utilized to bring the system up to the desired CO_2 level. Measurement of the existing CO_2 in the tank just before the lights are turned on will yield $\dot{P}_d^*$ as defined by Eq. (16.19), and as previously discussed for the oxygen problem the station keeping value of $\dot{A}_c$ can then be determined for the system. A 74 gram cartridge would last for 74/3.18 = 23.27 days (at 1 injection per day) considering start-up operations only. Obviously longer, should station keeping requirements be less.

Also keep in mind that should the desired target value of $P^* = 16$ PPM not be attained after T = 7 HRS, then the measured value of $P = P_d^*$ can be used in Eq. (16.23) in lieu of P^* as so to obtain f, namely to obtain the system calibration constant. The analysis can then be repeated with f used in all the pertinent equations of the process.

16.9 CRITICAL OXYGEN AND CO_2 OPERATIONAL CONSTRAINTS

Apart from the factor f which appears in Eqs. (16.17 and 16.23) which upon empirical determination calibrates the true air or CO_2 input flow that must be supplied to the reactors, some further system modeling is possible. As mentioned previously, there is no way that f can be obtained analytically because the oxygen consumption and CO_2 generation/demand are system parameters and depend upon the tank bio-load. However, the gas loss that occurs as a function of time at the surface of the tank or pond can be modeled or isolated by direct measurement.

To this end if a reference tank filled only with water is examined it will be evident that two factors or parameters come into play. These are called the *evection* parameters, namely, the duration, T, it takes for all the water in the tank to be replaced and the pump flowrate, $\dot{F}_o$ for all the tank water to be replaced once; it is known by Eq. (2.10) that $T = 9.2G/\dot{F}_o$ (see Section 16.1.1). Hence, for two different size tanks with the identical flowrate the duration ratio of exchange is $T_l/T_s = G_l/G_s$ where the subscripts denote large, l, and small, s. For a rectangular tank it is simple to observe that G_l/G_s is just the product of the ratio of surface areas of the respective tanks multiplied by the ratio of the water depths, d_l/d_s. It would be expected that the evection loss would be proportional to surface areas in contact with the atmosphere. But if the flowrate varies between both tanks then it would also be expected that the evection loss would also depend on the flowrate ratio, i.e., a greater flowrate implies more surface water movement. The rate of change of PPM can therefore be scaled by the appropriate ratios. Direct measurements would then yield a curve such as depicted in Figure 16.1.

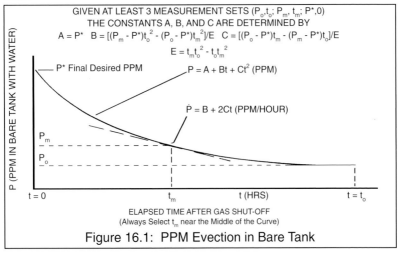

GIVEN AT LEAST 3 MEASUREMENT SETS (P_o, t_o; P_m, t_m; $P^*, 0$) THE CONSTANTS A, B, AND C ARE DETERMINED BY

$$A = P^* \quad B = [(P_m - P^*)t_o^2 - (P_o - P^*)t_m^2]/E \quad C = [(P_o - P^*)t_m - (P_m - P^*)t_o]/E$$

$$E = t_m t_o^2 - t_o t_m^2$$

P^* Final Desired PPM

$$P = A + Bt + Ct^2 \text{ (PPM)}$$

$$\dot{P} = B + 2Ct \text{ (PPM/HOUR)}$$

P (PPM IN BARE TANK WITH WATER)

P_m

P_o

$t = 0$ t_m t (HRS) $t = t_o$

ELAPSED TIME AFTER GAS SHUT-OFF
(Always Select t_m near the Middle of the Curve)

Figure 16.1: PPM Evection in Bare Tank

The slope of this curve at any time will then be, e.g., the actual CO_2 loss in PPM per unit time. This loss can be added to the target value of P^*.

Inclusion of this loss in the fundamental equations for gas addition is not warranted because measurements of the dissolved gas PPM must always be taken so as to account for bio-loading. If one is armed with these measurements the parameter f accounts for both bio-load and evection. It must be determined by trial and error and this operation cannot be avoided.

Nevertheless, it is interesting to determine the rate of evection of CO_2 in a bare tank. To this end the PPM CO_2 is measured as a function of elapsed time since cessation of CO_2 injection. From the previous discussion and the data a second order quadratic fit (Fig. 16.1) yields the total evection as :

$$P = 0.0811 \ (\dot{G}/G) \ (t^2 - 8.5t), \ t \leq 4,$$

which is again a function of elapsed time t hours. This equation can be used to obtain estimates of the CO_2 loss around the target operational level of 15 - 20 PPM. Remember this loss is a lower limit, the factor f must not be ignored. The evection loss for oxygen follows along the same path, and can be high (1.25 PPM/HR for each square foot of tank surface area).

For CO_2 addition it must be noted that it takes time for the CO_2 to be dissolved into the water passing through the reactor, i.e., if an injection of CO_2 is provided to the reactor it will take T_d hours for all the gas in the reactor to vanish. With a fair degree of approximation to dissolve 0.00149 LBS of CO_2 in a 3-1/8" diameter reactor measurements indicate:

$$T_1 = -6.84 \times 10^{-3}\dot{G} + 3.045, \ \dot{G} < 400 \ GPH,$$

where $\dot{G}$ is in gallons per hour and, T_1, the dissolve time is obtained in hours. But if the reactor diameter is D inches, a larger gas to water interface exists if $D > 3.15$ and T_1 would be reduced by the ratio of the reactor cross-sectional areas, namely:

$$T_2 = 9.765 \ T_1/D^2.$$

But since the PPM must be raised by $\Delta P = P^* - P_o$, it would take $\Delta P \times 10^{-6} \times 8.345G$ pounds of CO_2 as opposed to the 0.00149 pounds obtained by measurement. This will increase the time so that:

$$T_d = T_2 \ (8.345 \times 10^{-6}G)/0.00149.$$

By back substitution to eliminate T_1 and T_2:

$$T_d = (\Delta PG/D^2)(0.167 - 3.74 \times 10^{-4}\dot{G}). \tag{16.25}$$

This equation expresses the fact that when $\dot{G}$ is selected so that all the water has been carbonated ($\dot{G}$ = 9.2G/T), the minimum time for the CO_2 to dissolve is fixed, and the primary objective will be met only if T > T_d, i.e., T must always be taken greater than the value indicated by Eq. (16.25).

EXAMPLE

A 75 gallon tank is to have a total PPM increase of 20, i.e., P^* - P_o = 20 in a duration of 3 hours. An 8" diameter reactor is to be used. Can this be accomplished?

For total mixing:

$$\dot{G} = 9.2 \times 75/3 = 230 \text{ GPH.}$$

By Eq. (16.25):

$$T_d = (20 \times 75/8^2)(0.167 - 3.74 \times 10^{-4} \times 230)$$

$$= 23.44 \times 0.081 = 1.9 \text{ HRS,}$$

and the answer is yes. Note that if ΔP = 35 the answer is no.

   In closing this section it should be mentioned that addition of CO_2 will cause pH variations. The pH in the tank will drop as CO_2 is added. Therefore the pH should be monitored and whenever needed chemical alkalizers used to raise any undesired low level. Once the system is stabilized the effects are minimal.

16.10   CALCIUM ADDITION WITH A REACTOR

16.10.1 FUNDAMENTAL CALCIUM BACKGROUND

Calcium, a silvery white crystalline metal is an important additive to marine water. It is fundamental for reef life health in much the same manner as it is to humans that strive for strong bones and teeth. For marine tanks calcium can be added so that target values of about 400 - 425 PPM are satisfied. This addition can be achieved by use of calcium water solutions that are introduced into the tank via a drop-drip technique wherein the continuous flow of drops is provided by a reactor. There are two different methods currently in use to provide calcium. The first method uses calcium carbonate while the second uses calcium hydroxide. Calcium carbonate ($CaCO_3$) or chalk (Aragonite) is composed of the minute shells of marine animals (Foraminifera) and is virtually insoluble in water. It can be made soluble by addition of carbon dioxide, i.e., $CaCO_3 + H_2O + CO_2 \rightarrow Ca + 2HCO_3$, namely calcium carbonate plus water plus carbon dioxide yields calcium hydrogen carbonate. Use of $CaCO_3$ therefore necessitates the introduction of carbon dioxide This complication can be avoided by the second method that uses calcium hydroxide $Ca(OH)_2$ which is slightly soluble in water; and better so in cold water. Actually 0.17 grams will dissolve in 100 grams of water or 0.17 LBS/100 LBS which translates to 0.0142 LBS/Gallon. Hence, addition of 0.227 ounces (1/4 ounce or 6.44 grams) to a gallon of water upon mixing will yield a gallon of calcium water commonly called "*Kalkwasser.*" If slightly more calcium is used to make the Kalkwasser, from the German "chalkwater", it will just precipitate out of the solution. The clear effluent is to be used in the reactor. As can be seen it is very easy to make a 5 gallon stock solution in a water supply bottle by just adding 1.135 ounces, call it 1-1/4 ounces, to the container and then stir to mix. The use of Kalkwasser as an additive, as one might guess, originated in Germany, and is a very simple technique to achieve the objective of about a 410 PPM calcium level in the tank. Obviously a reactor can be used to mechanize the addition of this chemical but the reactor is ever so simple as opposed to reactors that use calcium carbonate. The calcium carbonate reactor, due to the needs of the carbonate needs to have carbon dioxide introduced from a supply cylinder. This in turn implies the need of expensive regulators to control the CO_2 plus a cut-off solenoid to shut the CO_2 off if a power failure occurs and then a water pump to circulate the carbonate/CO_2 mixture in the reactor. If all this complication and expense is accepted for the sake of a slightly more efficient or quicker calcium addition then so be it. Note that if CO_2 is added to the hydroxide it will go over to the carbonate form and nothing is gained. An examination of Table 16.4 will be useful at this point.

The addition of calcium as described in this chapter will appeal to the simpler calcium hydroxide technique which uses a simple inexpensive reactor. Actually, even an intravenous bag type feed can be used to drip the solution into the tank. But a reactor can be located under the tank, has a positive power feed and easily be shut off via an inexpensive mechanical timer.

As mentioned previously the solubility, s, of calcium hydroxide is 0.0017 LB/LB, i.e., this is the solubility of $Ca(OH)_2$ in water. The test kits usually available will determine the PPM of calcium carbonate ($CaCO_3$). Hence, a test kit that measures 1000 PPM $CaCO_3$, means exactly what it says: there are 1000 PPM of the chemical in the water. Since the atomic weight of calcium is 40.08, that of carbon 12 and oxygen

16, the total atomic weight of $CaCO_3$ is $(40 + 12 + 3 \times 16) = 100$. The percent of Ca is therefore $(40/100) \times 100 = 40\%$. Obviously for 1000 PPM of chemical there exist $1000 \times 0.4 = 400$ PPM of calcium metal in the tank. When hydroxide is used, i.e., $Ca(OH)_2$, the atomic weight (Hydrogen = 1) is $40 + 2 \times (16 + 1) = 74$ and the percent of calcium is $(40/74) \times 100 = 54\%$. Furthermore, test kits for the carbonate will tend to read about 10% high. Obviously, when the hydroxide is used the PPM of calcium present is given by PPM (Ca) = 0.54 PPM $(Ca(OH)_2)$ and depending on the test kit the reading should be reduced by 0.9. Strictly speaking a $Ca(OH)_2$ reading on a calcium carbonate test kit of 836 PPM implies a Ca PPM of $836 \times .54 \times .9$ or 406 PPM.

16.10.2 SIMPLE LIQUID SOLUTION POWER REACTOR
An air pump driven reactor is displayed in Figure 16.2. The operation could not be simpler. The hydroxide solution (clear effluent) is poured into the sealable loading port. An air pump placed on a timer delivers air to the reactor via tube A and pressurizes at point B. This will force water with the desired liquid additive, which is not limited to just calcium water but can have suspended medicines or nutriments, to be forced out of riser tube C. The small tubing line valve D is adjusted to control the drip rate, i.e., the drops introduced into the tank or sump. Note that the reactor can be placed under the tank. Should a power outage occur, the system just shuts down. The feed is under pressure for a more constant drip rate and to push via pressure any slight blockage or time induced constriction in drip tube E.

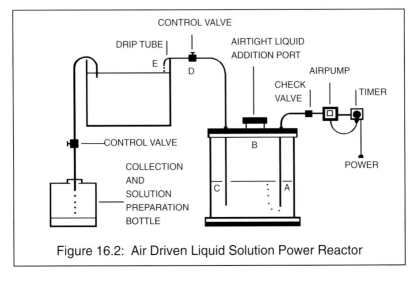

Figure 16.2: Air Driven Liquid Solution Power Reactor

16.10.3 DRIP-DROP ANALYSIS

Suppose the in-tank initial PPM concentration of the additive in question is measured via a reliable test kit, call it P_o. If a target value of P^* is desired, then $\Delta P = P^* - P_o$ PPM need be added to the tank in some reasonable duration, T, in say, hours. Since the additive liquid is to be introduced at some yet unspecified drip rate, d́, in drops per minute, the problem at hand is how to determine the drip rate. The drip rate can always be observed by just counting the drops that fall from the miniature "J" tube displayed as E in Figure 16.2. If the solubility, s, of the additive chemical but not necessarily the additive element in, say, pounds of additive to pounds of water is known and since there are 8.345 pounds of water per gallon it is evident that:

$$s_g = 8.345s,$$

namely, s_g is the solubility of the chemical in pounds per gallon. But by Appendix II, there are 76800 drops per gallon and so $s_g/76800$ is the number of pounds of additive per drop. If the number of drops is denoted by d, then by the definition of PPM for a tank with G net gallons:

$$\Delta P = [s_g d/(76800 \times 8.345 \ G)]10^6,$$

or

$$\Delta P = 13.02 \ sd/G. \tag{16.26}$$

This equation can be solved for d, namely,

$$d = 0.0768 \ \Delta PG/s, \tag{16.27}$$

or for a constant drip rate d́ = d/T, where T is measured in hours and d́ is observed in drops per minute:

$$d́ = 0.00128 \ \Delta PG/sT, \quad \text{drops/min.} \tag{16.28}$$

Note that this is the demand drip rate, d́, that must be provided by the reactor in duration T and this determines the total number of drops in the reactor which in turn specifies the volume of the reactor. In short the reactor need be sized so as to contain G_R gallons:

$$G_R = 1 \times 10^{-6} \ G\Delta P/s, \tag{16.29}$$

or the reactor must be filled such that the gallons predicted by Eq. (16.29) are available. Furthermore, s, the solubility of the chemical which is added, and the PPM of the chemical as measured by the requisite test kit should be used in the controlling equations of the process.

EXAMPLE

It is desired to add 60 PPM of calcium hydroxide to a tank (for purposes of station keeping) that holds 50 net gallons within a 24 hour period. Analyze the system; assume calcium hydroxide is to be used with a solubility of 0.0017 LBS/LB. Note this is the hydroxide level. As discussed the calcium level PPM = 0.54 x 0.9 x 60 = 29.16 PPM.

First the stock solution is prepared by adding 1-1/4 ounces of the hydroxide to a 5 gallon water bottle of marine water. The solution is mixed and left to clarify. Only the clear effluent will be used in the reactor. By Eq. (16.29):

$$G_R = 1 \times 10^{-6} \times 50 \times 60/0.0017 = 1.76 \text{ GAL},$$

namely, this is the amount of liquid the reactor should hold. Note that a smaller reactor can be used; it just would need to be filled more frequently. Note also that the main objective is to maintain the desired PPM so in actual operation the Kalkwasser would be added slowly and directly to the tank in order to reach the desired approximate level. By monitoring the calcium demand over a 24 hour period a reasonable value of ΔP, the station keeping PPM can be accurately determined and used in the next set of equations. The 60 PPM used herein is just this value and is adopted under the previous provisions, but just as an example.

Equation (16.28) provides the drip-drop rate, i.e.

$$\dot{d} = 0.00128 \times 60 \times 50/0.0017 \times 24$$
$$= 94.1 \text{ drops/minute.}$$

Note that a correctly designed reactor should have various outlet tubes so that the total drip rate to each "J" tube can be accurately determined. For example if two tubes are used then the drip rate out of each tube would be 94/2 = 47 drops/min; about 1 drop/sec. If this option is not available the control valve would be set so that it would fill a 1 ounce bottle (which holds 620 drops) in 620/94 = 6.6 minutes or a 4 ounce bottle in 26.4 minutes, etc. Obviously, the value of T can be increased so as to lower the drip rate.

16.10.4 OVERFLOW CONSIDERATIONS

Even though the liquid volume added to the tank is small, the same volume introduced into the tank should be subtracted. This is easily done by having a second stock bottle collect the same amount of water via a gravity siphon. The extraction rate would be adjusted by a valve and be equal to the input drip rate. When more stock solution is needed it is prepared in this collection bottle and added to the reactor. This operation is convenient and will ensure that the tank water level remains constant. The suction port of the "J" tube should project only slightly into the water surface so as to break suction should the reactor run out of fuel; in which case no harm will be done.

16.10.5 ENHANCING REACTOR SOLUTIONS WITH ADDITIONAL ELEMENTS

Many other elements are fundamental to fish and plant health. Sea water contains many minor and trace elements. Reference (16.13.2) lists the elemental constituents of seawater, and as mentioned previously calcium has a concentration of 0.409×10^{-3} LBS/LBS (water) which by multiplication by 10^6 is equivalent to 409 PPM. Since messing around with mother nature is bad operational procedure these levels of magnitude should be adopted. For the same reasons other necessary elements also should be added as they become exhausted. As an example dealing with the questions of how elements can be obtained from chemicals the important element strontium (Sr) will be examined. Other chemicals can be added by the same procedures. Strontium has a seawater concentration of 1×10^{-5} LB/LB (water) or 10 PPM. To obtain this element a water soluble chemical such as strontium chloride ($SrCl_2$) can be used. From Table 16.4 or any standard chemistry book the atomic weight of strontium is 87.63 while that of chlorine is 35.457 so that the atomic weight of the chemical to be used to obtain the strontium, namely $SrCl_2$ is $87.63 + 35.457 + 35.457 = 158.544$. The percent of Sr is thus $(87.63/158.544) \times 100 = 55.27\%$. The number of pounds of pure strontium, p_{sr}, that must be added to the tank such that mother natures value of 10 PPM is realized is:

$$p_{sr} = P \times 10^{-6} p_w,$$

where $P = 10$ and as usual the pounds of water in the tank are $8.345G$, where G is the net gallons in the tank. Therefore, in general:

$$p_{xx} = P \times 8.345 \times 10^{-6} G,$$

where P is the target PPM and p_{xx} is the pounds of elemental additive; obviously $p_{xx} = p_{sr}$ in this case. The number of pounds of the chemical is just $100p_{xx}$/(% of element in the chemical); in this case 55.27%, hence:

$$p(SrCl_2) = 10 \times 8.345 \times 10^{-6}G/.5527$$
$$= 1.51 \times 10^{-4}G, \quad LBS$$
$$= 0.0685G, \quad gms.$$

Specifically, for a 100 gallon tank 6.85 grams of strontium chloride can be added to the reactor. As long as the volume in the reactor is large enough to dissolve the strontium chloride, the powdered chemical can be added to the reactor. Since the physical data on strontium chloride (Table 16.4) indicates that 0.529 LBS/LBS (water) or 0.0634 LBS/gallon can be dissolved, only about a 0.24 gallon reactor will be needed for the 100 gallon tank. When the reactor is empty the prerequisite strontium will be present in the tank. Other fundamentally important candidate elements follow that same method of application. For simple station keeping of element levels, the amount of chemicals added to the reactor will be much smaller. Actually it is the slow additive element technique which is sought. Reactors can do many jobs. The last statement is quite banal but application of reactor technology has been greatly overlooked.

For those readers interested in the actual chemical constitution of seawater Table 16.4 is displayed. It will be most useful when the actual PPM of a fundamental element need be determined (see the last example). If magnesium sulfate is used to manufacture the mix, first compute the total atomic weight from the formula in Table 16.4

$$AT.WT.(MgSO_4) = (24.32 + 32.066 + 4 \times 16) = 120.386$$

$$\%Mg = (24.32/120.386) \times 100 = 20.2\%.$$

From Table 16.4 the PPM of magnesium sulfate is 6890 of which 20.2% is magnesium so that:

$$PPM \; Mg = 0.202 \times 6890 = 1391.76.$$

Reference (16.13.2) gives 1.30 gm/kilo or 1300 PPM. To add this element to 100 gallons of water, 6890 x 0.0008345 = 5.749 LBS of magnesium sulfate needs to be added—and, against Mr. Bond's wishes, stirred—not shaken.

Table 16.4

Synthetic Seawater Composition*
100 Gallons

Chemical	PPM
Major Elements	
Sodium Chloride (NaCl)	27561
Magnesium Sulfate ($MgSO_4$)	6890
Magnesium Chloride ($MgCl_2$)	5392
Potassium Chloride (KCl)	599.2
Calcium Chloride ($CaCl_2$)	1378
Sodium Bicarbonate ($NaHCO_3$)	209.7
Minor Elements	
Strontium Chloride ($SrCl_2$)	19.81
Manganese Sulfate ($MnSO_4 \cdot H_2O$)	3.96
Sodium Phosphate ($NaH_2PO_4 \cdot 7H_2O$)	3.96
Lithium Chloride (LiCl)	0.99
Sodium Molybdate ($NaMoO_4 \cdot 2H_2$))	0.99
Sodium Thiosulfate ($Na_2S_2O_3 \cdot 5H_2O$)	0.99
Trace Elements	
Potassium Iodide (KI)	0.089
Aluminum Sulfate ($Al_2[SO_4]_3$)	0.856
Potassium Bromide (KBr)	100.750*
Cobalt Sulfate ($CoSO_4$)	0.089
Rubidium Chloride (RbCl)	0.149
Cupric Sulfate ($CuSO_4 \cdot 5H_2O$)	0.001
Zinc Sulfate ($ZnSO_4 \cdot 7H_2O$)	0.096

*Transformed from Ref. (16.13.3) with bromine error corrected. According to Ref. (16.13.4) this number is 97.74. To obtain pounds multiply by 0.0008345.

Atomic Weights

Element	Symbol	Atomic Weight
Aluminum	Al	26.980
Bromine	Br	79.916
Calcium	Ca	40.080
Carbon	C	12.010
Chlorine	Cl	35.457
Cobalt	Co	58.94
Copper	Cu	63.54

Table 16.4 - continued

Synthetic Seawater Composition*
100 Gallons

Atomic Weights - continued

Element	Symbol	Atomic Weight
Hydrogen	H	1.008
Iodine	I	126.91
Lithium	Li	6.94
Magnesium	Mg	24.32
Manganese	Mn	54.93
Molybdenum	Mo	95.95
Oxygen	O	16.0
Phosphorus	P	30.975
Potassium	K	39.100
Rubidum	Rb	85.48
Strontium	Sr	87.63
Sulfur	S	32.066
Zinc	Zn	65.38

Solubilities
Pounds/100 Pounds of Water

Chemical	Solubility
Sodium Chloride	35.80
Magnesium Sulfate	34.44
Magnesium Chloride	54.50
Potassium Chloride	34.00
Calcium Carbonate	00.013
Calcium Chloride	73.19
Calcium Hydroxide	00.17
Calcium Sulfate	00.20
Sodium Bicarbonate	9.60
Strontium Chloride	52.90
Manganese Sulfate	39.31
Sodium Phosphate	85.21
Lithium Chloride	78.50
Sodium Thiosulfate	70.00
Potassium Iodide	144.00
Aluminum Sulfate	36.40
Potassium Bromide	65.20
Cobalt Sulfate	36.21
Rubidium Chloride	91.10
Cupric Sulfate	20.70
Zinc Sulfate	53.80

16.11 SUMMARY

The manner in which the injection of ozone, oxygen, CO_2 and other elements into reactors is performed was analyzed. Specific formulas for gas flow into the reactors and reactor degas time were developed. A description of the perfect gas law was outlined so as to permit correction of the pertinent gas flows. In the case of ozone all the disinfection is to be performed internally in the reactor and the degas line scrubbed free of the gas by passing the water through suitable carbon filters. When oxygen and carbon dioxide are injected, the objective is to raise the parts/million in the tank to some desired value. In the oxygen and ozone case the value of the degas time can be used to adjust the gas flowrate into the reactor. In the CO_2 and O_2 problem the reactor gas supply must be turned off at the desired target value PPM or else the safe concentrations of these gases might be exceeded. By noting the PPM decrease for an arbitrary duration after the target concentration of gas is achieved, the depletion rate of the gas due to natural causes can be determined and continuous gas input flowrates determined over any desired interval of time. The station keeping requirements to maintain specific PPM levels were outlined. Finally reactors which add calcium and other required elements were discussed. The composition of seawater was presented.

16.12 PROBLEMS

16.12.1 A 3" diameter cylindrical clear tube 16" in length which is capped on only one side is submerged in a tank of water, evacuated of all air and lifted vertically so that the water remains in the tube. It is lifted so that only 1/2 inch of the open end of the tube is below the tank waterline. An airpump line is slipped into the open end of the tube and the airpump is turned on. It is observed that it takes 30 seconds for the water to be forced out of the tube by the accumulated air provided by the pump. What is the airpump flow in cubic inches per minute at a pressure of 14.7 psi and 68°F?

Ans: 226.19 in^3/min.

16.12.2 The airflow obtained in Problem 16.12.1 is fed to a reactor that has an average pressure of 2 psi and temperature of 80°F. What is the resulting airflow into the reactor?

Ans: 203.62 in^3/min.

16.12.3 How would the airflow output from an airpump be determined as a function of the pressure the airpump senses from the reactor? What would a calibration curve for the airpump look like?

16.12.4 A 200 gallon tank that has 20% of its volume occupied by gravel, rocks and fish is to have a PPM oxygen level of 15 PPM. If the present level is 6 PPM, how many pounds of oxygen must the airpump deliver?

Ans: 0.012 LBS

16.12.5 In problem 16.12.4 what is the total air volume the airpump must deliver in 4 hours if the average reactor pressure is 3 psi and the water in the reactor is 84°F? What is the pump airflow rate?

Ans: 1018 in^3
Ans: 4.24 in^3/min.

16.12.6 A 4" diameter hyperbaric (oxygen) reactor with a 12" high column of bio balls is adjusted so that the degas time is 5 minutes. If the reactor gauge pressure is 3 psi and temperature is 78°F, how many PPM of oxygen is supplied to a 150 gallon tank in 3 hours whose initial oxygen level is 7 PPM? Assume $f = 1$ (or perfect oxygen absorbtion).

Ans: 19.3 PPM

16.12.7 Direct measurement of the O_2 level in a reactor indicates that from the point at which the target value of O_2 is attained the hourly loss k, where k is a measured constant, e.g., $k = 1$ or 1 PPM/HR. Modify Eq. (16.23) so that it can be used to determine that station keeping value of the pump airflow over a 24 hour period.

16.12.8 Since solubility of oxygen in water increases in direct proportion to the pressure should not the reactor pressure be as high as possible?

16.12.9 How many PPM of Aluminum are present in seawater? Bromine?

Ans: 0.135 PPM
Ans: 67 PPM

16.12.10 Rework Table 16.4 to get the number of pounds of each chemical that should be added to produce 100 gallons of synthetic seawater.

16.12.11 Calcium Chloride is quite soluble in water. What would you do to use this chemical in lieu of the hydroxide or carbonate form of the additive chemical?

16.13 REFERENCES

16.13.1 M. C. Sneed, J. L. Maynard, Robert C. Brasted, *General College Chemistry*, D. Van Nostrand Company, Princeton, New Jersey, 1956

16.13.2 M. A. Moe, Jr., *The Marine Aquarium Reference*, Green Turtle Publications, Plantation, Florida, 1992

16.13.3 S. Spotte, *Fish and Invertebrate Culture*, Wiley-Interscience, New York, N.Y., 1970

APPENDIX 1

Light Requirements

Candlepower is the quantitive measure of light generated by a sanctified and most holy candle of fixed dimensions manufactured with a specific type of wax. It is an index of the light output of a lamp but does not specify the actual light that reaches an object. A foot-candle describes the illumination falling on one square foot at a distance of one foot from the candle. For short, this is called a lumen, and is a measure of all the light which exits from the bulb in all directions at the surface of light.

The starting point for estimation of aquarium light requirements can be taken as L_o = 1000 lumens. This value can be adjusted to fit exact requirements but this will take observation. So how many watts are needed?

The number of watts required for a given tank depends on a number of factors. First, it depends on the bulb that is selected, and there are many bulbs from which to make this selection. For a more extensive discussion of this selection the reader is directed to the reference. However, some fundamental selection rules apply. Marine laboratories favor "cool white" bulbs for microalgae cultures. Wide spectrum bulbs such as Vita-Lite® and Chroma® which are classified as full spectrum bulbs supply a well rounded output, while Actinic 03 bulbs are biased to promote coral growth. In essence a selected mix of these bulbs is the best strategy to ensure proper lighting conditions. General selection might be twice as many full specturm bulbs as the equally divided number of cool white and actinic bulbs. High output (HO) bulbs which produce about double the light and thus imply less bulbs can be used. Metal halide or less expensive mercury bulbs that have very good spectral range and have high light output are also an option but these produce high heat levels. One way or another the goal is to achieve natural sunlight, which has a color rendering index (CRI) of 100.

The second factor of importance is the bulb efficacy, $\in$, which is a bulb characteristic measured in lumens per watt. Thirdly, there is a bulb utilization factor, μ which is an index of the total light from the bulb that actually strikes the water. The factor μ can be adopted as equal to 0.5 - 0.75 and depends on the reflector design.

When all these factors are considered the required number of watts for a given tank can be estimated by:

$$W = 6.945 L_o A/(1000 \in \mu),$$

where L_o is the adopted lumens, A is the tank surface area in in^2, $\in$ is the combined efficacy in lumens per Watt and $\mu = 0.5 - 0.75$ or an average value $= 0.625$. In this formula:

$$\in = (\in_1 N_1 + \in_2 N_2 + \ldots + \in_m N_m)/N,$$

where N_i are the subtotal number of bulbs with efficacy $\in_i$ and N is the total number of bulbs. Note $N_1 + N_2 + \ldots + N_m = N$. Obviously, N_i/N is also the percent fraction of each group of bulbs.

If μ and L_o are adopted as indicated then the previous formula just simplifies to:

$$W = 11.11 \, A/\in.$$

EXAMPLE

A tank 60" in length by 24" in width (top surface area) is to use twice as many full spectrum bulbs as cool white bulbs. How many bulbs are required?

From the table the Chroma 50 bulbs have an efficacy of 55.3 while the cool whites have 78.8. Therefore:

$$\in = 55.3 \times (2N) + 78.8 \times (N)/(2N + N)$$
$$= (55.3 \times 2 + 78.8)/3 = 63.13.$$

Note that N is not known but to estimate $\in$ it is not necessary; only the ratio need be known. The required watts are:

$$W = 11.11 \times (60 \times 24)/63.13 = 253.46 \text{ watts.}$$

Again from the Table each bulb has an output of 40 watts so:

$$N = 253.4/40 = 6.34 \text{ bulbs,}$$

or about 2 bulbs (cool whites) will be a reasonable estimate. Obviously L_o can always be adjusted as time goes by.

Typical Bulb Characteristics*

Description	Efficacy	Watts	Length	CRI
Fluorescent:				
Cool White	78.8	40	48	62
Cool White	84.0	75	60	62
Chroma 50	55.3	40	48	90
Chroma 75	50.0	40	48	92
Vita-Lite FS	60.0	40	48	91
Daylight	65.0	40	48	75
Daylight	72.7	75	60	75
Colortone	55	40	48	92
Verilux	54.2	40	48	93
Incandescent:				
60	14.5	60	—	99
100	17.5	100	—	99
Mercury Vapor:				
Clear	52.5	400	—	Good
Delux White	56.3	400	—	Good
Metal Halide:				
Clear (E23 1/2)	94.9	175	—	Excellent
Clear (E28)	82.0	250	—	Excellent
Clear (E37)	90.0	400	—	Excellent

*For a Detailed Listing See Reference.

REFERENCE

M.A. Moe Jr., *The Marine Aquarium Handbook*, Green Turtle Publications, Plantation, Florida, 1995.

APPENDIX 2

All the Math You Need to Know to Understand
Aquatic Systems Engineering

SQUARING AND ROOT EXTRACTION

A dot means to multiply

X^2 means $X \bullet X$; X^3 means $X \bullet X \bullet X$, etc.

$X^{1/2}$ means square root; $X^{1/3}$ means cube root, etc.

Square root means: Find the number which multiplied by itself is equal to X. Use a calculator.

Cube root means: Find the number which multiplied together three times is equal to X,

Et Cetera.

BRACKETS

These symbols are used to show the order of operations, especially in computer programs:

$\{[(x)]\}$

means do the ( ) operation first, the [ ] operation second, the operation { } last.

Basically, proceed numerical operations from the inner to outer brackets.

AVERAGES AND DIFFERENCES

The difference of two numbers is denoted by the symbol Δ, i.e., $\Delta T = T_2 - T_1$.

The Average of two numbers X and Y is $A = (X + Y)/2$, i.e., add X to Y (First bracket) then divide by 2.

The Average of three numbers X, Y, and W is $A = (X + Y + W)/3$,

Et Cetera.

EXPONENTIAL NOTATION

1×10^6 means 1 followed by 6 zeros or 1000000,

1×10^{27} means 1 followed by 27 zeros,

5.2×10^3 means 5.2 multiplied by $10 \bullet 10 \bullet 10$,

$\pi \times 10^4$ means π multiplied by $10 \bullet 10 \bullet 10 \bullet 10$,

π math constant = 3.1415,

5.2×10^{-3} means 5.2 divided by 1000,

25.6×10^{-6} means 25.6 divided by 1000000,

Et Cetera.

ALGEBRAIC EQUATIONS

If X, Y, W are parameters:

$X = Y + W$ means that X is equal to Y plus W.

Parameters can be moved across an equal sign; just change the sign:

$X - Y = W$ means that X minus Y is equal to W.

$X - Y - W = 0$ means that X minus Y and W is equal to zero.

If A, B, C, are constants, e.g., 5, 3.1, 2.5, then:

$AX = Y$ means that $X = Y/A$.

Specifically a constant can be moved across an equal sign by inverting
or dividing by the constant.

EXAMPLE

Note: AX means A times X; the dot is usually omitted.

If:
$$AX + BY + CW = 0,$$

solve for X. Operating as outlined:
$$AX = -BY - CW,$$
$$X = (-BY-CW)/A,$$

or
$$X = -BY/A - CW/A.$$

EXAMPLE

If:
$$AX^2 + BY = CW,$$

solve for X. Operating as outlined:
$$AX^2 = CW - BY$$
$$X^2 = (CW - BY)/A$$

Take the square root by use of a calculator:
$$X = [(CW - BY)/A]^{1/2}.$$

Note: Very inexpensive calculators are available at, e.g., Radio Shack,
that will extract square, cube, roots of any power, logarithms, etc.— A
wise investment.

FACTORING

If D is another constant so that:
$$AX + AY + AW = D,$$

then A can be factored:
$$A (X + Y + W) = D,$$
which says add the parameters in the brackets and multiply by A. If:
$$AX + BY + CW = D, \tag{1}$$
the factorization is:
$$A (X + BY/A + CW/A) = D.$$

Note that if A is multiplied into each term in the brackets Eq. (1) is obtained. A parameter can be factored as well, e.g., AW(X/W + BY/AW + C/A) = D.

LOGARITHMS

Logarithms basically transform the multiplication of two numbers into the addition of two numbers. In days of old (pre-computer age), imagine the work involved, especially for astronomical calculations, in the multiplication of two eight digit numbers. Construction of "log" tables permited scientists to take the logarithm of each number, add the two new numbers and then use the tables in backward fashion to obtain the product of the numbers. Today, any inexpensive calculator has logarithm functions—not for the purpose of multiplication, but to take the logarithms of equations that contain them.

Basically if X and Y are two numbers, then:
$$Log(XY) = Log\ X + Log\ Y$$
$$Log(X/Y) = Log\ X - Log\ Y.$$

HIGHER ORDER ALGERAIC EQUATIONS

These equations are of the form:
$$AX^2 + BX + C = 0$$
$$AX^3 + BX^2 + CX + D = 0$$
$$AX^4 + BX^3 + CX^2 + DX + E = 0,$$
etc. The problem is to solve for X, given the constants A, B, C, etc. Formulas for the above equations exist, e.g., in the quadratic case:
$$X = (-B \pm [B^2 - 4AC]^{1/2})/2A.$$
Closed form expressions for the cubic (X^3) and quartic (X^4) equation are also available, but they are much more complicated. Above degree 4, the solutions become intractable and the value of X is usually obtained by trial and error or other numerical means.

DIFFERENTIAL EQUATIONS

When a parameter, x, varies as a function of another parameter, y, the effect of a very small change in y, denoted by placing the letter d, i.e., dy (d is not a constant—it is just an operator) will result in a very small change in x, denoted by dx. Hence, the rate of change of these parameters can be expressed as dx/dy.

EXAMPLE

Let y be equal to time, T, and x be equal to gallons, G. Then gallons per hour can be symbolized by the "Derivative":

$$dx/dy = dG/dT. \tag{2}$$

Since time is such an important parameter, a shorthand notation which expresses the previous rate is usually adopted, i.e., an overhead dot:

$$dG/dT = \dot{G} = \text{Flowrate}.$$

In certain problems, the upper parameter in Eq. (2) x, along with $\dot{x}$ appears in an equation, e.g.,

$$\dot{x} + Ax = B.$$

This is a linear differential equation. These equations can be solved for x by the use of specialized formulas.

INTEGRATION

Integration or better said, the operation of integration, is usually denoted by an elongated s in front of a given parameter. This operation is the inverse of differentiation or the process of finding the anti-derivative. When integration is performed, one is actually finding the area under any given curve.

ARITHMETIC PROGRESSIONS

These are series with a finite number of terms wherein there is a common difference between all the numbers in the series, e.g., by direct summation:

$$1 + 3 + 5 + 7 + 9 + 11 = 36; \text{diff} = 2.$$

If n is the total number of terms, a is the first term and f is the final term, the sum can also be obtained by:

$$s = (n/2)(a+f) = (6/2)(1+11) = 36. \tag{3}$$

APPENDIX 3

A Compendium of Useful Conversion Factors

Units $\longrightarrow$ Multiply by $\longrightarrow$ Units
Units $\longleftarrow$ Divide by $\longleftarrow$ Units

British Thermal Units	252.	Calories (C)
Calories per Sec.	0.23889	Watts (W)
Centimeters	1/2.54	Inches (in)
Change in °C (ΔC)	1.8	Change in °F (ΔF)
Cubic Centimeters (water)	1.	Grams (gms)
Cubic Centimeters/sec.	26929.9	Gal/HR
Cubic Inches(in^3)	16.387	Cubic cm (cm^3)
Cubic Inches(in^3)	1/231.	Gallons (G)
Days	1440.	Minutes (min)
Feet^3	1728	in^3
Feet of Head	0.43208	lbs/in^2 (psi)
Feet^2	144.	in^2
Fluid ounces (U.S.)	29.573	cm^3
Gallons (G)	231.	in^3
Gallons (water)	8.345	lbs (pounds)
Gallons (water)	76800.	drops
Grams (gm)	1000.	mg (milligrams)
Inches	2.54	cm (centimeters)
In^3	1/1728.	ft^3
Liters (L)	61.025	in^3
Meters (M)	39.37	in
Millimeters (mm)	1/1000.	M (meters)
Parts per Million (PPM)	1000.	gms/L (grams/liter)
Pounds (lb)	453.6	gms
Pounds/in^2 (psi)	2.3144	feet of head
Seconds	1/3600.	hours

ANSWERS TO PROBLEMS

Chapter 1

No Answers supplied.

Chapter 2

2.5.1 $\dot{F}$ = 50 GPH, G = 100 GAL.

T = $9.2\,G/\dot{F}_o$ = 9.2 x 100/50 = 18.4 HRS.

2.5.2 $\dot{F}_o$ = 60 GPH, G = 70 GAL.

T = $9.2\,G/\dot{F}_o$ = 9.2 X 70/60 = 10.73 HRS.

2.5.3 T = $9.2\,G/\dot{F}_o$; Solve for $\dot{F}_o$.

$\dot{F}_o$ = $9.2\,G/T$. But T = 24/4 = 6 HRS, and the bio-tower contains 15 GAL, so $\dot{F}_o$ = 9.2 x (100+15)/6 = 176.3 GPH.

2.5.4 Purity Coefficient = 11.5. Twice daily means T = 24/2 = 12 HRS. So $\dot{F}_o$ = 11.5x400/12 = 383.3 GPH.

CHAPTER 3

3.9.1 $\dot{F}_o$ = 50 GPH, G = 100 GAL.

T = $12.75\,G/\dot{F}_o$ = 12.75 x 100/50 = 25.5 HRS.

3.9.2 Purity Coefficient = -13.8 (Table 2.1)

Use Eq. (3.8):

T = (-13.8x500/[-(1/2) x 400]) Log 2; Log 2 = 0.693
   = 23.9 HRS.

3.9.3 T = $12.75\,G/\dot{F}_o$, so

$\dot{F}_o$ = $12.75\,G/T$ = 12.75x500/12 = 531 GPH.

3.9.4 Gallons in system = 3x30+20 = 110 GAL.

Use Eq. (3.8) with e = 1/3, T = 6:

T = (-9.2x110/[-(1/3)$\dot{F}_o$]) Log 3.

Solve for $\dot{F}_o$:

$\dot{F}_o$ = 9.2x110x3xLog3/6 = 556 GPH.

CHAPTER 4

4.9.1 To attain proper flowrate; Yes.

4.9.2 Use Fig. 4.3; T = 8. For 3 turns enter at 8, go right to 200 GAL; read flowrate as 230 GPH.

4.9.3   Use Table 4.1.

4.9.4   Use Fig. 4.1. Enter at 92,000, intersect 25, 30, 64 watt line and read the flowrate below.

Enter at 22,000, intersect 25, 30, 64 watt line and read the flowrate below.

4.9.5   Use Fig. 4.3 For 3 turns T = 8 HRS. For 75 GAL, move up to the 8 hour line. Flowrate is halfway between 75 and 100 GPH radial lines, so;
$\dot{F}_o$ = (75+100)/2 = 175/2 = 87.5 = 88 GPH.

Use Fig. 4.1. Enter at 88 (90 GPH); 25 watt gives 52,000 (More than enough for algae); 30 watt gives 75,000; 64 watt gives (by extrapolation) 120,000.

4.9.6   Use Table 4.1. Fungus dose is 45,000. Enter Fig. 4.5 at 230 gallons and move up to intersect 30 watt curve. Note that dose is 45,000. Drop vertically down to the flowrate scale and read 175 GPH.

4.9.7   Use Fig. 4.5 at 22,000. Move horizontally and note that 64 watt unit can handle 833 gallons, with flowrate of 625 GPH. Two units will treat 2x833 = 1666 gallons (close enough).

CHAPTER 5

5.11.1   Use Table 5.1. Three turns = 8 HRS.
Use Eq. (5.13) and solve for $\dot{F}_o$:

T = $aG/\dot{F}_o$; $\dot{F}_o$ = aG/T = (9.2x500)/8 = 575 GPH.

5.11.2   A by-pass line will obtain the proper flowrate through the ultraviolet sterilizer.

5.11.3   Use Table 5.3. For one sterilizer (25 watt), dose at 500 GPH = 6512. Dose (new) = 6,512 x 500/600 = 5,426.6.

For two sterilizers, dose = 2 x 5426.6 = 10,853.

5.11.4   Flow through each sterilizer is 500 GPH. Use Table 5.5 and read Dose = 14,793. For three sterilizers Dose = 3 x 14,793 = 44,379.

5.11.5   Radiation decreases. Penetration of radiation into water decreases. Contact time increases. These three factors lead to an equation whose solution yields the optimum diameter.

CHAPTER 6

6.6.1 To force the water through the by-pass line.

6.6.2 The flowrate, $\dot{F}_o$, is given by:

$$\dot{F}_o = V/T = 15/45 \text{ GAL/sec}$$
$$= (15/45) \times 60 \text{ GAL/min}$$
$$= (15/45) \times 60 \times 60 = 1200 \text{ GPH.}$$

6.6.3 To prevent water from the main line backwashing into the reactor. By placing the reactor exit line as far removed as possible from the main return line, better circulation will be achieved.

6.6.4 Nitrogen could be forced into the water.

6.6.5 During the day, fill the reactor and turn down the water input valve of the by-pass connection until it is nearly shut. Observe how many hours it takes for the reactor to empty. If the time is greater than eight hours, shut the valve down even further. If the time is less than 8 hours, open the valve slightly. Continue until the exhaustion duration is about 8 hours. Tape down the input valve. This is the permanent setting of the valve. Note that if you miss filling the reactor 3 or 4 times a week, the world of the plants will not come to an end.

6.6.6 If you can not answer this question, please re-read the text (See 1.1.23).

CHAPTER 7

7.9.3 Use Eq. (7.3):

$$p_t - p_i = 3.1125 \times 10^{-7} \times [(4/3)^4 - 4^4] \times 650^2$$
$$p_t = 16 - 33.34 = -17.25 \text{ psi.}$$

7.9.4 Volume of tube = $\pi d^2 L/4 = V = 3.1415 \times 3^2 \times 20/4 = 141.37$ in^3. Air rate = $V/t = 141.37/27 = 5.236$ in^3/sec. Multiply this number by 60. Air rate = 314.2 in^3/min.

7.9.5 Convert 7 psi to feet. Depth = $7 \times 2.3144 = 16.2$ feet.

CHAPTER 8

8.5.1 Use Fig. 8.2. Enter the horizontal scale at 180. Move vertically up and read about 6. Read 135 below (75 + 4 squares of 15) GPH.

8.5.2 No filter elements to clog.

8.5.3   Enter Fig. 8.2 on lower horizontal scale at 315, read 420 gallons on scale above.

8.5.4   Enter Fig. 8.2 at 60 on horizontal scale. Read 4 on vertical scale.

Area $4'' = \pi\, 4^2/4 = 12.56$,
Area $3'' = 7.07 \times 2 = 14.14$.

Two $3''$ skimmers will work because their cross-sectional area is greater than that of the $4''$ skimmer.

8.5.5   Use Eq. (8.2) with the minus sign, and solve for D_s, noting that $R_B = 10$, $G = 400$ and $T = 12$:

$$d_s^2 = (R_B + 1.33) \times (G/T)/4.85$$
$$= (10 + 1.33) \times (400/12)/4.85 = 77.87$$
$$d_s = 8.82 \text{ in.}$$

The cross-sectional area of this skimmer is $\pi D_s^2/4 = 46.8 \text{ in}^2$. The cross sectional area of a $4''$ skimmer is 12.56 (12.56 x 4 = 50.24). The area of a $6''$ skimmer is 28.27 (28.27 x 2 = 56.54). Four $4''$ skimmers or two $6''$ skimmers will also work.

CHAPTER 9

9.10.1 $T = 9.2\, G/\dot{F}_o = 9.2 \times 80/60 = 12.26$ HRS.

9.10.2   Enter Fig. 9.3 at 80 gallons, move vertically to the 12 hour line and read off $4''$ or two $3''$ diameter skimmers.

9.10.3   Enter Fig. 9.3 at 200 gallons. Move vertically to the 12 hour line and read off $6''$. Drop down and obtain the flowrate as 150 GPH. If two $4''$ diameter skimmers are used, split the flowrate in two.

9.10.4   Four turns means $T = 6$ HRS.

The standard turnover formula is:

$T = 9.2\, G/\dot{F}_o$. Solve for $\dot{F}_o$.

$\dot{F}_o = 9.2\, G/T = 9.2 \times 100/6 = 153.3$ GPH.

9.10.5   Enter Fig. 9.3 at 400 gallons; read the flowrate on the lower axis as 300 GPH. Move vertically from this point and find the diameter equal to $9''$ at the two turn per day limit line.

CHAPTER 10

10.8.1 The water never touches the motor shaft of the motor.

10.8.2 If one pump fails, the other will continue to operate until repairs can be made.

10.8.3 Inlet pressure - 5 psi.

Pressure = -5 + 10 + 10 + 10 = +25 psi.

10.8.4 Flowrate = 500 + 500 + 500 = 1500 less 10% = 1350 GPH. Five percent of 1500 is 75, so the flowrate is 1425 GPH.

CHAPTER 11

11.8.1 Use Fig. 11.1 for a 1″ pipe carrying 1000 GPH to obtain k_f = 0.017. Since L/D = 200/(1/12) = 2400; k = k_f (L/D) = 40.8. From Table 11.1, k for the two elbows is 2 x 0.9 = 1.8, so that K = 42.6. Use Eq. (11.1) to obtain the head loss:

h_f = 42.6 x 7.2035 x 10^{-7} x $1000^2/1^4$
= 30.68 ft. = 30.68/2.3144 = 13.25 psi.

11.8.2 Let N be the number of elbows. From Table 11.1, each elbow has k = 0.9. The head loss, by Eq. (11.1) is:

h_f = N x 0.9 x 7.2035 x $500^2/0.75^4$,

which must equal the pump head of 10 psi = 2.3144 x 10 = 23.144 ft. So N x 0.5122 = 23.144. Solve for N; N = 45.19.

11.8.3 Apply Eq. (11.5):

a $(p_1 - p_2)$ = bk$\dot{G}^2/D^4$; a $(p_1 - p_2)$ = 2.3144 x 6.
Solve for k$\dot{G}^2$ = 6.1 x 10^6.

Assume $\dot{G}$ = 600, solve for k = 16.9. Enter Fig. 11.4 at 600 and read off k = 11; the k's do not agree.

Assume $\dot{G}$ = 750, solve for k = 10.8. Enter Fig. 11.4 at 750 (extrapolate) and read off k = 11. This is close enough. $\dot{G}$ = 750 GPH.

11.8.4 Use Fig. 11.4. K increases by 13 x 1.5 = 19.5. H = 40.406 (See the example). Therefore H_p = 15 - 2 + 40. 406 = 53.4 ft., or 23.1 psi. To obtain the flowrate at a one foot head, use Eq. (11a) with L/D = 24; K = 0.012 x 24 + 0.1 = 0.388. Assume $\dot{G}$ = 1600 GPH.

CHAPTER 12

12.12.2 Select Eq. (12.7) with $W = 12$, $H = 24$, $L = 60$,
$m_T = 3/8 \ / \ 1/8 = 3$, $m_B = 3/8 \ / \ 3/8 = 1$,
$m_C = 0.00009/0.002$ (Table 12.2). This yields $A = 5648.4$ in^2.
$\Delta T = 70° -55° = 15°$. Use Eq. (12.5)

$W \ = 0.3371 \times 0.002 \times 5648.4 \times 15/(0.90 \times 0.375)$

$= 169.25$ watts; or one 150 watt and one 25 watt heater.

12.12.3 Select Eq. (12.12); $V = 60 \times 12 \times 24$.

Select Eq. (12.15); $g_w = 16.38 \ V$
$= 283046. \ 4$ gm. Weight $= g_w/453.6 = 624$ LBS.

12.12.4 Select Eq. (12.16); $m_T = 3$ (Eq. 12.12.2),
$V_r \ = [2\times24\times60+2\times24\times12+12\times60/3+12\times60/1]\times0.375$

$= 1656$ in^3.

Use Table 12.1; $S = 2.53$. Use Eq. (12.19):

$g_r \ = 16.387 \times 2.53 \times 1656 = 68656.28$ gm, which upon
dividing by $453.6 = 151.35$ LBS.

12.12.5 Select Eq. (12.6) with $G = 1.1 \ (g_w + sg_r)$;

g_w, g_r are obtained from the previous two problems and s
from Table 12.3.

$t \ = 0.0003685 \times 2.56 \times (1.1[283046.4+0.21\times68656.28])$

$\times 15/169.25$

$= 2.74$ HRS.

12.12.6 Tank length $= 14 \times 28 \times 80$; $\Delta T = 77 - 55 = 22°F$.
Select Eq. (12.7) with

$m_T = (1/2)/(1/4) = 2$, $m_B = (1/2)/(3/4) = 0.666$,
$m_C = 0.00009/0.0004 = 0.225$, $H = 28$, $W = 14$, $L = 160$.

$A \ = 2 \times 28 \times 160 + 2 \times 28 \times 14 + 2 \times 14 \times 160 + 0.666 \times 0.225$
$\times 14 \times 160 = 14247.98$ in^2.

Use the Wattage Equation:

$W \ = 0.337 \times 0.0004 \times 22 \times 14247.98/(0.9\times0.5)$,

$W \ = 93.93$ watts; or select two 50 watt heaters.

12.12.7 Select Eq. 12.7 with $W = 12$, $H = 12$, $L = 36$,
$m_T = (1/4)/(1/16) = 4$, $m_B = (1/4/1/4) = 1$,
$m_C = 0.00009/0.0004 = 0.225$, so that:

A = 2 x 12 x 36 + 2 x 12 x 12 + 4 x 12 x 36 +
1 x 0.225 x 12 x 36 = 2977.2 in^2.

Use the Wattage Equation:

W = 0.337 x 0.0004 x 2977.2 x 22 /(0.9x0.25)
= 39.25 watts; add a 50 watt heater.

12.12.8 The wattage equation need be applied once as opposed to an application to each individual panel.

CHAPTER 13

13.8.1 Electric discharge or ultraviolet radiation.

13.8.2 One part per million.

13.8.3 Vary the air input or use a mechanical sleeve over the bulb.

13.8.4 Reversability of the reaction.

13.8.5 From Fig. 13.1 for 5 LPM, R = 0.55. Use Eq. (13.4):

$\dot{O}_3$ = 270.144 x 0.55 x 5 = 742.8 mg/HR.

13.8.7 Generator diameter, wattage, arc length of the bulb.

13.8.8 Use Eq. (13.6) with L = 34, r = 3, $\dot{A}$ = 6, W = 34.5:

From Fig. 13.1, R = 0.54

$\dot{O}_3$ = 0.6525 x [1 - (3 - 1)/6] x 34 x 34.5 x 6 x 0.54
= 1653.2 mg/HR.

13.8.9 It depends on the input air flow.

CHAPTER 14

Class projects; no answers supplied.

CHAPTER 15

15.12.1 The average mean grain size is (0.45 + 0.55)/2 = 0.5. Enter Fig. 15.4 with 0.5 and read the surface area as 4750 + 1/2(250) = 4875 ft^2/ft^3.

15.12.2 Compute the ratio of the last two terms of Eq. (15.8) as $(\pi^3/4g^3)/(\pi^2/2g^2) = \pi/2g$. This is the common ratio. Multiply the last term by the common ratio to obtain $\pi^4/8g^4$.

15.12.3 Read the surface density of the grains of sand via Fig. 15.4. Since the graph uses millimeters for the mean diameter d_g = 0.25 x 1000/39.37 = 6.35 millimeters. With this value read S_g = 500 + .75 x 250 = 6.87.5 ft^2/ft^3. The volume of the filter bed is:

V = 80" x 18" x 5" = 7200 in^3 = 7200/1728 = 4.166 ft^3.

Note that the 22" tank height does not enter into the problem. Equation (15.11) yields the surface area of the bed, namely S = kS_gV = 1 x 687.5 x 4.166 = 2864 ft^2. Enter Fig. 15.5 with 2864 and $\hat{G}$ = 300GPH and read O_p = 2.5 + 0.2 x 0.5 = 2.6 mg/min. More exactly use Eq. (15.10) so that O_p = 2864/ (1009.2 + 11.095 x 2864/300) = 2.57 mg/min.

15.12.4 From Table 15.2, the weight of the standard platy is 1.35 gram. Since these platies have a length of 2" the actual weight would be given by scaling the weight of 1.35, i.e., B = 1.35 x 2/1.50 = 1.8 gram. This is also the average weight $\bar{B}$. Adopting f = 0.0132 Eq. (15.13) yields:

P = 0.051 x 0.0132 x 300 + 0.01 x $1.8^{0.544}$ x 300

= 0.202 + 3 x $1.8^{0.544}$

To obtain the fractional exponential term use Fig. 15.6 (or a computer) to yield $1.8^{0.544}$ = 1.38, and so:

P = 0.202 + 3 x 1.38 = 4.34 mg/min.

15.12.5 Since the polution potential is 4.34 and the oxidation is 2.6, the answer is an obvious no. The number of fish can be reduced or a fluidized bed can be added to the system.

15.12.6 There are 150 fish (q = 150). From Table 15.2 the Angels weigh 1.25 grams and the gourami weigh 3.85 x 4/2.50 = 6.16 grams. The average weight is therefore (1.25 x 100 + 6.16 x 50)/150 = 2.88 grams, i.e., $\bar{B}$ = 2.88 grams. The mean gravel diameter d_g = 0.25 x 1000/39.37 = 6.35 mm. Enter Fig. 15.4 with d_g and read S_g = 500 + .75 x 250 = 687.5 ft^2/ft^3. Equation (15.14) can be solved for O_p:

O_p = 150 (0.051 x 0.0132 x 2.88 + 0.01 x $2.88^{0.544}$)

= 2.96 mg/min.

Next use Eq. (15.10b) to obtain the tank filter bed volume:

V = 1009.2 x 2.96/(1 - 11.095 x 2.96/500) x 1 x 687.5

= 4.65 ft^3.

The cross sectional area of the bed which is 6" (= 0.5') deep is 4.65/0.5 = 9.3 ft^2. Since the area of the circle is $\pi D^2/4$, solving for the diameter, D gives D^2 = 9.3 x 4/π = 11.84 ft^2 or D = 3.44 ft = 41.29 in. Hence a tank with a 42" diameter will be acceptable. This tank holds 4.65 x 1728/231 = 34.78

gallons of gravel. So by Eqs. (15.16 and 15.17) a tank of 34.78 x 5 = 173.9 gallons would be selected.

15.12.7 External Mechanical devices are used to remove the pollution potential. These consist of fluidic beds, mechanical and chemical filters, wet/dry filters, bio-towers, etc. Once the pollution potential of the tank is exceeded, there is no recourse except to add these devices.

CHAPTER 16

16.12.1 Tube volume = $\pi \times 3^2 \times 16/4$; Time = 30/60 min. $\dot{A}$ = volume/time = $\pi \times 9 \times 16 \times 60/(30 \times 4)$ = 226.19 in^3/min. Note that the pressure at the surface of the water is 14.7 psi; the 1/2" is negligible. The standard atmospheric temperature is 68°F; the pressure 14.7. No correction.

16.12.2 Use Eq. (16.5):
C_v = (14.7 + 0) (80° + 460)/(14.7 + 2)(68 + 460) = 0.90
$\dot{A}_{cor}$ = A/t = AC$_v$/t = 226.19 x 0.9 = 203.62 in^3/min.

16.12.3 Use the tube method outlined in Exercise 16.12.1 but place a valve between the tube and the air pump (in the air line). Next place a pressure gauge between the valve and the air pump. Measure the duration it takes for the tube to be evacuated of water with the valve fully open. Divide the tube volume by the duration to get the airflow and note the gauge pressure. Repeat the procedure each time slightly closing the valve. Plot a curve of airflow (in^3/min) on a vertical scale versus pressure (psi) on a horizontal scale.

16.12.4 Use Eq. (16.6):
LBS_{02} = (15 - 6) x 10^{-6} LBS_{H2O}
          = 9 x 10^{-6} x 8.345 x (200 - 0.2 x 200)
          = 0.012 LBS.
LBS_{air} = 0.012/.23 = 0.05224 LBS.

16.12.5 Use Eq. (16.2), i.e., the perfect gas law.
Since w = 0.012 LBS, R_o = 1545,
M (oxygen); Table 16.1; = 32:
V = 0.012 x (1545/32) x (84 + 460)/(14.7 +3) x 144
   = 0.124 ft^3 of oxygen
   = 0.124 x 1728 = 213.68 in^3 of oxygen.
V(air) = 213.68/0.2099 = 1018 in^3.

$\dot{A}$ = 1018/4 x 60 = 4.24 in^3/min.
Another approach is to use Eq. (16.17). First compute
C_d = (3 + 14.7)(68 + 460)/(14.7)(84 + 460) = 1.17, then:
$\dot{A}$ = 0.0138 x 1 x (15 - 6) x 160/1.17 x 4 = 4.26 in^3/min
and V = 4.26 x 4 x 60 = 1022 in^3. The error in the approaches is
negligible.

16.12.6 The density correction is given by Eq. (16.5):
C_d = (3 + 14.7) x (68 + 460)/14.7 x (78 + 460) = 1.182
Since the degas time is 10 min. Eq. (16.18) yields:
$\dot{A}$ =0.3742 x 4^2 x 12/10 = 7.18 in^3/min.
Use Eq. (16.17):
P* = (C$_d$T$\dot{A}$/0.0138fG) + P$_o$,
so:
P* = (1.182 x 3 x 7.18/0.0138 x 1 x 150) + 7
  = 12.3 + 7 = 19.3 PPM.

16.12.7 Over 24 hours the PPM loss would be 24k. The process
starts when P$_o$ = P*, i.e., at the desired PPM, so P = P* - 24k.
The value of P must be boosted by 24k and so:
$\dot{A}$ = 0.0138 (24k) fG/C$_d$ x 24
  = 0.0138kfG/C$_d$.

16.12.8 No. Nitrogen would also be forced into the water but less so.

16.12.9 From Table 16.4 the formula for Aluminum Sulfate is Al$_2$[SO$_4$]$_3$.
Aluminum has an atomic weight of 26.98; Al$_2$ = 2 x 26.98; Sulfur
has a weight of S = 32.066; Oxygen 16 or O$_4$ = 4 x 16 so:
SO$_4$ = 32.066 x 4 x 16 = 96
but there exist 3 [SO$_4$] or
[SO$_4$]$_3$ = 96 x 3 = 288.
Therefore:
Al$_2$[SO$_4$]$_3$ = 53.96 + 288 = 341.96,
and % Al = (53.96/341.96) x 100 = 15.8%.
So PPM = 0.856(PPM of the sulfate) x .158
     = 0.135 PPM.
For Bromine, the salt is KBr (K = 39.1, Br = 79.916); KBr = 119.
%Br = (79.916/119) x 100 = 66.5%,
and
PPM = 100.75 x .665 = 67 PPM.

16.12.11 Remove the resulting chlorine by venting and chemical
neutralizers.

INDEX

For Information On Many Of The Products Discussed In This Book Please Fill Out The Enclosed Slip And Mail To:

Filtronics, P.O. Box 2457, Oxnard, CA 93033

PRINT CLEARLY

NAME: _____

ADDRESS: _____

_____ Zip _____

Enclose $2.00 for your catalog, plus $0.50 for postage ($2.50). Check or money order. **NO CASH PLEASE.**

EXCHANGE FORM
TO OBTAIN SECOND EDITION

F: Fax Orders: (805) 486-2491

T: Telephone Orders: (805) 487-2248; Have your credit card number ready

P: Postal Orders: Dimension Engineering Press
P.O. Box 2457, Oxnard, California 93033

**PLEASE RETURN EDITION 1 TO RECEIVE EDITION 2
AT PRICE BELOW:**

Please Print

Name _____

Address: _____

_____ Zip_____

Telephone: _____

COST: $14.98

S: **Sales Tax.** Please add 7.75% for books shipped to California addresses ($1.16).

Shipping: Book Rate: $2.00 for 1 copy and $0.80 for each additional copy. (Surface shipment may take 3-4 weeks). For airmail add $3.50 per book.

Payment: ___Check ___Credit Card ___Visa ___Mastercard

Card Number _____

Name on Card: _____

Expiration Date: _____

───────── **ORDER FORM** ─────────

BOOK

F: Fax Orders: (805) 486-2491

T: Telephone Orders: (805) 487-2248; Have your credit card number ready

P: Postal Orders: Dimension Engineering Press
                     P.O. Box 2457, Oxnard, California 93033

PLEASE SEND THE FOLLOWING TO:

Please Print

Name _____

Address: _____

_____Zip_____

Telephone: _____

COST: $29.95

S: **Sales Tax.** Please add 7.75% for books shipped to California addresses ($2.32).

Shipping:
     Book Rate: $2.00 for 1 copy and $0.80 for each additional copy. (Surface shipment may take 3-4 weeks). For airmail add $3.50 per book.

Payment: ___Check   ___Credit Card   ___Visa   ___Mastercard

Card Number _____

Name on Card: _____

Expiration Date: _____

───────── **ORDER FORM** ─────────

COMPUTER DISK

F: Fax Orders: (805) 486-2491

T: Telephone Orders: (805) 487-2248; Have your credit card number ready

P: Postal Orders: Dimension Engineering Press
                     P.O. Box 2457, Oxnard, California 93033

PLEASE SEND THE FOLLOWING CD'S TO:

Please Print

Name _____

Address: _____

_____Zip_____

Telephone: _____

COST: $34.95

S: **Sales Tax.** Please add 7.75% for CD's shipped to California addresses ($2.70).

Shipping:
     CD Rate: $2.00 for 1 copy and $0.80 for each additional copy. (Surface shipment may take 3-4 weeks). For airmail add $3.50 per CD.

Payment: ___Check   ___Credit Card   ___Visa   ___Mastercard

Card Number _____

Name on Card: _____

Expiration Date: _____